ON BEING JEWISH:
American Jewish Writers
from Cahan to Bellow

"Perhaps no ethnic group in America could produce so rich a body of writing about itself as American Jewry. Certainly, browsing through this fat collection, which was probably put together for academic use but will serve as well for a bedtime reader, makes one think so. Because much of the Jewish experience has been sad, some of these excerpts are sad, but some are hilarious and full of Jewish wit— though it often has a cutting edge. Above all the extracts reflect the experience of the immigrant and his children. Many are excellently written, as one would expect from the like of Saul Bellow, Howard Nemerov, Philip Roth and Herbert Gold. Walden provides a sober running commentary."

—Publishers Weekly

Other Fawcett Books of Interest:

On Being Jewish: American Jewish Writers from Cahan to Bellow

Edited by Daniel Walden

A FAWCETT PREMIER BOOK

Fawcett Publications, Inc., Greenwich, Conn.

For REBA EDITH WEINROTH
my mother

*ON BEING JEWISH: American Jewish Writers from Cahan
to Bellow*

A Fawcett Premier Original

Library of Congress Catalog Card Number: 74-80850

Printed in the United States of America
July 1974

CONTENTS

Introduction

THE FIRST JEWS who came to America in 1654 were descendants of those who had been expelled from Spain and Portugal in the 1490s. At the time of the American Revolution, these Sephardic Jews,* who numbered less than 2,500, had made extraordinary contributions to their new homeland. By the eve of the Civil War they had gained a large measure of economic rights, and political and religious acculturation followed. In turn, acculturation led to widespread intermarriage and conversion on the one hand, and the establishment of Reform Judaism on the other. As Rabbi Gustavus Poznanski, Charleston's German-educated leader of the Sephardic congregation, put it, "America is our Zion, and Washington is our Jerusalem."

Beginning with the 1830s, thousands of German Jews

* *Sephardic* refers to those Jews deriving from Spain and Portugal. Ashkenazic Jews, originally from Central and Eastern Europe, now include only those from Russia—Poland; since the late nineteenth century, German Jews have been called *"Yahudim"* or *"Die Deitschen."*

· *11*

arrived in the United States. There were now about fifty
thousand Jews in America, mostly on the East Coast. Since
they came from a country where the Enlightenment had
spread its doctrine of rationalism, these Jews embraced
and extended Reform Judaism. With the organization of
the Central Conference of American Rabbis in 1889, however, the religious issue was joined. The Russo-Polish Jews,
who began arriving in the 1880s, came from an orthodox
tradition, and though they subsequently diluted their religion, they were not yet ready to abandon it. Another issue
soon emerged. The German Jews, many of whom began as
itinerant peddlers, succeeded magnificently in everything
material. Unfortunately, though much biography, history,
and sociology attests to the German and Sephardic Jews'
accession to wealth, little more than the poetry of Penina
Moise, Adah Isaacs Menken, and Emma Lazarus (a Sephardic Jew) reflects their spiritual-creative life. Com-
menting on what had happened to her people, Lazarus
regretted that "the light of the perpetual lamp is
spent/That an undying radiance was to shed." With the
news of the assassination of Czar Alexander II in 1881 and
the subsequent massacres of Jews in Russia, she extended
her heart to the "huddled masses yearning to breathe free."
Between 1881 and 1914, more than two million Jews from
Russia–Poland arrived in America. It was the "promised
land" to Mary Antin, fresh from Polotzk. It was also the
land of opportunity where Abraham Cahan's David Levinsky was told, "It isn't Russia. . . . Judaism has not much of
a chance here. . . . A man must make a living here."

Coming from Russia–Poland, most from *shtetls,*† the
Jews of the New Immigration and their descendants have

---

† The *shtetl* was a Jewish town within a town, usually in a
three-hundred-thousand-square-mile area called The Pale, on
Russia's western border. Made up of rickety houses, mud
streets, anti-Jewish restrictions, and constant danger, and grinding poverty, these *shtetlach* became more highly structured and
theocratically oriented as the pressures increased.

dominated American Jewish life numerically, economically, and culturally almost since they arrived. But they have lived with a paradox: At the same time that they wanted more than anything else to be American, they wanted to remain Jews. Like one of America's foremost scholars, W. E. B. DuBois, who experienced the "double vision" and "two-ness" of being both American and black, they were troubled by the efforts to integrate themselves into the society while retaining and passing on an ethnic identity: as Jews, as American Jews, and—since World War II—increasingly as Americans who are Jews. The attempts to define what it meant to be a Jew in the Old Country, what it meant to be a Jew here, and how a Jew was acculturated (and perhaps assimilated in an ever-changing culture) while still holding to an ethnic identity, are grist for the writers who have described the unique experience of being Jewish. That set of experiences, these problems, this people, are the source and reason for the American Jewish writers included here.

The new immigrants, numbering perhaps five hundred thousand by 1900 and close to three million in 1914, came to the New World with little or no money and few skills. Arriving too late to duplicate or even carry on the experience of the German Jews, they were received with hostility by most Christians and viewed with contempt by the German Jews. Speaking a despised language, Yiddish, they were called coarse peasants and were seen as a threat to the comfortable assimilation and economic stability of their predecessors. The threat proved to be real; as we know from historians Moses Rischin and Ronald Sanders and from Abraham Cahan's classic, *The Rise of David Levinsky,* the Russian Jews succeeded the German Jews as entrepreneurs, owners, and workers in the clothing industry in New York City. As Russian Jews became more visible, anti-Semitism surfaced and grew. Fortunately, the plans to cut off immigration did not become effective until well after World War I. By that time, three-and-a-half million Jews

had landed. Ironically, though it is often forgotten, Catholic
immigrants from Russia, Poland, Italy, and Greece were
far more numerous and visible.

Most Jews who arrived here between 1881 and 1914
were nominally Orthodox. Those willing to venture to the
New World were those least committed to the practice of
their religion. Beaten down by several hundred years of
persecution and ghettoization, the Jews of Eastern Europe
came alive only in the eighteenth century under the twin
spurs of Chasidism and the Jewish Enlightenment. Chasidism taught them to find God everywhere and in everything;
to pray with joy and enthusiasm was more important than
rote, ritual, and exegesis. These latter elements, along with
a new emphasis on scholarship, would come later. From
the Enlightenment, Jews learned how to enter European
civilization; literature from outside the Jewish community
(like Dostoyevsky, Tolstoy, and Marx), science, and the
impact of urbanism combined to dissolve the medieval isolation of the ghettos. As a synthesis developed, it became
clear that the ideas of the Enlightenment had been diluted
even as they penetrated the ghetto, while the orthodoxy of
extreme piety and ritual crumbled even as the essence of
the Jewish heritage held on. That there would be two Zions
in their lifetime, one in the United States and the other in
Israel, was not foreseen. That Yiddish culture, Eastern
European culture, would endure, though the Yiddish language would diminish, was also not seen. Driven by
pogroms at home and lured by the American Dream, they
chanced the journey to what was literally a New World.

For most Jews in America the question of observing the
Sabbath and the dietary laws was often related to their
feelings about becoming American and climbing out of the
ghetto. Those who insisted on adhering to orthodox practice were in the minority. Those who erected a façade or
who chose to pursue American ways and a new identity
were in the majority. It was a shock, for instance, to discover that success meant learning the way things were done,

doing them better than anyone else, and becoming (and even looking) American as soon as possible. Shaving off beards and sideburns (*payess*) and married women not wearing wigs (*shaytls*) were serious religious matters. The wearing of American clothes paled by comparison. Looking to material values was even more traumatic, even for free-thinkers. In the Old Country, one achieved prestige (*yiches*) by learning and Torah study, and one's duty on Friday night and Saturday was simply to welcome the Sab-bath. In America, as Cahan's David Levinsky and Samuel Ornitz's Meyer Hirsch learned, one achieved prestige and social acceptance at greater costs. That many Jews worked for themselves or for other Jews so as not to be forced to work on the Sabbath is a fact; that many decided to be Jews outside their homes, regardless of the cost (though they could not see the future cost), is also a fact. Their chil-dren and their children's children have departed even further from the old ways. In a society dominated by acquisitiveness and technology, people chose whatever roots and pillars were available, hoping to temper the mix with humanism whenever possible.

By the 1920s, America's Jews, now American Jews, with one foot in the Old Country and one in the New, were strug-gling with problems no longer tied to the ghetto. As Jews, their adherence to traditional values and ethics was hon-ored. As American Jews, shown in Samuel Ornitz's anony-mously published novel *Haunch, Paunch and Jowl* (1923), the compulsion to succeed and to wield power, no matter how corruptly, surfaced for the first time. Though it was an isolated case, surrounded by pathos and humor, it went beyond David Levinsky's acceptable entrepreneurship in its earthiness—so much in the Yiddish tradition—and gro-tesqueness. Myron Brinig's Singermann family saw some of the same forces and emotions. In a country in which an allegedly "lost generation" flourished, emulation was com-mon. As the drama of the generations was played out, Jews as Jews and as American Jews rebelled against their parents, struggled for their own identities, succeeded and failed, cried and laughed, as did others. Jews were in the forefront in creative areas. The success of George and Ira Gershwin, Irving Berlin, Eddie Cantor, and Al Jolson in the world of entertainment matched the success of Albert Einstein, Marc Chagall, and Ben Shahn and many others in science and in the creative arts.

In the 1930s, in the grip of the Great Depression, Jews moved into prominence in movies, in the theater, and in literature. Luther and Stella Adler, John Garfield, and the playwright Clifford Odets made their marks in legitimate theater; Paul Muni, Edward G. Robinson, Irving Thalberg, and many producers in Hollywood enriched the screen. In literature, whether through proletarian novels or novels with social impact, writers fought the system that bound and fought their families as well. Nathanael West, Tillie Lerner, Albert Halper, Daniel Fuchs, Michael Gold, Henry Roth, Nelson Algren, Meyer Levin, and Edward Dahlberg were some of those in whose works social and economic and generational and religious problems appeared. Writing about intellectuals and workers, hoboes and farmers, they concentrated on the attempts of people to identify with the poor and the oppressed. Some glorified the new energy of the Soviet Union or the Communist Party at home, as alternatives to what appeared a sick society. Michael Gold's *Jews Without Money* (1934), a novel from an ideologue, surprisingly kept to its last pages a plea for communist brotherhood. Most, characteristically, reflected the external pressures of a depression-ridden society in which Jews struggled to be Americanized and survive. Many also joined in the decade's widely supported protests, spearheaded by President Roosevelt's New Deal for some and the Communists' program for others. Exchanging religious attachments for secularism, they sought new answers, perhaps new messiahs, in the social order. As Mike Gold wrote, "We had no Santa Claus, but we had a Messiah." No wonder he promised his mother, ideologically, "I must remain faithful to the poor because I cannot be faithless to you."

Caught up in the conflict of generations, young Jewish writers sometimes moved beyond acculturation. Nathanael West, escaping from Nathan Weinstein, was refused admission to a gentile fraternity at Brown University and expanded his rebellion; turning his anger inward, he attacked Jews in his novels. Ben Hecht, on the first page of *A Jew in Love* (1931), described "Jew faces in which race leers and burns like some biologic disease." Within a few years, however, he had become an ardent Zionist; spurred by Hitler's horrors, the inability of the West to act, and the efforts of Jews to escape to Palestine and elsewhere, Hecht strongly criticized those (including Rabbi Stephen Wise) who did not act as quickly as he. As other examples of questionable taste or Jewish anti-Semitism, Ornitz, Halper, and Dahlberg were named. Even Ludwig Lewisohn was criticized by fellow Jews, though he early became a Zionist and a Judeophile. That their motives were good, they argued, ranging from a belief in assimilation to a belief in class over religion, meant little. To a people recently arrived from Eastern European persecution, sensitive to overt anti-Semitism in America, excuses or rationales were hard to accept.

It was almost unique that Henry Roth's *Call It Sleep* (1934) shifted focus in so many ways. Unlike any other novel of the era, this superb psychological work, seen through the eyes of a child, summed up the truths and the traumas of the immigrants' experience. Confronted by a father who was maddened by ghosts of the past and present poverty and despair, little David Schearl's existence balanced precariously between the traditional values of his mother and the *cheder* (religious school) and those of the outside world. The most Freudian of the interwar novels, involved with oedipal conflict, God, and phallic imagery, it is, said Leslie Fiedler, "the best single book by a Jew about Jewishness written by an American, certainly through the

thirties and perhaps ever." Whether *Call It Sleep* is a proletarian novel, which I doubt, is unimportant. What comes
across is the inner psychic pain of the second generation
and its social and familial revolts. In Ludwig Lewisohn's
view, the literary reflections of the historical and generational circumstances were part of an ongoing dialectical
process that would eventuate in a return to Judaism, characteristically liberal not only in the religious field but in politics and love and sex as well. Although Lewisohn was a
prophet for the Thirties through the Fifties, it appears that
the continuing process has wreaked havoc with his words
since World War II.

Even before 1930, American Jewish novelists used the
themes of sex and love. They are persistent needs in the
works of Bruno Lessing, Anzia Yezierska, and James Oppenheim. Cahan's David Levinsky, a kind of Jewish Horatio
Alger, continually tried to find love. That he ended with
loneliness, a millionaire, only highlighted the paradox: His
success was a measure of his estrangement from the community of old. "There are cases when success is a tragedy,"
David knew. He never forgot the Jewish greenhorn who
arrived here penniless and without friends. He never forgot
what might have been if he had gone to the City College of
New York. Similarly, the Jew as Don Juan conflicted with
the traditions of the Old Country, as Ludwig Lewisohn,
Myron Brinig, and Meyer Levin found out. The hold of
ghetto mores, the fear of what "they" would say, were
barriers. Until the 1960s, American Jewish writers did not
easily use these themes. In any case, the image of the Jew
was more meaningful than it had been. An inarticulate
sense of inherited identity, later to be articulated, reflected
a growing interest. Secular and cultural Judaism, generational problems, intermarriage, all vied with traditional
forms. Apparently there were millions of Americans who
wondered about the God of their fathers, the American
Dream, man's manipulation of man, and the necessary per-

sistence of the natural and compulsory Jewish communities of earlier days.

American Jewish writers have had to fashion their product out of the life they knew, and they worked usually in an uncaring or hostile framework. For too long, as in the case of black literature, stereotypes persisted, drawn mainly by the host culture but aided and abetted by the minority. Even as Sambo and Amos and Andy perpetuated the Negro stereotype, so Potash and Perlmutter, Cohen on the telephone, the Goldbergs, Mickey Katz, and chocolate matzos continued the travesty of Jews by Jews. Overcoming these images was one aspect of the writers' problem. Learning the language and the symbols was another. Most important, the writers had to deal with a Jewish image brought into existence by gentiles and Jews and then create what had never existed before—an American Jewish literature.

America's major writers from the early nineteenth century on have been preoccupied with man's condition and his attempts to find meaning in it. Observing the tendency to overintellectualize and pervert the humanistic spirit of the Founders, Hawthorne, Melville, Whitman and Twain stressed the importance of following the dictates of the heart, of the spiritual as against the material values of society. They were conscious of the disparity between what Americans said they believed in and what they did. Sensitive to this gap, to the fraudulent, self-righteous, commercial aspects of American culture that overshadowed the ethical–human, they used their insights to hold mirrors up to us all.

In the twentieth century this socio-literary examination and analysis continued in the works of Dreiser, James, Hemingway, Dos Passos, Faulkner, Fitzgerald, and Wolfe, to name a few. In this tradition the American Jewish writers came of age. They are American writers, of course, but they are also American Jewish writers because they were born Jewish, and, regardless of the intensity of their religious or cultural commitment, they have written about some essential aspect of the Jewish experience in America. Unlike the Lost Generation writers—gentiles who seldom wrote about urban or ethnic conditions—the Jewish writers had to wait until they had become American Jews and the Jewish community was defined enough to support their work. In the cultural vacuum that existed in the early 1940s, American Jewish writers responded as no other group to the country's urgent cultural need. The biblical past, the rise of Hitler, the Holocaust, the new State of Israel, and the need of Americans to again believe in humanity helped. As Saul Bellow put it, affirming his belief in the humanity of the patriarch Abraham, he knew his debt —it had to do with the presence and continuation of life.

For the American Jewish writers, from the cities, towns and *shtetls* of Russia–Poland, arriving at a time of national reform and psychic crisis, of primary importance were the problems of adjustment to the new culture and reconciliation of their Old Country culture with that of the New World. Scrambling for a dollar, everyone working, they endured so that their children might become Americans. "Who has ever seen such optimism?" asked Harry Golden. For the American Jewish writer, under the pressures of the Americanizing process, new problems were added. With disdain for his parent's ways, dress, and accent, he often opted for the New at the expense of the Old. Traditions, values, religion—all were subordinated to the need to emulate the Americans or the Jews who were no longer greenhorns. The joys and the tragedies of the generational experience were not unique, of course, but the works of those writers from Cahan on in the first generation, and from Ornitz through Henry Roth in the next, show that the context, the insights, and the style of the generational experience are novel, a breakthrough. For the first time, Jews who bridged the two cultures in a host country wrote of the ongoing bridging experience. Their literary talents explored the sociological dimensions of a minority. And as the up-from-the-ghetto literature gave way to fiction as a living form, as Jewish self-consciousness benefited from the national and international processes, so the American Jewish writer wrote of himself, his people, anti-Semitism, the War, middlebrow America, and the attempt to understand himself and the society he inhabited. That some of the works fall short of excellence may be true; that they are therefore irrelevant to the main lines of development of American fiction is absurd. The fact of their quest for identity, the effort to create a literature in a non-WASP context, the excellent and near-excellent quality of the work seem to me significant because they created a new genre in literature and demonstrated that the American Jew was beginning to feel at home. Because of the writings of the "Jewish Thirties," fertile, talented minds, conversant with the subject, created the images of the American Jew; the gross, distorted portraits of the past, as a result, have been dissolved in the subtler and more artful, and thus truer, images of the American Jewish moderns.

When Abraham Cahan's *The Rise of David Levinsky* appeared, it was seen by some, incorrectly, as an anti-Semitic book. "Had the book been published anonymously," observed one critic, "we might have taken it for cruel caricature of a hated race by some anti-Semite." In the succeeding decades, anti-Semitism has been denounced readily, whenever it appeared—if at times questionably. Recently most of the animus in American Jewish literature has been directed at Philip Roth, though novels like Budd Schulberg's *What Makes Sammy Run?* and Herman Wouk's *Marjorie Morningstar* have come in for their share of denunciation. The question of what constitutes anti-Semitism (or more correctly anti-Judaism) is a ticklish one. When Roth's *Goodbye, Columbus* (1959) was published, with "The Conversion of the Jews," "Defender of the Faith," and "Epstein" included, the issue was again raised. *Portnoy's Complaint* and *The Breast* have exacerbated the problem. To the charges that he was an anti-Semite and a pornographer, Roth answered that he was a writer who was a

Jew. "How are you connected to me as another man is not?" is one of the questions he started with. The question really, he believed, was who was going to address men and women like men and women—and who would address them like children. Castigating the oratory of self-congratulation and self-pity too often heard from the pulpits, he argued that many Jews found the stories the novelists told more provocative and pertinent than the sermons of the rabbis. Maybe so, but as Irving Howe says, Roth, since *Portnoy's Complaint,* has not really been involved in the Jewish tradition. He is "one of the first American Jewish writers who finds that it yields him no sustenance, no norms or values, from which to launch his attacks on middle-class complaisance."

When a gentile commits an anti-Judaic act, the deed is usually clear and can be recognized and dealt with. Organizations like B'nai B'rith's Anti-Defamation League, backed by law, stand ready to discuss, persuade, or act. When a Jew is accused, the facts are harder to come by. The forces can be exceedingly subtle, pro and con. For example, when a Jew describes another Jew in gross terms and the description does not proceed out of love or honest concern, there is little room for argument. To describe a Jew as a lecher or a parvenu or a corrupt businessman in the 1960s or 1970s, even if he is good to his mother, is another thing. Thus, Philip Roth says that in his "Epstein" he was interested in the condition of a man who was a lecher and who was Jewish, in that order. It is understandable that the older generation, still so close to the pogroms in Russia–Poland, the Holocaust, and overt anti-Semitism, would be hostile to a writer washing dirty linen in public. In my youth I remember being called "Kike," and hit by rocks as I walked to school in a Catholic neighborhood in Philadelphia. I recall crossing the street when I saw a priest or a nun approaching. I was in a unit in World War II that helped liberate a concentration camp. But since World War II, in the United States, the situation has changed; public opinion and law are antagonistic—officially—to anti-Judaism, and the tendency to cut the ties that bind, to forgive and forget, is strong. Many of America's Jews have succeeded materially. Their children, fortunate to have middle-class parents, are Americans who are Jewish. Their dress, their likes and dislikes, their speech, their music, their foods, are urban- and exurban-oriented, with no memories of Europe's death camps and little active acquaintance with anti-Judaism at home. A generation brought up on the Jewish experiences of Allen Ginsberg, Abbie Hoffman, Bob Dylan, and Don Rickles is not likely to look to Dachau or the cheder for its reference points. Yet, uncertain as they are of their precise Jewish identity, for many there is no struggle with being identified as Jewish. Influenced by the Kennedys, Martin Luther King, the Vietnamese War, rock 'n' roll, and the Youth Cult, they are also possessed by the desire to understand the human condition, themselves, and the country they live in. Rejecting that part of America where the bland lead the bland, they seek roots and truth. In the same way, the contemporary American Jewish writers were influenced by the same forces, as well as those of the Depression, the Spanish Civil War, Hitler and World War II, Franklin D. Roosevelt, and the Korean War and McCarthyism. In their common quest, compelled by an indefinable feel of one's heritage, it is the writers who have asked the questions about other Jews, because that is whom they know, and love, and hate, and because they, care deeply and want to find out what it means to be a Jew or an American Jew or an American who is a Jew.

Jews in the United States have responded in many ways to the pressures of the New World. Some from the beginning and into the present desired to be and were quickly or eventually assimilated. Some attempted to find a middle way by which they could become Americans and still retain their sense of being Jews. Some were so alienated or estranged as to drop out and pass into the great other—the gentile world. Still others were doubly alienated, no longer at home either in the Jewish or non-Jewish context. And some didn't care one way or the other. Arthur Koestler, for example, after World War II, bade goodbye to Judaism, opting for total assimilation. Meyer Levin, accepting biculturalism, wrote, "Godless though I profess myself, I have responded with more than warmth to the mystical elements of Chasidism. As a writer, I have considered that I accept the material as folklore. But in my soul I know that I take more than this from these legends." Albert Halper spoke of Yiddish as a "bastardized language," while Edward Dahlberg, a Jew who was in a Catholic, and then a Jewish, orphan asylum, sought a faith he could not find. And Ben Hecht vacillated from self-hating and nearly anti-Semitic prose to some essays and stories in the 1940s calling on Jews to defend Jewish rights. For Saul Bellow, who has had no struggle in identifying himself as Jewish, there has been unconcern for the definition of what that means. As for Herbert Gold, who has traveled far, he has returned to his Jewishness, as he describes his pilgrimage in *My Last Two Thousand Years* (1972).

These opinions and these insights have been used by American Jewish writers since World War II. Though some critics would call the authors collectors of pathological characters, anti-Semitic, or simply non-writers because their concerns are not in accord with a set of predefined goals, it is clear to me that they are writers first, who are Jews. I realize that some will ask that a writer be held to a specific commitment (individually defined) to a specific religious framework in which the writing goes on. In my view, the duty of a writer is clear: a story that is on the right side of God but is not well-written will neither make an impression nor live. Similarly, a tale that is sexy, if it is not honest and well-crafted, will not persist. Searching for truth takes many forms. One form it will take only perilously will be that of the didactic story or essay; however, the search must take the form that the characters and their situations determine. If Jews in America are religious or not, or are rooted in the values of the past or not, so be it. If they are engaged in a generational conflict, so be it. And if they are Americans who are Jews, who are trying to find their way in a world that has meanings and structure somewhat different from that of the past, or that seems to lack meaning, or that needs new interpretations of the past—as is the way of the Talmud—so be it. The writer's province is insight and honesty, not religious or political activism, and the degree to which he succeeds as a writer, as an American Jewish writer, is the most important criterion.

Since the early 1940s millions of Americans have read the works of Bellow, Mailer, Salinger, Malamud, Miller, Friedman, Roth, Wouk, Heller, Ozick, Rosen, Schwartz, Trilling, Potok, Singer, and Wiesel. Because I. B. Singer usually writes in Yiddish and Elie Wiesel in French, and their concerns are for Jews outside of America, they can not be considered as American Jewish writers. Similarly, though Mailer, Salinger, Trilling, and Heller are Jewish, because they deal only peripherally with Jews they will not be considered American Jewish writers, though I would contend that they write as they do because they are Jewish. Bellow, Malamud, Roth, and the others, however, are American Jewish writers because their novels and stories, whose literary and cultural reference points are Jewish, reflect their essential concerns. In spite of their individual differences, they usually deal with Jews in the American experience.

From World War I through World War II, American literature was dominated by concepts like alienation and the wasteland. In spite of the fact that estrangement produced some masterpieces, its time passed. When the older generation passed on, there seemed to be few replacements. At this point in time, in Bellow's opinion, the writer had to exercise his own intelligence, to think, and not merely of his own narrow interests and needs. For Bellow, who had no fight about being a Jew—"I simply must deal with the facts of my life, a basic set of primitive facts," he said in 1964

—the Jewish people's experience was a universal metaphor. Inasmuch as the modern writer specializes in what are called grotesque facts, and cannot compete with the news itself, as both Bellow and Roth pointed out, he must go beyond reality. He must turn away from current events, but without losing focus. For what seems lacking, concluded Bellow, was a firm sense of a common world, a coherent community, a genuine purpose in life. Man had to strive for a life of significant pattern.

With the same goals in mind, Malamud quested for moral salvation and self-realization. Whether he is writing about Morris Bober and his assistant, or Fidelman, or a Levin who would like to be a "Free-man" in a world that is not easy for Jews, the theme of meaningful suffering was present. Bober, for example, knew painfully that he had been a failure in the eyes of the world. But, as became clear in the end, he was a good man in the biblical sense of the word. As one of the Chasidic rabbis said, I would rather be devout than clever, but rather than both devout and clever, I should like to be good. Achieving the essential Jew, therefore, by his own actions is what was sought. But that goal, shared by Philip Roth, is at least distantly related to what Bellow refers to as consummation of a heart's need.

That there are similarities in the works of some American Jewish writers can be demonstrated. The differences are more striking. Roth, for instance, has written most often about extreme behavior in ordinary situations. From the beginning, he was concerned with men and women whose moorings had been cut, who had been swept away from their native shores and out to sea, sometimes on a tide of their own righteousness or resentment. Take "The Conversion of the Jews," a story of a little Jewish boy who could no longer stomach his rabbi's evasions and rote—answers a child who could no longer act like a little rabbi. Take Alexander Portnoy, a productive member of society on the job, whose problems, rightly or wrongly understood, lead him to live beyond his psychological and moral means. In short, we learn from Roth, the fantastic situation must be accepted as reality at the same time as the reality of the fantastic and horrible. Or, to go back to an earlier explanation, the world of fiction, wrote Roth, "frees us of circumscriptions that society places upon feeling . . . and allows both writer and the reader to respond to experience in ways not always available in day-to-day conduct."

Through writing and reading, a people passes on its collective experience. From Yiddish literature the Old Country can be remembered; even some of that whole wonderful body of literature, in English translation, can bring back the hard, dirty, primitive life of the *shtetls*. It will also bring back the warmth and earthiness of life in a Jewish family in a Jewish community in a world that no longer exists. So it is with the sensitively written recollections of Harry Golden and Alfred Kazin, and the creative memories of the American Jewish writers from Abraham Cahan into the present. Thus, Bellow, as he recreates the joys and sadnesses of growing up in Montreal and Chicago, or describes an Augie March or a Herzog, also demonstrates an ambivalent faith in man's ability to realize himself in an ambiguous world. The resonance of two-ness is always present. For Malamud, redemptive suffering is what comes through, from a New York City past; for Roth, who grew up outside of Elizabeth, New Jersey, insanity or estrangement are not what he sees as the good life, yet an examination of what appears insane in a framework of normality is compelling. For others, the flight from impotence into *machismo,* in Bruce Jay Friedman, and the significance of the existential, in Edward Lewis Wallant, are important. And no wonder. If one recalls the *shtet* (in spite of the romanticized "Fiddler on the Roof"), or the Holocaust, as in Wallant's *The Pawnbroker* (1961), then pain is an everyday experience that coexists with love and comfort. What Jew over forty can ever forget the death camps in Germany and Poland? How many can forget how their grandparents hid in the forests from the Cossacks or townspeople, or fled Russia to avoid the draft, persecution, humiliation, and often forced conversion? But, the question must be asked, what has all this to do with the 1970s? Today?

To young Americans who are Jews, the memories and suffering of the past are subordinated to the middle-class comforts and security of post-World War II America, as they should be. Like Descartes, they ask: "I am certain that I am, but what am I?" The case of Franz Kafka, an acculturated Jew, might be a help. Conscious of being an outsider, he somehow felt his way into Jewishness. "The Metamorphosis" was "no dream," he wrote. What was at stake, according to young Jewish Americans, was that many struggles were going on, the outcomes of which were dreadfully important to them. They had to find a way to bring peace to the contending forces; to find some harmonic middle way between the material–hedonistic and the ethical–moral was necessary. No longer capable of determining their destinies, though taught individualism as a supreme virtue, they alternately pursued the chimera of achievement and escape from the frustration of despair. It was clear to them that the love of suffering, of what they saw as the dead past, was a waste of time. It was not clear that playing the doomsday theme, or playing at crises, alienation, apocalypse, and desperation, with tools like mind expanders and religious cults, were also suffering. They didn't see that individualism cut two ways: A triumph on the one hand for justice and self-realization, it was also a bearer of possible trouble with its dream of unlimited leisure and liberty. Why can't I do anything I want? they asked. Why can't I have everything I want? The answer is not in the power of money to buy. The answer is in the nature of being Jewish, in the time-honored, ages-long meaning. Perhaps as Bellow's Dr. Sammler put it, the best is "to have some order within oneself. Better than what many call love. Perhaps it *is* love." That is, to be a Jew because of anti-Semitism is not enough. Similarly, to be a Jew because of the bravery of the State of Israel cannot be convincing. And to be a Jew because your parents say so is also a transparent excuse. But the experience *of being Jewish,* of living the warmness of community, with or without ritual, of having roots, as in [Henry] Roth, Bellow, Malamud, and Gold, of being a part of an organic, progressive community that has existed proudly and contributed mightily for thousands of years—this might be enough.

Longfellow, after visiting the Jewish cemetery in Newport in the 1850s, lamented, "What once has been shall be no more." But he forgot that nothing remains the same. Jews have always disappeared, but the Jew lived on. And just as the Jews of antiquity differed from those of the Middle Ages, so the Jews of Eastern Europe differed from the American Jews and they from the Jewish Americans. But as the American Jewish writers have made plain, they were all Jews, and they are still ethically and morally committed, still concerned with right behavior, and, as the Bible commands, in spite of the secular and assimilative tendencies of American life, they still choose life. After all, wrote Salo Baron, what really matters is not personal immortality but the immortality of the Jewish people. It was once given, it cannot be lost or taken away. It is what people care about. It is the meaning of life that we seek.

For a long time many people have accepted the premise that a work of art is important in itself, that it is a social action in itself. So it is with the American Jewish writer. Asking, What do people think? he has ignored the question, What do *they* say? Exposing the sensitive issues others avoid, he is not held back by criticism. Concerned with the honesty and depth of his work, it is the human predicament and the human condition that engage him. In defense of values, he rejects pessimism, and quests for values. The possibility of meaningful individual life is what he seeks, in whatever way he can. For if it is man, a little lower than the angels, in whom we are interested, then it is man's questionable or diminished state in the real world that is at stake. To that challenge, the American Jewish writer has risen. The record to this point is a promising one.

1. The Immigrant Experience

BETWEEN 1880 and the 1920s, the immigrant Jews struggled with the problem of their removal from an Eastern Europe *shtetl* or town to a modern urbanized American metropolis. Coming from a rich religio-cultural tradition that was in the process of being splintered, they entered a world where all one needed, as David Levinsky learned, was success; in America tradition and religion followed not only the flag but the prevailing economic winds. They exchanged communities in which the Torah was meaningful for cities and neighborhoods in which the factory, shop, and cold-water flat circumscribed their existence. Given the pressures, arriving on the heels of Reconstruction, with its national compulsion to get back to business as usual, at a time when big business and monopoly and electric power and social Darwinism prevailed, it is only natural that the Jews' responses included the release of energies that had been bottled up for centuries. It was an outpouring, wrote historian Mark Sullivan, of such growth in culture and

capacity for transmission through influence and example
as had never before been seen.

By the turn of the century, more than one-third of the
Jews in Eastern Europe had left their homes for the New
World, most of them settling in New York. After a journey
begun in precarious financial straits and carried through
under threats of uncertainty and hostility, they left family
and friends for Western Europe and thence to "Columbus'
medina." "We were homeless, houseless and friendless in
a strange place," wrote Mary Antin, but six weeks later,
"our eyes beheld the Promised Land," and her father held
her and her family in his arms.

The Promised Land meant many things. There was the
longing for the past seen in Cahan's *Yekl* and in David
Levinsky. For some, there was a pride in being Americanized; for Mary Antin, and Shadrach Cohen's boys, it was an
overpowering force. There was the chance to reform, to
heal. Dr. Rast, for instance, tried to heal bodies and spiritual disorders. There was also the search for love so poi-
gnantly described by Anzia Yezierska, and the struggle to
grasp the opportunities offered in this strange, new land—
if not for oneself then for one's children. Finally, there was
the paradox presented by the success or failure, adjustment,
or assimilation, of the American Dream. To David Levinsky, being a millionaire could not erase the pull of his
roots; to Sara Reisel, in Yezierska's *Hungry Hearts,* her
"hungry heart" found fulfillment. Already in the first generation it was apparent that for the Eastern European Jews
to become American Jews, there would be costs.

The reality of the Lower East Side, the cradle for most
Eastern European Jews, was a compound of long hours,
sweatshop conditions, poverty, and the struggle to maintain
community. From the crowded tenements in which some
families kept boarders, the parents went forth to work.
From the same tenements the kids ran out to do chores, to
go to school, to go to *cheder* (religious school). The people met and talked in hundreds of meeting halls, in *shuls*

(synagogues)—including storefront *shuls,* in cafés; everywhere they could the people, the philosophers, intellectuals, and poets came together. They went to the public baths, to the *schvitz* (the steam bath)—the more genteel ladies washed at home. They helped each other, they contributed to causes, *pushkes* (contribution boxes) were all over. They bought cottage cheese and noodles, herring and potatoes, pickles, rye and pumpernickel, *kishke* (stuffed derma, a flour stuffing in cows' intestinal skins); they made *cholent* (a slow-cooking pot roast made with bits of meat, bones, potatoes and lima beans) on Fridays, kept it cooking all night on banked fires in the breadbaker's ovens, and ate it Saturday after *shul.* They took freshly killed chickens, plucked the feathers, cleaned the chicken, and made chicken soup with *mandelen* (croutons). They rendered the chicken fat and ate the *gribbaness* (crackles). They made brisket and *flanken* when they could afford them. They drank seltzer delivered in heavy, tinted syphon bottles. The Yiddish press and the Yiddish theater thrived, people took courses at the Educational Alliance; never was there such a ravenous drive for education and culture. And they laughed—they had to, coming from a Yiddish culture, pogroms and anti-Semitism; their humor was broad, often earthy, often an escape valve. But it was also warm. How they lived!

In this milieu their kids grew up, a generation motivated by the possibilities and the optimism that suffused the people. These were the years when they became citizens as soon as they could. It was a country in which on July 4, 1911, the *Jewish Daily Forward* claimed, "It is our holiday. . . . It shows us that that which is not can be . . . that the thought of freedom is the beginning of true freedom." In spite of the fact that they were Eastern European Jews, America gave them hope and life. These were the decades in which the Lower East Side throbbed, and the past and the present met, and from it came the American Jew.

ABRAHAM CAHAN (1860–1951), born in Vilna, arrived in the United States in 1882 and became the long-time, innovative editor of the influential *Jewish Daily Forward. Yekl* (1896), well-received by William Dean Howells and Hutchins Hapgood, led him to write other stories in English—and eventually *The Rise of David Levinsky* (1917), a tale of an immigrant boy who, though he achieved great success, never forgot his roots or got over the loneliness his wealth brought him. Writing fluently in both Yiddish and English, a powerful orator and editor, Cahan was also a leading Socialist.

In the Grip of His Past
from
YEKL

Jake had never even vaguely abandoned the idea of supplying his wife and child with the means of coming to join him. He was more or less prompt in remitting her monthly allowance of ten rubles, and the visit to the draft and passage office had become part of the routine of his life. It had the invariable effect of arousing his dormant scruples, and he hardly ever left the office without ascertaining the price of a steerage voyage from Hamburg to New York. But no sooner did he emerge from the dingy basement into the noisy scenes of Essex Street, than he would consciously let his mind wander off to other topics.

Formerly, during the early part of his sojourn in Boston, his landing place, where some of his townsfolk resided and where he had passed his first two years in America, he used to mention his Gitl and his Yosselé so frequently and so enthusiastically, that some wags among the Hanover Street tailors would sing "Yekl and wife and the baby" to the tune of "Molly and I and the Baby." In the natural course of things, however, these retrospective effusions gradually became far between, and since he had shifted his abode to New York he carefully avoided all reference to his antecedents. The Jewish quarter of the metropolis, which is a vast and compact city within a city, offers its denizens incomparably fewer chances of contact with the English-speaking portion of the population than any of the three separate Ghettos of Boston. As a consequence, since Jake's advent to New York his passion for American sport had considerably cooled off. And, to make up for this, his enthusiastic nature before long found vent in dancing and in a general life of gallantry. His proved knack with the gentle sex had turned his head and now cost him all his leisure time. Still, he would occasionally attend some variety show in which boxing was the main drawing card, and somehow managed to keep track of the salient events of the sporting world generally. Judging from his unstaid habits and happy-go-lucky abandon to the pleasures of life, his present associates took it for granted that he was single, and instead of twitting him with the feigned assumption that he had deserted a family—a piece of burlesque as old as the Ghetto —they would quiz him as to which of his girls he was "dead struck" on, and as to the day fixed for the wedding. On more than one such occasion he had on the tip of his tongue the seemingly jocular question, "How do you know I am not married already?" But he never let the sentence cross his lips, and would, instead, observe facetiously that he was not "shtruck on nu goil," and that he was dead struck on all of them in "whulshale." "I hate retail beesnesh, shee? Dot'sh a' kin' a man *I* am!" One day, in the course of an intimate conversation with Joe, Jake, dropping into a philosophical mood, remarked:

"It's something like a baker, *ain't it?* The more *cakes* he has the less he likes them. You and I have a *lot* of girls; that's why we don't *care* for any one of them."

But if his attachment for the girls of his acquaintance collectively was not coupled with a quivering of his heart for any individual Mamie, or Fanny, or Sarah, it did not, on the other hand, preclude a certain lingering tenderness for his wife. But then his wife had long since ceased to be

what she had been of yore. From a reality she had gradually
become transmuted into a fancy. During the three years
since he had set foot on the soil, where a "shister* becomes
a mister and a mister a shister," he had lived so much more
than three years—so much more, in fact, than in all the
twenty-two years of his previous life—that his Russian past
appeared to him a dream and his wife and child, together
with his former self, fellow characters in a charming tale,
which he was neither willing to banish from his memory
nor able to reconcile with the actualities of his American
present. The question of how to effect this reconciliation,
and of causing Gitl and little Yosselé to step out of the
thickening haze of reminiscence and to take their stand by
his side as living parts of his daily life, was a fretful subject from the consideration of which he cowardly shrank.
He wished he could both import his family and continue his
present mode of life. At the bottom of his soul he wondered
why this should not be feasible. But he knew that it was
not, and his heart would sink at the notion of forfeiting the
lion's share of attentions for which he came in at the hands
of those who lionized him. Moreover, how will he look
people in the face in view of the lie he has been acting? He
longed for an interminable respite. But as sooner or later
the minds of his acquaintances were bound to become disabused, and he would have to face it all out anyway, he was
many a time on the point of making a clean breast of it,
and failed to do so for a mere lack of nerve, each time letting himself off on the plea that a week or two before his
wife's arrival would be a more auspicious occasion for the
disclosure.

Neither Jake nor his wife nor his parents could write
even Yiddish, although both he and his old father read
fluently the punctuated Hebrew of the Old Testament or the
Prayer Book. Their correspondence had therefore to be
carried on by proxy, and, as a consequence, at longer intervals than would have been the case otherwise. The mis-

* Yiddish for shoemaker.

sives which he received differed materially in length, style, and degree of illiteracy as well as in point of penmanship; but they all agreed in containing glowing encomiums of little Yosselé, exhorting Yekl not to stray from the path of righteousness, and reproachfully asking whether he ever meant to send the ticket. The latter point had an exasperating effect on Jake. There were times, however, when it would touch his heart and elicit from him his threadbare vow to send the ticket at once. But then he never had money enough to redeem it. And, to tell the truth, at the bottom of his heart he was at such moments rather glad of poverty. At all events, the man who wrote Jake's letters had a standing order to reply in the sharpest terms at his command that Yekl did not spend his money on drink; that America was not the land they took it for, where one could "scoop gold by the skirtful"; that Gitl need not fear lest he meant to desert her, and that as soon as he had saved enough to pay her way and to set up a decent establishment she would be sure to get the ticket.

Jake's scribe was an old Jew who kept a little stand on Pitt Street, which is one of the thoroughfares and market places of the Galician quarter of the Ghetto, and where Jake was unlikely to come upon any people of his acquaintance. The old man scraped together his livelihood by selling Yiddish newspapers and cigarettes, and writing letters for a charge varying, according to the length of the epistle, from five to ten cents. Each time Jake received a letter he would take it to the Galician, who would first read it to him (for an extra remuneration of one cent) and then proceed to pen five cents' worth of rhetoric, which might have been printed and forwarded one copy at a time for all the additions or alterations Jake ever caused to be made in it.

"What else shall I write?" the old man would ask his patron, after having written and read aloud the first dozen lines, which Jake had come to know by heart.

"How do *I* know?" Jake would respond. "It is you who can write; so you ought to understand what else to write."

And the scribe would go on to write what he had written on almost every previous occasion. Jake would keep the letter in his pocket until he had spare United States money enough to convert into ten rubles, and then he would betake himself to the draft office and have the amount, together with the well-crumpled epistle, forwarded to Povodye.

And so it went month in and month out.

The first letter which reached Jake after the scene at Joe Peltner's dancing academy came so unusually close upon its predecessor that he received it from his landlady's hand with a throb of misgiving. He had always labored under the presentiment that some unknown enemies—for he had none that he could name—would some day discover his wife's address and anonymously represent him to her as contemplating another marriage, in order to bring Gitl down upon him unawares. His first thought accordingly was that this letter was the outcome of such a conspiracy. "Or maybe there is some death in the family?" he next reflected, half with terror and half with a feeling almost amounting to reassurance.

When the cigarette vender unfolded the letter he found it to be of such unusual length that he stipulated an additional cent for the reading of it.

"Alla right, hurry up now!" Jake said, grinding his teeth on a mumbled English oath.

"Righd evay! Righd evay!" the old fellow returned jubilantly, as he hastily adjusted his spectacles and addressed himself to his task.

The letter had evidently been penned by some one laying claim to Hebrew scholarship and ambitious to impress the New World with it; for it was quite replete with poetic digressions, strained and twisted to suit some quotation from the Bible. And what with this unstinted verbosity, which was Greek to Jake, one or two interruptions by the old man's customers, and interpretations necessitated by difference in dialect, a quarter of an hour had elapsed before the scribe realized the trend of what he was reading.

Then he suddenly gave a start, as if shocked.

"Vot'sh a madder? Vot'sh a madder?"

"*Vot's der madder?* What should be the *madder?* Wait—a—I don't know what I can do"—he halted in perplexity.

"Any bad news?" Jake inquired, turning pale. "Speak out!"

"Speak out! It is all very well for you to say 'speak out.' You forget that one is a piece of Jew," he faltered, hinting at the orthodox custom which enjoins a child of Israel from being the messenger of sad tidings.

"Don't *bodder* a head!" Jake shouted savagely. "I have paid you, haven't I?"

"*Say,* young man, you need not be so angry," the other said, resentfully. "Half of the letter I have read, have I not? so I shall refund you one cent and leave me in peace." He took to fumbling in his pockets for the coin, with apparent reluctance.

"Tell me what is the matter," Jake entreated, with clinched fists. "Is anybody dead? Do tell me now."

"*Vell,* since you know it already, I may as well tell you," said the scribe cunningly, glad to retain the cent and Jake's patronage. "It is your father who has been freed; may he have a bright paradise."

"Ha?" Jake asked aghast, with a wide gape.

The Galician resumed the reading in solemn, doleful accents. The melancholy passage was followed by a jeremiade upon the penniless condition of the family and Jake's duty to send the ticket without further procrastination. As to his mother, she preferred the Povodye graveyard to a watery sepulcher, and hoped that her beloved and only son, the apple of her eye, whom she had been awake nights to bring up to manhood, and so forth, would not forget her.

"So now they will be here for sure, and there can be no more delay!" was Jake's first distinct thought. "Poor father!" he inwardly exclaimed the next moment, with deep anguish. His native home came back to him with a vividness which it had not had in his mind for a long time.

"Was he an old man?" the scribe queried sympathetically.

"About seventy," Jake answered, bursting into tears.

"Seventy? Then he had lived to a good old age. May no
one depart younger," the old man observed, by way of
"consoling the bereaved."

As Jake's tears instantly ran dry he fell to wringing his
hands and moaning.

"Good-night!" he presently said, taking leave. "I'll see
you tomorrow, if God be pleased."

"Good-night!" the scribe returned with heartfelt con-
dolence.

As he was directing his steps to his lodgings Jake wondered why he did not weep. He felt that this was the proper
thing for a man in his situation to do, and he endeavored
to inspire himself with emotions befitting the occasion. But
his thoughts teasingly gambolled about among the people
and things of the street. By-and-by, however, he became
sensible of his mental eye being fixed upon the big fleshy
mole on his father's scantily bearded face. He recalled the
old man's carriage, the melancholy nod of his head, his
deep sigh upon taking snuff from the time-honored birch
bark which Jake had known as long as himself; and his
heart writhed with pity and with the acutest pangs of homesickness. "And it was evening and it was morning, the sixth
day. And the heavens and the earth were finished." As the
Hebrew words of the Sanctification of the Sabbath resounded in Jake's ears, in his father's senile treble, he could
see his gaunt figure swaying over a pair of Sabbath loaves.
It is Friday night. The little room, made tidy for the day of
rest and faintly illuminated by the mysterious light of two
tallow candles rising from freshly burnished candlesticks, is
pervaded by a benign, reposeful warmth and a general air
of peace and solemnity. There, seated by the side of the
head of the little family and within easy reach of the huge
brick oven, is his old mother, flushed with fatigue, and with
an effort keeping her drowsy eyes open to attend, with a

devout mien, her husband's prayer. Opposite to her, by the window, is Yekl, the present Jake, awaiting his turn to chant the same words in the holy tongue, and impatiently thinking of the repast to come after it. Besides the three of them there is no one else in the chamber, for Jake visioned the fascinating scene as he had known it for almost twenty years, and not as it had appeared during the short period since the family had been joined by Gitl and subsequently by Yosselé.

Suddenly he felt himself a child, the only and pampered son of a doting mother. He was overcome with a heart-wringing consciousness of being an orphan, and his soul was filled with a keen sense of desolation and self-pity. And thereupon everything around him—the rows of gigantic tenement houses, the hum and buzz of the scurrying pedestrians, the jingling horse cars—all suddenly grew alien and incomprehensible to Jake. Ah, if he could return to his old home and old days, and have his father recite Sanctification again, and sit by his side, opposite to mother, and receive from her hand a plate of reeking *tzimess,** as of yore! Poor mother! He *will* not forget her—But what is the Italian playing on that organ, anyhow? Ah, it is the new waltz! By the way, this is Monday and they are dancing at Joe's now and he is not there. "I shall not go there tonight, nor any other night," he commiserated himself, his reveries for the first time since he had left the Pitt Street cigarette stand passing to his wife and child. Her image now stood out in high relief with the multitudinous noisy scene at Joe's academy for a discordant, disquieting background, amid which there vaguely defined itself the reproachful saintlike visage of the deceased. "I will begin a new life!" he vowed to himself.

He strove to remember the child's features, but could only muster the faintest recollection—scarcely anything beyond a general symbol—a red little thing smiling, as he, Jake, tickles it under its tiny chin. Yet Jake's finger at this

* A kind of dessert made of carrots or turnips.

moment seemed to feel the soft touch of that little chin, and
it sent through him a thrill of fatherly affection to which he
had long been a stranger. Gitl, on the other hand, loomed
up in all the individual sweetness of her rustic face. He
beheld her kindly mouth opening wide—rather too wide,
but all the lovelier for it—as she spoke; her prominent red
gums, her little black eyes. He could distinctly hear her
voice with her peculiar lisp, as one summer morning she
had burst into the house and, clapping her hands in despair,
she had cried, "A weeping to me! The yellow rooster is
gone!" or, as coming into the smithy she would say:
"Father-in-law, mother-in-law calls you to dinner. Hurry
up, Yekl, dinner is ready." And although this was all he
could recall her saying, Jake thought himself retentive of
every word she had ever uttered in his presence. His heart
went out to Gitl and her environment, and he was seized
with a yearning tenderness that made him feel like crying.
"I would not exchange her little finger for all the American
ladas," he soliloquized, comparing Gitl in his mind with
the dancing-school girls of his circle. It now filled him with
disgust to think of the morals of some of them, although it
was from his own sinful experience that he knew them to be
of a rather loose character.

He reached his lodgings in a devout mood, and before
going to bed he was about to say his prayers. Not having
said them for nearly three years, however, he found, to his
dismay, that he could no longer do it by heart. His landlady
had a prayer book, but, unfortunately, she kept it locked
in the bureau, and she was now asleep, as was everybody
else in the house. Jake reluctantly undressed and went to
bed on the kitchen lounge, where he usually slept.

When a boy his mother had taught him to believe that to
go to sleep at night without having recited the bed prayer
rendered one liable to be visited and choked in bed by some
ghost. Later, when he had grown up, and yet before he had
left his birthplace, he had come to set down this earnest
belief of his good old mother as a piece of womanish super-

stition, while since he had settled in America he had hardly ever had an occasion to so much as think of bed prayers. Nevertheless, as he now lay vaguely listening to the weird ticking of the clock on the mantelpiece over the stove, and at the same time desultorily brooding upon his father's death, the old belief suddenly uprose in his mind and filled him with mortal terror. He tried to persuade himself that it was a silly notion worthy of womenfolk, and even affected to laugh at it audibly. But all in vain. "Cho-king! Cho-king! Cho-king!" went the clock, and the form of a man in white d clothes never ceased gleaming in his face. He resolutely turned to the wall, and, pulling the blanket over his head, he huddled himself snugly up for instantaneous sleep. But presently he felt the cold grip of a pair of hands about his throat, and he even mentally stuck out his tongue, as one does while being strangled.

With a fast-beating heart Jake finally jumped off the lounge, and gently knocked at the door of his landlady's bedroom.

"*Eshcoosh me, mishesh,* be so kind as to lend me your prayer book. I want to say the night prayer," he addressed her imploringly.

The old woman took it for a cruel practical joke, and flew into a passion.

"Are you crazy or drunk? A nice time to make fun!"

And it was not until he had said with suppliant vehemence, "May I as surely be alive as my father is dead!" and she had subjected him to a cross-examination, that she expressed sympathy and went to produce the keys.

The Meeting

A few weeks later, on a Saturday morning, Jake, with an unfolded telegram in his hand, stood in front of one of the desks at the Immigration Bureau of Ellis Island. He was freshly shaven and clipped, smartly dressed in his best clothes and ball shoes, and, in spite of the sickly expression of shamefacedness and anxiety which distorted his features, he looked younger than usual.

All the way to the island he had been in a flurry of joyous anticipation. The prospect of meeting his dear wife and child, and, incidentally, of showing off his swell attire to her, had thrown him into a fever of impatience. But on entering the big shed he had caught a distant glimpse of Gitl and Yosselé through the railing separating the detained immigrants from their visitors, and his heart had sunk at the sight of his wife's uncouth and un-American appearance. She was slovenly dressed in a brown jacket and skirt of grotesque cut, and her hair was concealed under a voluminous wig of a pitch-black hue. This she had put on just before leaving the steamer, both "in honor of the Sabbath" and by way of sprucing herself up for the great event. Since Yekl had left home she had gained considerably in the measurement of her waist. The wig, however, made her seem stouter and shorter than she would have appeared without it. It also added at least five years to her looks. But she was aware neither of this nor of the fact that in New York even a Jewess of her station and orthodox breeding is accustomed to blink at the wickedness of displaying her natural hair, and that none but an elderly matron may wear a wig without being the occasional target for snowballs or stones. She was naturally dark of complexion, and the nine or ten days spent at sea had covered her face with a deep bronze, which combined with her prominent cheek bones, inky little eyes, and, above all, the smooth black wig, to lend her resemblance to a squaw.

Jake had no sooner caught sight of her than he had averted his face, as if loth to rest his eyes on her, in the presence of the surging crowd around him, before it was inevitable. He dared not even survey that crowd to see whether it contained any acquaintance of his, and he vaguely wished that her release were delayed indefinitely.

Presently the officer behind the desk took the telegram from him, and in another little while Gitl, hugging Yosselé with one arm and a bulging parcel with the other, emerged from a side door.

"Yekl!" she screamed out in a piteous high key, as if crying for mercy.

"Dot'sh alla right!" he returned in English, with a wan smile and unconscious of what he was saying. His wandering eyes and dazed mind were striving to fix themselves upon the stern functionary and the questions he bethought himself of asking before finally releasing his prisoners. The contrast between Gitl and Jake was so striking that the officer wanted to make sure—partly as a matter of official duty and partly for the fun of the thing—that the two were actually man and wife.

"*Oi* a lamentation upon me! He shaves his beard!" Gitl ejaculated to herself as she scrutinized her husband. "Yosselé, look! Here is *taté*!"

But Yosselé did not care to look at taté. Instead, he turned his frightened little eyes—precise copies of Jake's—and buried them in his mother's cheek.

When Gitl was finally discharged she made to fling herself on Jake. But he checked her by seizing both loads from her arms. He started for a distant and deserted corner of the room, bidding her follow. For a moment the boy looked stunned, then he burst out crying and fell to kicking his father's chest with might and main, his reddened little face appealingly turned to Gitl. Jake continuing his way tried to kiss his son into toleration, but the little fellow proved too nimble for him. It was in vain that Gitl, scurrying behind, kept expostulating with Yosselé: "Why, it is taté!" Taté was forced to capitulate before the march was brought to its end.

At length, when the secluded corner had been reached, and Jake and Gitl had set down their burdens, husband and wife flew into mutual embrace and fell to kissing each other. The performance had an effect of something done to order, which, it must be owned, was far from being belied by the state of their minds at the moment. Their kisses imparted the taste of mutual estrangement to both. In Jake's case the sensation was quickened by the strong steerage odors which were emitted by Gitl's person, and he involuntarily recoiled.

"You look like a *poritz*," * she said shyly.

"How are you? How is mother?"

"How should she be? So, so. She sends you her love," Gitl mumbled out.

"How long was father ill?"

"Maybe a month. He cost us health enough."

He proceeded to make advances to Yosselé, she appealing to the child in his behalf. For a moment the sight of her, as they were both crouching before the boy, precipitated a wave of thrilling memories on Jake and made him feel in his own environment. Presently, however, the illusion took wing and here he was, Jake the Yankee, with this bonnetless, wigged, dowdyish little greenhorn by his side! That she was his wife, nay, that he was a married man at all, seemed incredible to him. The sturdy, thriving urchin had at first inspired him with pride; but as he now cast another side glance at Gitl's wig he lost all interest in him, and began to regard him, together with his mother, as one great obstacle dropped from heaven, as it were, in his way.

Gitl, on her part, was overcome with a feeling akin to awe. She, too, could not get herself to realize that this stylish young man—shaved and dressed as in Povodye is only some young nobleman—was Yekl, her own Yekl, who had all these three years never been absent from her mind. And while she was once more examining Jake's blue diagonal cutaway, glossy stand-up collar, the white four-in-hand necktie, coquettishly tucked away in the bosom of his starched shirt, and, above all, his patent leather shoes, she was at the same time mentally scanning the Yekl of three years before. The latter alone was hers, and she felt like crying to the image to come back to her and let her be *his* wife.

* Yiddish for nobleman.

Presently, when they had got up and Jake was plying her with perfunctory questions, she chanced to recognize a certain movement of his upper lip—an old trick of his. It was as if she had suddenly discovered her own Yekl in an apparent stranger, and, with another pitiful outcry, she fell on his breast.

"Don't!" he said, with patient gentleness, pushing away her arms. "Here everything is so different."

She colored deeply.

"They don't wear wigs here," he ventured to add.

"What then?" she asked, perplexedly.

"You will see. It is quite another world."

"Shall I take it off, then? I have a nice Saturday kerchief," she faltered. "It is of silk—I bought it at Kalmen's for a bargain. It is still brand new."

"Here one does not wear even a kerchief."

"How then? Do they go about with their own hair?" she queried in ill-disguised bewilderment.

"Vell, alla right, put it on, quick!"

As she set about undoing her parcel, she bade him face about and screen her, so that neither he nor any stranger could see her bareheaded while she was replacing the wig by the kerchief. He obeyed. All the while the operation lasted he stood with his gaze on the floor, gnashing his teeth with disgust and shame, or hissing some Bowery oath.

"Is this better?" she asked bashfully, when her hair and part of her forehead were hidden under a kerchief of flaming blue and yellow, whose end dangled down her back.

The kerchief had a rejuvenating effect. But Jake thought that it made her look like an Italian woman of Mulberry Street on Sunday.

"Alla right, leave it be for the present," he said in despair, reflecting that the wig would have been the lesser evil of the two.

When they reached the city Gitl was shocked to see him lead the way to a horse car.

"*Oi* woe is me! Why, it is Sabbath!" she gasped.

He irately essayed to explain that a car, being an uncommon sort of vehicle, riding in it implied no violation of the holy day. But this she sturdily met by reference to railroads. Besides, she had seen horse cars while stopping in Hamburg, and knew that no orthodox Jew would use them on the seventh day. At length Jake, losing all self-control, fiercely commanded her not to make him the laughingstock of the people on the street and to get in without further ado. As to the sin of the matter he was willing to take it all upon himself. Completely dismayed by his stern manner, amid the strange, uproarious, forbidding surroundings, Gitl yielded.

As the horses started she uttered a groan of consternation and remained looking aghast and with a violently throbbing heart. If she had been a culprit on the way to the gallows she could not have been more terrified than she was now at this her first ride on the day of rest.

The conductor came up for their fares. Jake handed him a ten-cent piece, and raising two fingers, he roared out: "Two! He ain' no maur as tree years, de liddle feller!" And so great was the impression which his dashing manner and his English produced on Gitl, that for some time it relieved her mind and she even forgot to be shocked by the sight of her husband handling coin on the Sabbath.

Having thus paraded himself before his wife, Jake all at once grew kindly disposed toward her.

"You must be hungry?" he asked.

"Not at all! Where do you eat your *varimess?*" *

"Don't say varimess," he corrected her complaisantly; "here it is called *dinner.*"

"*Dinner?*† And what if one becomes fatter?" she confusedly ventured an irresistible pun.

This was the way in which Gitl came to receive her first

* Yiddish for dinner.
† Yiddish for thinner.

lesson in the five or six score English words and phrases which the omnivorous Jewish jargon has absorbed in the Ghettos of English-speaking countries.

BRUNO LESSING (Rudolph Block: 1870–1940), born in New York, became famous as a journalist and editor for *The New York Sun* and *The New York Recorder,* and as a writer for the slick magazines of the time. *Children of Men* (1903), was a series of short stories about the problems and the troubles of the Jews on the Lower East Side. He also wrote *With the Best of Intentions* and *Lapidowitz.*

The Americanization of Shadrach Cohen
from
CHILDREN OF MEN

There is no set rule for the turning of the worm; most worms, however, turn unexpectedly. It was so with Shadrach Cohen.

He had two sons. One was named Abel and the other Gottlieb. They had left Russia five years before their father, had opened a store on Hester Street with the money he had given them. For reasons that only business men would understand they conducted the store in their father's name— and, when the business began to prosper and they saw an opportunity of investing further capital in it to good advantage, they wrote to their dear father to come to this country.

"We have a nice home for you here," they wrote. "We will live happily together."

Shadrach came. With him he brought Marta, the serving-woman who had nursed his wife until she died, and whom, for his wife's sake, he had taken into the household. When

the ship landed he was met by two dapper-looking young
men, each of whom wore a flaring necktie with a diamond
in it. It took him some time to realise that these were his
two sons. Abel and Gottlieb promptly threw their arms
around his neck and welcomed him to the new land. Behind his head they looked at each other in dismay. In the
course of five years they had forgotten that their father
wore a gaberdine—the loose, baglike garment of the Russian Ghetto—and had a long, straggling grey beard and
ringlets that came down over his ears—that, in short, he was
a perfect type of the immigrant whose appearance they
had so frequently ridiculed. Abel and Gottlieb were proud
of the fact that they had become Americanised. And they
frowned at Marta.

"Come, father," they said. "Let us go to a barber, who
will trim your beard and make you look more like an
American. Then we will take you home with us."

Shadrach looked from one to the other in surprise.

"My beard?" he said; "what is the matter with my
beard?"

"In this city," they explained to him, "no one wears a
beard like yours except the newly landed Russian Jews."

Shadrach's lips shut tightly for a moment. Then he said:

"Then I will keep my beard as it is. I am a newly landed
Russian Jew." His sons clinched their fists behind their
backs and smiled at him amiably. After all, he held the
purse-strings. It was best to humor him.

"What shall we do with Marta?" they asked. "We have
a servant. We will not need two."

"Marta," said the old man, "stays with us. Let the other
servant go. Come, take me home. I am getting hungry."

They took him home, where they had prepared a feast
for him. When he bade Marta sit beside him at the table
Abel and Gottlieb promptly turned and looked out of the
window. They felt that they could not conceal their feelings.
The feast was a dismal affair. Shadrach was racking his
brains to find some explanation that would account for the

change that had come over his sons. They had never been demonstrative in their affection for him, and he had not looked for an effusive greeting. But he realised immediately that there was a wall between him and his sons; some change had occurred; he was distressed and puzzled. When the meal was over Shadrach donned his praying cap and began to recite the grace after meals. Abel and Gottlieb looked at each other in consternation. Would they have to go through this at every meal? Better—far better—to risk their father's displeasure and acquaint him with the truth at once. When it came to the response Shadrach looked inquiringly at his sons. It was Abel who explained the matter:

"We—er—have grown out of—er—that is—er—done away with—er—sort of fallen into the habit, don't you know, of leaving out the prayer at meals. It's not quite American!"

Shadrach looked from one to the other. Then, bowing his head, he went on with his prayer.

"My sons," he said, when the table had been cleared. "It is wrong to omit the prayer after meals. It is part of your religion. I do not know anything about this America or its customs. But religion is the worship of Jehovah, who has chosen us as His children on earth, and that same Jehovah rules supreme over America even as He does over the country that you came from."

Gottlieb promptly changed the subject by explaining to him how badly they needed more money in their business. Shadrach listened patiently for a while, then said:

"I am tired after my long journey. I do not understand this business that you are talking about. But you may have whatever money you need. After all, I have no one but you two." He looked at them fondly. Then his glance fell upon the serving-woman, and he added, quickly:

"And Marta."

"Thank God," said Gottlieb, when their father had retired, "he does not intend to be stingy."

"Oh, he is all right," answered Abel. "After he gets used to things he will become Americanised like us."

To their chagrin, however, they began to realise, after a few months, that their father was clinging to the habits and customs of his old life with a tenacity that filled them with despair. The more they urged him to abandon his ways the more eager he seemed to become to cling to them. He seemed to take no interest in their business affairs, but he responded, almost cheerfully, to all their requests for money. He began to feel that this, after all, was the only bond between him and his sons. And when they had pocketed the money, they would shake their heads and sigh.

"Ah, father, if you would only not insist upon being so old-fashioned!" Abel would say.

"And let us fix you up a bit," Gottlieb would chime in.

"And become more progressive—like the other men of your age in this country."

"And wear your beard shorter and trimmed differently."

"And learn to speak English."

Shadrach never lost his temper; never upbraided them. He would look from one to the other and keep his lips tightly pressed together. And when they had gone he would look at Marta and would say:

"Tell me what you think, Marta. Tell me what you think."

"It is not proper for me to interfere between father and sons," Marta would say. And Shadrach could never induce her to tell him what she thought. But he could perceive a gleam in her eyes and observed a certain nervous vigour in the way she cleaned the pots and pans for hours after these talks, that fell soothingly upon his perturbed spirit.

As we remarked before, there is no rule for the turning of the worm. Some worms, however, turn with a crash. It was so with Shadrach Cohen.

Gottlieb informed his father that he contemplated getting married.

"She is very beautiful," he said. "The affair is all in the hands of the Shadchen."

His father's face lit up with pleasure.

"Gottlieb," he said, holding out his hand, "God bless you! It's the very best thing you could do. Marta, bring me my hat and coat. Come, Gottlieb. Take me to see her. I cannot wait a moment. I want to see my future daughter-in-law at once. How happy your mother would be if she were alive to-day!"

Gottlieb turned red and hung back.

"I think, father," he said, "you had better not go just yet. Let us wait a few days until the Shadchen has made all the arrangements. She is an American girl. She—she won't—er—understand your ways—don't you know? And it may spoil everything."

Crash! Marta had dropped an iron pot that she was cleaning. Shadrach was red in the face with suppressed rage.

"So!" he said. "It has come to this. You are ashamed of your father!" Then he turned to the old servant:

"Marta," he said, "to-morrow we become Americanised —you and I."

There was an intonation in his voice that alarmed his son.

"You are not angry——" he began, but with a fierce gesture his father cut him short.

"Not another word. To bed! Go to bed at once."

Gottlieb was dumbfounded. With open mouth he stared at his father. He had not heard that tone since he was a little boy.

"But, father——" he began.

"Not a word. Do you hear me? Not a word will I listen to. In five minutes if you are not in bed you go out of this house. Remember, this is my house."

Then he turned to Abel. Abel was calmly smoking a cigar.

"Throw that cigar away," his father commanded, sternly.

Abel gasped and looked at his father in dismay.

"Marta, take that cigar out of his mouth and throw it into the fire. If he objects he goes out of the house."

With a smile of intense delight Marta plucked the cigar from Abel's unresisting lips, and incidentally trod heavily upon his toes. Shadrach gazed long and earnestly at his sons.

"To-morrow, my sons," he said, slowly, "you will begin to lead a new life."

In the morning Abel and Gottlieb, full of dread forebodings, left the house as hastily as they could. They wanted to get to the store to talk matters over. They had hardly entered the place, however, when the figure of their father loomed up in the doorway. He had never been in the place before. He looked around him with great satisfaction at the many evidences of prosperity which the place presented. When he beheld the name "Shadrach Cohen, Proprietor" over the door he chuckled. Ere his sons had recovered from the shock of his appearance a pale-faced clerk, smoking a cigarette, approached Shadrach, and in a sharp tone asked.

"Well, sir, what do you want?" Shadrach looked at him with considerable curiosity. Was he Americanised, too? The young man frowned impatiently.

"Come, come! I can't stand here all day. Do you want anything?"

Shadrach smiled and turned to his sons.

"Send him away at once. I don't want that kind of young man in my place." Then turning to the young man, upon whom the light of revelation had quickly dawned, he said, sternly:

"Young man, whenever you address a person who is older than you, do it respectfully. Honour your father and your mother. Now go away as fast as you can. I don't like you."

"But, father," interposed Gottlieb, "we must have someone to do his work."

"Dear me," said Shadrach, "is that so? Then, for the present, you will do it. And that young man over there—what does he do?"

"He is also a salesman."

"Let him go. Abel will take his place."

"But, father, who is to manage the store? Who will see that the work is properly done?"

"I will," said the father. "Now, let us have no more talking. Get to work."

Crestfallen, miserable, and crushed in spirit, Abel and Gottlieb began their humble work while their father entered upon the task of familiarising himself with the details of the business. And even before the day's work was done he came to his sons with a frown of intense disgust.

"Bah!" he exclaimed. "It is just as I expected. You have both been making as complete a mess of this business as you could without ruining it. What you both lack is sense. If becoming Americanised means becoming stupid, I must congratulate you upon the thoroughness of your work. To-morrow I shall hire a manager to his store. He will arrange your hours of work. He will also pay you what you are worth. Not a cent more. How late have you been keeping this store open?"

"Until six o'clock," said Abel.

"H'm! Well, beginning to-day, you both will stay here until eight o'clock. Then one of you can go. The other will stay until ten. You can take turns. I will have Marta send you some supper."

To the amazement of Abel and Gottlieb the business of Shadrach Cohen began to grow. Slowly it dawned upon them that in the mercantile realm they were as children compared with their father. His was the true money-maker spirit; there was something wonderful in the swiftness with which he grasped the most intricate phases of trade; and where experience failed him some instinct seemed to guide

him aright. And gradually, as the business of Shadrach
Cohen increased, and even the sons saw vistas of prosperity
beyond their wildest dreams, they began to look upon their
father with increasing respect. What they had refused to
the integrity of his character, to the nobility of his heart,
they promptly yielded to the shrewdness of his brain. The
sons of Shadrach Cohen became proud of their father. He,
too, was slowly undergoing a change. A new life was un-
folding itself before his eyes, he became broader-minded,
more tolerant, and, above all, more flexible in his tenets.
Contact with the outer world had quickly impressed him
with the vast differences between his present surroundings
and his old life in Russia. The charm of American life, of
liberty, of democracy, appealed to him strongly. As the field
of his business operations widened he came more and more
in contact with American business men, from whom he
learned many things—principally the faculty of adaptability.
And as his sons began to perceive that all these business
men whom, in former days, they had looked upon with
feelings akin to reverence, seemed to show to their father
an amount of deference and respect which they had never
evinced toward the sons, their admiration for their father
increased.

And yet it was the same Shadrach Cohen.

From that explosive moment when he had rebelled
against his sons he demanded from them implicit obedience
and profound respect. Upon that point he was stern and
unyielding. Moreover, he insisted upon a strict observance
of every tenet of their religion. This, at first, was the bit-
terest pill of all. But they soon became accustomed to it.
When life is light and free from care, religion is quick to
fly; but when the sky grows dark and life becomes earnest,
and we feel its burden growing heavy upon our shoulders,
then we welcome the consolation that religion brings, and
we cling to it. And Shadrach Cohen had taught his sons
that life was earnest. They were earning their bread by

the sweat of their brow. No prisoner, with chain and ball, was subjected to closer supervision by his keeper than were Gottlieb and Abel.

"You have been living upon my charity," their father said to them: "I will teach you how to earn your own living."

And he taught them. And with the lesson they learned many things; learned the value of discipline, learned the beauty of filial reverence, learned the severe joy of the earnest life.

One day Gottlieb said to his father:

"May I bring Miriam to supper to-night? I am anxious that you should see her."

Shadrach turned his face away so that Gottlieb might not see the joy that beamed in his eyes.

"Yes, my son," he answered. "I, too, am anxious to see if she is worthy of you."

Miriam came, and in a stiff, embarrassed manner Gottlieb presented her to his father. The girl looked in surprise at the venerable figure that stood before her—a picture of a patriarch from the Pentateuch, with a long, straggling beard and ringlets of hair falling over the ears, and clad in the long gaberdine of the Russian Ghettos. And she saw a pair of grey eyes bent keenly upon her—eyes of shrewdness, but soft and tender as a woman's—the eyes of a strong man with a kind heart. Impulsively she ran toward him and seized his hands. And, with a smile upon her lips, she said:

"Will you not give me your blessing?"

When the evening meal had ended, Shadrach donned his praying cap, and with bowed head intoned the grace after meals:

"We will bless Him from whose wealth we have eaten!"

And in fervent tones rose from Gottlieb's lips the response:

"Blessed be He!"

JAMES OPPENHEIM (1882–1932), was born in Minnesota but brought up in New York City. In the 1890s and into the 1900s he worked as a steamship and express company clerk, a social worker and teacher, and as head of the Hebrew Technical School for Girls. The stories in *Dr. Rast* (1909) reflect his intimate acquaintance with the Lower East Side. Among his other novels were *The Nine-Tenths* (1911), and *The Olympians* (1912). In 1916 he became an editor of *The Seven Arts*. After 1915 he had given up novel-writing, concentrating on poetry, plays and essays. He called his stories "bad prose with a streak of suppressed poetry in them." His two best-known books of poetry are *Songs for a New Age* (1914) and *The Sea* (1924).

Groping Children
from
DR. RAST

A little before dawn the old Mother awoke the old Father, and then both dressed quietly. Added to their own breathing rose the deep breathing of four others through the thick air—the two little girls huddled on a heap of goods in the corner, the eldest daughter in the inner room, the son in the room beyond. The dirty window-panes let in a ghostlike glimmer and in the glimmer stood visible the double bed, the sewing machine, the heap of "piece-work" on the floor, and the paper ornaments on the mantelpiece.

The old couple passed quietly through the inner rooms— glancing timidly, as they went, on the dim red hair of the daughter Johanna—now called Jane—and on the black hair and white pimply face of the son Ivan—now called John. The Mother went deftly to work at the stove and the table of the kitchen, and the Father sat down and ate in silence.

Not good to look upon was the old Father. His clothes were several sizes awry and several years too old. His face was oily and cut off by a shattered beard. His big, rolling brown eyes were bloodshot. Nor had the Mother any beauty —she was clumsily fat and straggle-haired, and her face was sewed by lines like a soft quilt.

The Father arose to go. He trudged over to the busy woman.

"Good-by, dear one," he said softly in Yiddish. "Are you well?"

He kissed her.

"Ach, good," sighed the Mother, "but you heard little Esther breathing?"

He shook his head.

"She is always sick," he murmured, "but have faith, sweet one, for soon Johanna and Ivan will bring us money and fame and comfort!"

The Mother sighed heavily.

"But it takes so long," she muttered, and then suddenly she seized his arm, and her face showed pain. "Oh, my man, they grow further and further away from us! They do not love us! They are angry with us!"

He controlled his sudden-aching heart, and fondled her.

"Have faith," he murmured; "the children mean well enough. They do not understand. They speak English. They are struggling very hard—I know, I know how hard it is for them! But they are good, and how proud I am to see them grow in beauty and learning and power!"

She smiled feebly. "But they do not grow humanly; they do not grow in love and unselfishness. Ach, this America, it calls the child from the mother and father, and we are," she broke into English with a queer grin, "out-of-date!"

He shook his head sadly, and trudged out through the doorway, fumbled for the banisters and went slowly down two flights of steep stairs. He emerged in the cool of the May morning, in the twilight of the roofed street—for overhead ran the elevated road structure. He trudged under this to the corner, and followed the "el" road, which curved uptown. One block up was the station, and under the stairway was his news-stand. He unlocked the door of a little

closet, and pulled out a child's "express wagon." Then he
waited in the empty, gray street, until the quick news company wagon came thundering up, and the driver's assistant
cried, "Here, Uncle Ike!" and tossed a tied bundle of morning papers to the pavement. The wagon raced away to sow
the city with news of the world, and the old Father stooped,
labored at his bundle, sorted his papers, stacked them on
the "express," locked up his closet, and dragged his load
toward the dawn. Few people saw the strange sight—one of
the city's oldest children pulling his express wagon, his
prophet's face dreamy and unaware, his back bent, his burden trundling after him.

The Mother, after preparing the food for her children,
went back to the front room and roused the two little girls.
They arose mechanically, though little Esther moaned
feverishly and had much ado to dress herself.

"I got sick," she told her Mother.

"Hush! you wake Johanna!" said the busy Mother. She
was already hard at work doing hand-sewing. She did not
dare do machine-work until Jane and John were up.

The two little girls got their own breakfast, but Esther
crawled back without eating a bite, and fell in a faint at the
Mother's feet. The Mother cried out, and picked up the
frail bundle of fleshless bones, and put the child on the bed.
She moaned as she applied water to the face, until Esther
looked up.

"I get up," cried Esther, struggling. "I must work. I get
up. I'm all right!"

And the brave little body managed somehow to get to
her feet and hold her piece of cloth and her needle, but she
was too dizzy to speak or sew. The Mother cried over her
—affectionate words of fear and love and doubt. Her heart
was torn between the awful need of having the day's work
done and desire to protect the little child. Finally she went
to the next room.

"Jane," she called softly.

Jane sat upright.

"Is breakfast ready?" she asked sharply.

"Excuse," said the Mother tremblingly, "but could you to look at Esther?"

"Sick again?" cried Jane. "She's always sick." Then her harsh voice softened. "I'll look in later. Let me sleep, Mother!"

The Mother walked back blindly and stood at the window. Right below were the elevated tracks, and as she glanced out a train swept by with a flash of human faces, and suddenly the Mother thought of her meager world. All that she knew was that for ten blocks in any direction the world was a choked ruin of crumbling tenements, gashed by a brilliant street or two of glaring shop-windows. Save that she knew the path that had brought her here—first, Broadway, up which she had come years ago in an open truck, sitting on her luggage and minding her absent-minded husband and two little children. Beyond that lay the Atlantic, and beyond that a rattling ride in a train, and beyond the ride the massacre in the Russian village of Pleynoff. And she thought a moment of how she had saved her children's lives, on a wild January night, by flight through a howling storm.

Jane went to sleep again—slept until eight—then she joined her brother at the breakfast table.

The neatly dressed, pimply-faced boy looked up from his coffee and rolls.

"Well, sis," he remarked, "how goes it?"

She stood frowningly, arranging her fiery red hair. Her face had little beauty, but it was strangely animated and fascinating. The eyes were brilliant brown, the cheeks flushed, the cheek-bones high. She was distinctly of the American Indian type.

"Oh, John," she exclaimed, dropping in a chair, "I'll explode soon!"

His face darkened.

"Don't blame you!" he muttered. "It's the deuce here!"

"Worse!" she cried. "I feel every afternoon as if I were

coming back to a graveyard. I can't stand it any longer."

"I can't, either," he echoed. "I sweat night and day, and nothing comes of it. *They*"—he nodded toward the front room—"think it's easy to study law all day, and then sell men's furnishings at night in a Pollacken Grand Street store. They always look at me as if I were a criminal—such looks! They always remind us what ungrateful children we are. Ungrateful!" he snorted. "What have we to be grateful for?"

She bit her lips.

"Yes, John," she whispered, "but you're a boy—it's easy for you. But I—" her eyes filled. *"Look at the rags I have to wear!* Everybody notices. And I can't even ask a friend to come down here—to see what kikes we are! what Pollacks! Oh, I can't stand it!"

They ate in bitter silence, these poor children who could not understand.

"I suppose," Jane murmured, "they haven't got it easy; I suppose they get mighty little out of life—but they're used to that! But," she added fiercely, her eyes blazing under the red hair, "why did they train us differently? Why did they make us so unlike themselves?" She clutched the table with her hands, and then suddenly blurted out: "But what's the use of talking?"

He gave vent to anger.

"I wish I had money," he exclaimed. "I'd skip out of here!"

He pulled out his dollar watch.

"But say, sis, it's late—it's twenty after! Beat it!"

They arose and rushed for their hats and books, called a hasty good-by to the front room, ran down the steps, hurried through the crowded street to the "el" station, and passed the Father without greeting.

Four o'clock that afternoon Jane came out of the uptown Medical College in the center of an excited group of men and women students. Among the dark heads hers shone

out, and among the faces hers seemed to flash. In any group
she was the natural hub, animated and quick-tongued. The
students had just been testing the efficacy of ultra-violet
rays in the treatment of cancer, and she was full of the
glory and mystery of running a ray of healing light through
a diseased human body.

The group stopped at the corner of Fifty-ninth Street to
wait for the crosstown car. It was a yearning May-day, blue
and shining, and they breathed the keen air deeply.

"We young doctors, I tell you," Jane cried breathlessly,
"are coming into a future of miracles! The world is ours!
The fate of the race is in our hands! We shall take Nature
and use her as a tool to shape a new human breed! I'm
almost too excited to speak!"

A peal of delighted laughter went up.

"And Miss Grabo," commented a big, dark, spade-
bearded specimen in a kindly voice, "says she's a material-
ist! Why, her idealism is rank!"

She whirled on him.

"Ideals? Yes," she cried, "but practical ones—scientific
ones. Your scientist is your only idealist—he alone throws
out his vision into experiments and makes it real, human,
workable! But there's nothing wishy-washy about that!
There's no sentiment in it! It's just work!"

"Just work?" said the spade-bearded specimen, frowning
moodily. "I fear, Miss Grabo, you're a dreamer like the rest
of us. It'll all be knocked into a cocked hat, though, when
you get into your practice! You'll leave the future alone and
get busy on catarrh and rheumatism and grip and tonsilitis!
And you'll curse the human breed, not improve it!"

She laughed.

"We'll see!" she cried, "we'll see! I won't be tied to
money-grubbing, not I!"

The group laughed merrily, for they liked her and her
wildfire enthusiasm, and they shouted good-by as the car
stopped, gathered them in and whisked them away. Jane
walked rapidly across town and took the Second Avenue

elevated. She sat down in a corner, flushed and excited, in a fever of the future. For the moment she was herself, far removed from the rags on her body and the Russian twang in her speech—all absorbed in the world of her work, her strength, her dreams. Medicine to her was the breath of life; it led her through marvel on marvel of adventure and discovery. Into her tenement-house hands—hands that had sturdily groped out and out until they touched the shining world beyond—had been put unimagined powers, and the thrill of this new strength made her blood sing through her. Her fine Jewish mentality needed only the stimulus of daily work to grow by leaps and ...ds. There seemed to be nothing she could not achieve.

But then, like a shock, came Canal Street. She hurried out, and down the steps, and to the street. She turned. And there, as ever, a bill-post advertisement of her mean condition, stood the Father, leaning against a post and buried in a Yiddish paper. The flashing, brilliant face looked toward the Old Testament prophet, on whose head was jammed an absurd faded derby.

She took a sharp breath and had half a mind to hurry by without speaking, but the deep dreamer instinctively felt the presence of a customer and glanced up.

"Ach!" he murmured, "Johanna!"

She paused near him, and flushed red.

"Father," she snapped, "can't you call me *Jane?*"

He shook his head, and smiled.

"Excuse," he breathed; "I forget much. Jane," he suddenly seemed to awaken, "hurry home. Little Esther is took sick."

"Sick?" echoed Jane. *"She* sick? Again?"

He shrugged his shoulders and said nothing. Where the English word slipped him, there was nothing to say, for Jane did not tolerate Yiddish.

"Sick?" Jane repeated. "Oh, everything's spoiled!"

Then, for the first time, she remembered her Mother's words in the morning and trudged on guiltily down the street under the elevated structure. The street was so narrow that this structure roofed it over and made it a gloomy arcade everlastingly damp and muddy. A stream of people moved up and down. At the next corner the "el" road curved into Division Street, and in the center of this was home.

Jane's mood went bitter. Uptown lay her own kingdom, her work, her personality—the Jane Grabo who was the intellectual center of a group of bright minds; down here was only the crass realness, the obscurity, the shame and the squalor. She suddenly remembered the afternoon's experiment, and thought of her home as the cancer in her life and no ultra-violet rays to dissipate it—a cancer she had to ashamedly hide, and that ate her heart out.

The tenement was four-story wood, painted green. On the ground floor was an artificial flower factory; in the cellar lived the Matches Man, the beggar who made his way into uptown brownstone houses with a single box of unbuyable matches. Jane entered the narrow, hump-sided hall and went up the steep stairs, and knocked on the front door. After a minute it was narrowly opened—as if she were the landlord or the instalment man, she thought—and her Mother peered out.

"Ach, you!" she muttered, and flung the door wide.

"What's the matter with Esther?" snapped Jane, as she strode into the bedroom. At the edge of the bed sat one of the thin, big-eyed girls, sewing feverishly. In the bed lay Esther, tossing and groaning.

"Oh!" Jane snorted. "Why, this air is enough to stifle a person! Can't you keep the window open, Mother? Won't you ever learn that?"

The fat, bloodless woman sighed heavily.

"But it makes draught," she murmured, "and dirt and noise what hurts."

Jane strode over and flung up the dirty windows.

"There! We can breathe at least in this hole."

"But Esther's took sick," the Mother put in weakly. "Fell down yesterday—fell down to-day."

Jane went over to the bed.

"Esther," she said sharply, "let me feel your pulse."

Esther turned a terrified face toward her sister.

"Stick out your tongue!"

The little girl began sobbing violently.

"Sh!" said the Mother, "take care! She's very, very sick!"

Jane seized the little wrist. The pulse was galloping. It needed but a touch to reveal the rage of high fever.

"Oh, you'll have to call Dr. Rast," she muttered. "I ca[n] handle this!"

"Dr. Rast!" cried the Mother, aghast, "but we got no money."

Esther began to cry out deliriously. Jane groaned.

"Call him anyway! Here—I'll go myself!" Then sudden[ly] she blurted out: "I can't understand all this! Here I've got loads of things to study, and now my whole afternoon's smashed up! It's a nuisance!"

She turned just as her brother entered.

"What's up?" he exclaimed.

"Oh, Esther's sick," cried Jane, "and everything's upset again!"

"Same old story!" snapped the boy.

The Mother looked sadly from one to the other.

"Ach, my little Esther!" she cried out, and put her hands to her face.

"Now we'll have a scene!" Jane sputtered. "I'll be back soon."

And she rushed out. Dr. Rast's office on East Broadway was three blocks away. Nell opened the door in the musty hallway.

"Is Dr. Rast in?" asked Jane.

"Yes, Miss Grabo; come in!"

She was ushered into the little dark waiting-room.

"Morris!" called Nell, "Miss Grabo!"

The tall, dark doctor emerged from the front office.

"Any trouble?" he asked kindly.

He shook hands with her, and she smiled.

"My little sister's sick—high fever, quick pulse; I think it's serious!"

"Well," he exclaimed, "that's bad! Wait a moment."

He went back to the office.

Nell sighed: "He's working himself to death! He's been on the jump all day. He's killing himself to help others!"

"He's foolish to do it," said Jane.

Nell looked at the medical student sharply—a look Jane did not forget—but just then the doctor came in with coat on and satchel in hand. He kissed Nell good-by.

"Now, little wife," he laughed, "mind the house till I come back!"

He and Jane hurried out and down the crowded street.

"Well, how's medicine?" he asked gaily.

Jane's face suddenly became brilliant.

"Oh, it's glorious!" she cried. "To-day we experimented on cancer with ultra-violet rays!"

"H'm! Interesting!" he murmured.

"Yes." She was breathless again with excitement. "It's a hint of what the future holds. We doctors shall be the new creators—we shall start a new race of human beings! It's wonderful!"

He smiled sadly. "Is that the kind of a doctor Miss Grabo is going to be?"

"Why not?" she challenged.

He laughed a bit.

"Well, I guess I'm an old-fashioned doctor," he murmured, "and I have queer ideas about things. Do you know my definition of a doctor?"

"What is it?"

Dr. Rast looked at her queerly.

"Why, he's just an ordinary man, like Jesus, who lays his hand on the filth of the world's flesh, but who lays his heart and his soul on—" he paused, and held his breath, "bruised hearts and broken souls."

"Like Jesus?" she cried, shocked. "You, a Jew, say that?"

"Why not?" he smiled. "Jesus was a Jew. And as a doctor I revere him. He was our greatest doctor—he cured multitudes! I wish there was one such in these roaring slums."

A shadow of contempt passed over her face.

"But that's not being a doctor," she cried; "that's grubbing in a garbage-can!"

He smiled sadly again.

"You don't understand," he said gently. "This city has a disease—a cancer." She looked up quickly. "That cancer is this very district we live in, and that cancer isn't only a growth of the flesh, it's a mental disorder—a spiritual disorder! We need people to clean cellars, to open windows, to heal bodies—but more, to bring in those mysterious ultra-violet rays of the spirit that dissolve the knot in the heart and the kink in the soul! We need Christs of the common people!"

His face was so dead in earnest that she said nothing. The fire of his conviction could not help but touch her and thrill her in spite of herself. They walked in silence down through the crowd, through the arcade, into the black hall, and up the steep stairs.

The whole family was in the bedroom. The Father was bending over the bed. The one little girl was still sewing. The Mother and son had evidently been quarreling.

The Mother came forward.

"Och, Dr. Rast!" she cried, "my little Esther is dying!"

"Don't get so excited!" snapped John.

Dr. Rast turned to John.

"Step out," he said sharply; "you too, Miss Grabo. I want quiet!"

Dr. Rast was seldom angry, but when he was those about him trembled. The boy sullenly went out.

"Come on back, sis," he muttered.

Jane's eyes flashed as she followed him.

"Now, Beth," the doctor murmured, "hadn't you better run out and take a walk?"

The little seamstress looked up with big eyes.

"Got to sew," she muttered wearily.

He took the material and needle from her hands, and lifted her up level with his eyes.

"Little sweetheart," he murmured, "doctor says out you go!" He walked to the open door, and kissed her. "And out you go!"

She laughed merrily, and he swung her out and shut the door.

"Now, Mr. Grabo, sit down!" the doctor commanded, "and Mrs. Grabo, too! Quiet, now!"

The old people grinned and seated themselves. The doctor bent over the bed. The little girl was tossing and crying incoherently. He whispered to her:

"Come, Esther, it's Dr. Rast! Show me how brave you are. Come! There's my little girl!"

She looked up into his face and cried out. He took a quick look at the convulsed lips; then he felt the pulse and put his big head to the restless, shrunken chest.

"How long was she sick?" he asked sharply.

Mrs. Grabo sobbed: "A week!"

"A week! You let it run on? Why?"

"She works on piece-work, and makes us money!"

"I thought she went to school," said Dr. Rast.

Mr. Grabo lifted his voice.

"She and Elizabeth got to help," he explained. "I work, mine wife works, they works—need the money."

Dr. Rast's face darkened.

"For what?"

"For Johanna and Ivan!"

Dr. Rast breathed quickly. He went over to the Mother and took one of her big hands between his own.

"Now, tell me," he said quietly, "how sick was she?"

The poor woman looked at him with terrified expression.

"She fall down," she gasped, "yesterday—to-day; she spit

blood—she cry. She's a good girl—she try to sew, and fall
—and get up, and try to sew—and fall—and is like dead.
I put her to bed!"

A strange pain and pity tightened his heart and showed
in his struggling face.

"Dear Mrs. Grabo!" he whispered, his hand pressing
hers, "Esther is very, very sick!—Hush, now! She hears!"

The Mother looked at him wildly.

"She die? My baby die?" she cried hoarsely.

The doctor gulped.

"Maybe not! We'll work hard, won't we? We'll have
quiet? You'll do as I say?"

The Father arose and tottered toward them. His eyes
seemed to bulge from their sockets.

"We let Esther die?" he moaned in a ghastly voice.

The Mother rocked back and forth.

"Ach, my little Esther, my little baby!" she wailed. Dr.
Rast seized Mr. Grabo's arm.

"Come, brace up!" he cried. "Come, both of you! Help
—get to work—don't kill her!"

The man and woman seemed stricken down—terrified
and helpless. But Dr. Rast gave quick, clear directions.
Then he wrote out a prescription and hurried through the
two dark middle rooms to the kitchen in back. John was
walking about, and Jane was seated at the table, her head
in her hands. They both turned as he entered.

"John," said Dr. Rast, in a sharp tone, "run and get
this prescription filled. There isn't a moment to lose!"

John took it, muttered under his breath, and sullenly
went out.

Dr. Rast sat down at the table near Jane.

"How is Esther?" she muttered.

He leaned toward her, and spoke harshly:

"She has a terrible case of pneumonia—the last stages,
in fact!"

In spite of herself, she felt as if she were suddenly
frozen.

"Last stages? You mean she'll——"

The edge of his voice cut like a knife:

"Die! Yes—a matter of a few hours, or less! Where have you been all this week?"

She choked, and held to the table with her hands.

"This week?"

"Yes," he went on terribly; "*you* should have known this!"

"Why, the girl had a cough—she's always complaining —she's always been a sickly thing—she's always been full of pains——"

He broke in roughly:

"And you never paid attention! Always!" His eyes flashed a look she could not meet. "Always! Miss Grabo, your sister has been sick for years! This is only the breakdown! And *you* want to be a doctor!"

She shivered, but anger suddenly staved her.

"And what of it?" she cried. "I'm too busy to bother with these people here!"

He sat back, shocked.

"These people!" he echoed. "No, no, it can't b˞ It can't be that you are one of those vulgar second-generation girls—one of those children of immigrants who are ashamed of their parents!"

A rush of red overspread her face.

"Is it for you to tell me this?" she muttered, but, nevertheless, went on in self-defense: "Why shouldn't I be ashamed? Look at them—kikes, Yiddish; hear their broken English; see how they live, in a pigsty—and their manners —their ignorance—and look at—" She stopped.

"You!" he added. "Now, let me tell you something! They are Russian Jews—true! But who are you? Whose blood is in you? From whose brain and body and soul are you born? Why, haven't you learned yet that you can't shake off your race? It's the breath you breathe! *You*, too, are a Russian Jew—" he leaned forward, and whispered harshly, *"polished up!"*

She bit her lip.

"You compare me to them?"

"Be proud if I do!" he cried, "but I can't! There's little comparison! *They* are of the nobility of earth——"

"Nobility!" she broke in.

He looked at her queerly.

"Come, come!" he said quickly, "who is giving you an education! Whose money?—I mean outside the scholarship."

"Why shouldn't they?" she said shrilly. "That's all they're good for. I have talent—it's for the good of the race—it's their duty to develop it!"

"Now, wait a minute," he went on; "we're going too quickly. First of all, your Father has more talent, more learning, more character, more breeding than a dozen of you!"

"Dr. Rast!" she cried, "what right have you to tell me these things?"

"A curious right," he exclaimed—"the right of a doctor over his patient, and of a friend over his friend, and of a human being over a human being! Now, let me go on. As I said, your Father has wonderful talent. How else could he dream of making a doctor of his daughter? Do you think an ordinary man could grasp so great a vision? Was it his idea?"

She was silent, her eyes wide. A strange pang of remorse hurt her heart.

"Yes," she murmured.

"And learning?" he laughed. "Why, your Father and I have had many long talks together at the news-stand, and he's the most learned man I know! He has absorbed big washes of history; he has studied Rabbinical literature; he knows the Bible backward; he knows Russian literature thoroughly. He's perfectly marvelous. Oh, you blind young American girl—you don't know your own parents—you never became acquainted with them! You have separated yourself from them by the wall of a new language!"

She seemed stunned, and said nothing. He was letting into her mind a flood of new knowledge.

"And character? Perfectly wonderful!" cried the doctor. "Don't you know the story of the massacre? How your parents saved your lives when the mob was raging through Pleynoff? How they refused to give in—to declare themselves Christians? How they escaped at night and worked their way to America? Why, if I had a parent who was such a hero, I would—would know what the word reverence means! And that's not the greatest!"

"What is?" she asked breathlessly.

"This," he murmured, "that all these years a man of his accomplishments, of his sensitive nature, of his heroic heart, has, without a complaint, without a pang of hesitation, been content to humble himself in the very dust for his children, been content to get up at five in the morning and trudge about with newspapers, been content to a long day, in the hot summer or the terrible winter, of standing at his post. And all for you!"

Her hand went to her mouth; she looked as if she were frightened.

"But, worst of all," he muttered, "your Mother has worn her eyes out on piece-work, and your parents have broken the law and set your little sisters to work, that *you* might have your wishes, that *you* might be free of the sweat and the dust of life, that *you* might have the big and real things of life! Why, aren't those little girls worth as much as you? Oh, you don't see yourself as you are!" he cried. "What kind of a decent girl would let her mother go blind, her sisters be cut off from childhood, from education, from all the future, her father freeze or burn in the street, all to give her peace and joy and plenty?"

She bowed her head in her hands. His voice came near, and was final and terrible.

"And your little sister! How she worked this last week, I can't dream. She has been consumed in a living fire—the poor, shrunken little baby. She fainted away, spit blood,

and got up and worked on—worked until she fell senseless
—till she was delirious. And all for you. All this week, and
you here every day!"

During the pause that followed a hand seemed to grasp
her heart and crush it. She waited for what worse was to
come.

"Miss Grabo," he said slowly and with infinite pity,
"you have killed your little sister!"

She gave a cry, but when she looked up he had gone.

Her mind went hurrying back over her life with a search-
light. She saw strange things. She felt like sobbing—she
that never sobbed. A fearful remorse clutched at her. Her
Mother and Father, under the rays of the new light, suddenly appeared in a weird radiance; learned, heroic,
talented, martyrs. She could not shut out the truth; it ate
into her; it seared her heart; it scalded her mind; it made
her soul writhe. And then came vividly a thousand memories of sad faces when she had mocked her parents or
shocked them—a thousand memories of selfishness, of care-
lessness. And now? That little shrunken creature in the
front room was her sister—and she— She cried out: "No,
no! I haven't killed her, not I!"

But Dr. Rast had said it, and he never lied. *She* had
done this; *she* had neglected her duty—had trampled the
little things that make life, to grasp the big thing which is
only a dream— had— Suddenly Dr. Rast's words came
back: "A doctor is merely an ordinary man like Jesus,"
and "bruised hearts and broken souls," and the "ultra-violet
rays that dissolve the knot in the heart and the kink in the
soul." She was utterly miserable, all crumpled up. She saw
herself a base, selfish girl, who had deliberately shunned
the truer life for the false. And her sister? No, it was not too
late! She herself would nurse the child—would warm it
back to life; she would earn money, too—study shorthand
at night—anything—and Esther and Beth should be
wrenched loose. She would change all. It could not be too
late.

John came bounding in.

"Has that softy doctor gone yet?" he asked.

She leaped up, eyes flaming.

"John," she cried, "be careful! Esther is dying! You and I have got to change things here!"

"Jane!" he exclaimed, "what has happened?"

His face suddenly paled, and he clutched the back of a chair.

There was a step, and he turned, and Jane turned. It was Doctor Rast. Even in the late twilight his face was lividly white and his eyes burning. They read death in his face. He cleared his throat; his words seemed to come from far away.

"John," he said, "and Jane! Come in to your Mother and Father!"

They followed him in awed silence. Every detail came clear: the dark rooms; the glimmer of twilight beyond in the front windows; the roaring of the elevated train; and the terrible, stifled sobs of the Mother. They saw, in the dim light, the Mother flung over the child, and the Father standing in the far corner.

They heard the Mother's cries:

"My little baby—oh, my little Esther—my little dead baby!"

And as they entered, the Father suddenly took a step toward them, and his wail seemed to rip open the ceiling and find its way to other worlds.

"Oh, weh! oh, weh! oh, weh!"

And then, as if his throat were strangled, he followed the Jewish custom by seizing with his hand the top of his shirt and tearing it down to his waist. The rip was like the audible shredding of a human heart. The Mother staggered to her feet with a wild cry.

Jane stood transfixed, tottered, cried:

"Mother! my Mother!"

And took her Mother to her arms and to her heart.

And as it came to the poor, tear-blinded Father that his

Johanna was again cradled at the Mother's breast, and as he saw his Ivan breaking down and sobbing over the bed-post, and as he looked on his dead, he groped his way to Dr. Rast, he sank his head on the Doctor's shoulder, and he murmured in Yiddish:

"The children of me have come back through death!—through living death! We are stricken, yea, stricken holy! Now there is light and understanding!"

And Dr. Rast was full of love for human beings.

MONTAGUE GLASS (1877–1934), son of an English napkin manufacturer, came to the United States in 1890. After going to the City College of New York and New York University Law School, he practiced law. His stories were based on his association with a firm whose practice was largely "commercial" and dealt with clients in the women's outer garment business. His first tales of *Potash and Perlmutter* (1910) were followed by *Abe and Mawruss* (1911), both of which became stage successes. His last book on the petty tycoons of the garment industry was *Keeping Expenses Down* (1932), done with Dan Jarrett.

R.S.V.P.
from
ABE AND MAWRUSS

It was the tenth of the month, and Abe Potash, of Potash & Perlmutter, was going through the firm mail with an exploratory thumb and finger, looking for checks.

"Well, Mawruss," he said to his partner, Morris Perlmutter, "all them hightone customers of yours they don't take it so particular that they should pay on the day, Mawruss. If they was only so prompt with checks as they was to claim deductions, Mawruss, you and me would have no worries. I think some of 'em finds a shortage in the shipment before they open the packing-case that the goods come in. Take your friend Hyman Maimin, of Sarahcuse—nothing suits him. He always kicks that the goods ain't made up right, or we ain't sent him enough fancies, or something like that. Five or six letters he writes us, Mawruss, when he gets the goods; but when he got to pay for 'em, Mawruss, that's something else again. You might think postage stamps was solitaire diamonds, and that he dassen't use 'em!"

"Quit your kicking," Perlmutter broke in. "This is only the tenth of the month."

"I know it," said Abe. "We should have had a check by the tenth of last month, but"—here Abe's eye lit upon an envelope directed in the handwriting of Hyman Maimin —"I guess there was some good reason for the delay," he went on evenly. "Anyhow, here's a letter from him now."

He tore open the envelope and hurriedly removed the enclosed letter. Then he took the envelope, blew it wide open, and shook it up and down, but no check fell out.

"Did y'ever see the like?" he exclaimed. "Sends us a letter and no check!"

"Why, it ain't a letter," Morris said. "It's an advertisement."

Abe's face grew white.

"A meeting of creditors!" he gasped.

Morris grabbed the missive from his partner and spread it out on the table.

"Hello!" he exclaimed, a great smile of relief spreading itself about his ears. "It's a wedding invitation!" He held it up to the light. " 'Mr. and Mrs. Marcus Bramson,' " he read, " ' request the pleasure of Potash & Perlmutter's company at the marriage of their daughter Tillie to Mr. Hyman Maimin, Sunday, March 19, at seven o'clock, P.M., Wiedermayer's Hall, 2099 South Oswego Street. R.S.V.P. to residence of bride, care of Advance Credit Clothing Company, 2097 South Oswego Street.' "

"What is that 'R.S.V.P. to residence of bride'?" Abe Potash asked.

Morris reflected for a moment.

"That means," he said at length, "that we should know where to send the present to."

"How do you make that out?" said Abe.

" 'R.S.V.P.'," Morris replied, emphasizing each letter with a motion of his hand, "means 'Remember to send vedding present.' "

"But," Abe rejoined, "when I went to night school, we spelt 'wedding' with a W."

"A greenhorn like Maimin," said Morris, "don't know no better."

"He knows enough to ask for a wedding present, Mawruss," Abe commented, "even if he don't know how to spell it. We'll send him a wedding present, Mawruss! We'll send him a summons from the court, that's what we'll send him!"

Morris shook his head.

"That ain't no way to talk, Abe," he said. "If a customer gets married, we *got* to send him a wedding present. It don't cost much, and if Hyman Maimin gets a couple of thousand dollars with this Miss—Miss——"

"Advance Credit Clothing Company," Abe helped out.

Morris nodded.

"Then he buys more goods, ain't it?" he concluded.

"Let him pay for what he's got," Abe rejoined.

"It just slipped his mind. He'll pay up fast enough, after he gets married."

"All right! Wait till he pays up, and then we'll give him a present."

"Now lookyhere, Abe," Morris protested, "you can't be small in a matter of this kind. I'll draw a check for twenty-five dollars, and——"

"Twenty-five dollars!" Abe screamed. "You're crazy! When you was married last year, I'd like to know who gives you a present for twenty-five dollars?"

"Why you did, Abe," Morris replied.

"Me?" Abe cried. "Say, Mawruss, I want to tell you something. If you can buy a fine sterling silver bumbum dish, like what I give you, for twenty-five dollars, I'll take it off your hands for twenty-seven-fifty any day!"

"But, Abe——"

"Another thing, Mawruss," Abe went on. "If you don't like that dish, there ain't no law compelling you to keep it, you understand. Send it back. My Rosie can use it. Maybe we ain't so stylish like your Minnie, Mawruss; but if we don't have bumbums every day, we could put dill pickles into it!"

"One moment," Morris protested. "I ain't saying anything about that bumbum dish, Abe. All I meant that if you give *me* such a high-price present when *I* get married, that's all the more reason why we should give a high-price present to a customer what we will make money on. I ain't no customer, Abe."

"I know you ain't," said Abe. "You're only a partner, and I don't make no money on you, neither."

Morris shrugged his shoulders.

"What's the use of wasting more time about it, Abe?" he said. "Go ahead and buy a present."

"Me buy it?" Abe cried. "You know yourself, Mawruss, I ain't a success with presents. You draw the check and get your Minnie to buy it. She's an up-to-date woman, Mawruss, while my Rosie is a back number. She don't know nothing but to keep a good house, Mawruss. Sterling silver bumbum dishes she don't know, Mawruss. If I took her advice, you wouldn't got no bumbum dish. Nut-picks, Mawruss, from the five-and-ten-cent store, that's what you'd got. You might appreciate them, Mawruss; but a sterling silver——"

At this juncture Morris took refuge in the outer office, where Miss Cohen, the bookkeeper, was taking off her wraps.

"Miss Cohen," he said, "draw a check for twenty-five dollars to bearer, and enter it up as a gratification to Hyman Maimin."

At dinner that evening Morris handed the check over to his wife.

"Here Minnie," he said, "Abe wants you should buy a wedding present for a customer."

"What kind of a wedding present?" Mrs. Perlmutter asked.

"Something in solid sterling silver, like that bumbum dish what Abe gave us."

"But, Mawruss," she protested, "you know we got that bonbon dish locked away in the sideboard, and we never take it out. Let's give 'em something useful."

"Suit yourself," Morris replied. "Only don't bother me about it."

"All right," Mrs. Perlmutter said. "Leave me the name and address, and I'll see that they send it direct from the store. I'll put one of your cards inside."

"And another thing," Morris concluded. "See that you don't hold nothing out on us by way of commission."

Mrs. Perlmutter smiled serenely.

"I won't," she said, in dulcet tones.

It was the fourth day after Potash & Perlmutter's receipt of the wedding invitation. When Morris Perlmutter entered the private office he found Abe Potash in the absorbed perusal of the *Daily Cloak and Suit Record*. Abe looked up and saluted his partner with a malignant grin.

"Well, Mawruss," he said, "I suppose you sent that present to Hyman Maimin?"

"I sent it off long since already," Morris replied.

"I hope it was a nice one, Mawruss," Abe went on "I hope it was a real nice one. I'm sorry now, Mawruss, we didn't spend fifty dollars. That would have made it an even seven hundred, instead of only six hundred and seventy-five, that Hyman Maimin owed us."

"What d'ye mean?" cried Morris.

"I don't mean nothing, Mawruss—nothing at all," Abe said, with ironical emphasis. He handed the paper to Morris. "Here, look for yourself!"

He pointed with a trembling forefinger at the "business-troubles" column, and Morris's eyes seemed to bulge out of his head as he scanned the printed page:

A petition in bankruptcy was filed late yesterday afternoon against Hyman Maimin, 83 West Tonawanda Street, Syracuse. It is claimed that he transferred assets to the amount of eight thousand dollars last week. Mr. Maimin says that he has been doing business at a heavy loss of late, but that he hopes to be able to resume. A ‎⁀lement of thirty cents is proposed.

Morris sat down in a revolving-chair too crushed for comment, and drummed with a lead pencil on the desk.

"I wonder if he done up his intended father-in-law, too?" he said at length.

"No fear of that, Mawruss," Abe replied. "He ain't no sucker like us, Mawruss. I bet you his father-in-law—what's his name——"

"The Advance Credit Clothing Company," Morris suggested.

"Sure," Abe went on. "I bet you this clothing concern says to him: 'If you want to marry my daughter, you gotter go into bankruptcy first. Then, when you're all cleaned up, I'll give you a couple of thousand dollars to start as a new beginner in another line.' Ain't it?"

Morris nodded gloomily.

"No, Mawruss," Abe continued. "I bet you his father-in-law is a big crook like himself."

He rose to his feet and opened the large green-and-red covered book furnished by the commercial agency to which they subscribed.

"I'm going to do now, Mawruss, what you should have done before you sent that present," he said. "I'm going to look up this here Advance Credit Clothing Company. I bet you he ain't even in the book—what?"

Before Morris could reply, the letter-carrier entered with the morning mail. While Abe continued to run his thumb down the columns of the commercial agency book, Morris began to open the envelopes. Both their heads were bent over their tasks, when an exclamation arose simultaneously from each.

"Now, what d'ye think of that?" said Abe.

"Did y' ever see anything like it?" Morris cried.

"What is it?" Abe asked.

For answer, Morris thrust a letter into his partner's hand. It was headed, "The Advance Credit Clothing Company—Marcus Bramson, Proprietor," and read as follows:

MESSRS. POTASH & PERLMUTTER.
GENTS:

Your shipment of the 5th is to hand, and in reply would say that we are returning it *via* Blue Line on account Miss Tillie Bramson's engagement is broken. We understand that lowlife H. Maimin got into you for six hundred and fifty dollars. Believe me, he done us for more than that. Our Mr. Bramson will be in New York shortly, and will call to look at your line. Hoping we will be able to do business with you,

Yours truly,
THE ADVANCE CREDIT CLOTHING COMPANY,
Per T. B.

Abe Potash laid down the letter with a sigh, while his thumb still rested caressingly on the open page of the mercantile agency book.

"So he's going to send back the present!" he said. "That man Marcus Bramson, proprietor, has a big heart, Mawruss. He's a man with fine feelings and a fine disposition, Mawruss. He's got a fine rating too, Mawruss—seventy-five to a hundred thousand, first credit!" He closed the book almost lovingly. "D'ye think they would give the money back for that present, Mawruss?"

"I don't know," said Morris. "Minnie bought it, and she told me it was a big bargain. It was a sale, she said, but I guess they'll take it back."

MARY ANTIN (1881–1949), born in Polotzk, Russia, came to the United States with her mother and family in 1894; her father, who had arrived a few years before, was a grocer in Chelsea, Massachusetts. A precocious child, she was educated at Teachers College and Barnard College where she met and married Amadeus Grabau, a paleontology professor. *From Polotzk to Boston* (1899), a sketch, her first work, was followed by *The Promised Land* (1912), which strongly emphasized the melting pot, and *They Who Knock at the Gates* (1914). In her later years she worked as a social worker and "sought the face of God." According to Rabbi Cronbach, who knew her, "the atheist of *The Promised Land* had, amidst deprivation and suffering, discovered the reality of God."

The Exodus
from
THE PROMISED LAND

On the day when our steamer ticket arrived, my mother did not go out with her basket, my brother stayed out of heder, and my sister salted the soup three times. I do not know what I did to celebrate the occasion. Very likely I played tricks on Deborah, and wrote a long letter to my father.

Before sunset the news was all over Polotzk that Hannah Hayye had received a steamer ticket for America. Then they began to come. Friends and foes, distant relatives and new acquaintances, young and old, wise and foolish, debtors

and creditors, and mere neighbors,—from every quarter of
the city, from both sides of the Dvina, from over the Polota,
from nowhere,—a steady stream of them poured into our
street, both day and night, till the hour of our departure.
And my mother gave audience. Her faded kerchief halfway off her head, her black ringlets straying, her apron
often at her eyes, she received her guests in a rainbow of
smiles and tears. She was the heroine of Polotzk, and she
conducted herself appropriately. She gave her heart's
thanks for the congratulations and blessings that poured in
on her; ready tears for condolences; patient answers to
monotonous questions; and handshakes and kisses and hugs
she gave gratis.

What did they not ask, the eager, foolish, friendly people? They wanted to handle the ticket, and mother must
read them what is written on it. How much did it cost? Was
it all paid for? Were we going to have a foreign passport
or did we intend to steal across the border? Were we not
all going to have new dresses to travel in? Was it sure that
we could get koscher food on the ship? And with the questions poured in suggestions, and solid chunks of advice
were rammed in by nimble prophecies. Mother ought to
make a pilgrimage to a "Good Jew"—say, the Rebbe of
Lubavitch—to get his blessing on our journey. She must be
sure and pack her prayer books and Bible, and twenty
pounds of zwieback at the least. If they did serve trefah on
the ship, she and the four children would have to starve,
unless she carried provisions from home.—Oh, she must
take all the featherbeds! Featherbeds are scarce in America.
In America they sleep on hard mattresses, even in winter.
Haveh Mirel, Yachne the dressmaker's daughter, who
emigrated to New York two years ago, wrote her mother
that she got up from childbed with sore sides, because she
had no featherbed.—Mother must n't carry her money in a
pocketbook. She must sew it into the lining of her jacket.
The policemen in Castle Garden take all their money from

the passengers as they land, unless the travellers deny having any.

And so on, and so on, till my poor mother was completely bewildered. And as the day set for our departure approached, the people came oftener and stayed longer, and rehearsed my mother in long messages for their friends in America, praying that she deliver them promptly on her arrival, and without fail, and might God bless her for her kindness, and she must be sure and write them how she found their friends.

Hayye Dvoshe, the wig-maker, for the eleventh time repeating herself, to my mother, still patiently attentive, thus:—

"Promise me, I beg you. I don't sleep nights for thinking of him. Emigrated to America eighteen months ago, fresh and well and strong, with twenty-five ruble in his pocket, besides his steamer ticket, with new phylacteries, and a silk skull-cap, and a suit as good as new,—made it only three years before,—everything respectable, there could be nothing better;—sent one letter, how he arrived in Castle Garden, how well he was received by his uncle's son-in-law, how he was conducted to the baths, how they bought him an American suit, everything good, fine, pleasant;—wrote how his relative promised him a position in his business— a clothing merchant is he—makes gold,—and since then not a postal card, not a word, just as if he had vanished, as if the earth had swallowed him. *Oi weh!* what have n't I imagined, what have n't I dreamed, what have n't I lamented! Already three letters have I sent—the last one, you know, you yourself wrote for me, Hannah Hayye, dear —and no answer. Lost, as if in the sea!"

And after the application of a corner of her shawl to eyes and nose, Hayye Dvoshe, continuing:—

"So you will go into the newspaper, and ask them what has become of my Möshele, and if he is n't in Castle Garden; maybe he went up to Balti-moreh,—it's in the neighborhood, you know,—and you can tell them, for a mark, that he has a silk handkerchief with his monogram in Russian, that his betrothed embroidered for him before the engagement was broken. And may God grant you an easy journey, and may you arrive in a propitious hour, and may you find your husband well, and strong, and rich, and may you both live to lead your children to the wedding canopy, and may America shower gold on you. Amen."

The weeks skipped, the days took wing, an hour was a flash of thought; so brimful of events was the interval before our departure. And no one was more alive than I to the multiple significance of the daily drama. My mother, full of grief at the parting from home and family and all things dear, anxious about the journey, uncertain about the future, but ready, as ever, to take up what new burdens awaited her; my sister, one with our mother in every hope and apprehension; my brother, rejoicing in his sudden release from heder; and the little sister, vaguely excited by mysteries afoot; the uncles and aunts and devoted neighbors, sad a solemn over their coming loss; and my father away over i.. 'ston, eager and anxious about us in Polotzk, —an American citizen impatient to start his children on American careers,—I knew the minds of every one of these, and I lived their days and nights with them after an apish fashion of my own.

But at bottom I was aloof from them all. What made me silent and big-eyed was the sense of being in the midst of a tremendous adventure. From morning till night I was all attention. I must credit myself with some pang of parting; I certainly felt the thrill of expectation; but keener than these was my delight in the progress of the great adventure. It was delightful just to be myself. I rejoiced, with the younger children, during the weeks of packing and preparation, in the relaxation of discipline and the general demoralization of our daily life. It was pleasant to be petted and spoiled by favorite cousins and stuffed with belated sweets by unfavorite ones. It was distinctly interesting to catch my mother weeping in corner cupboards over precious

soaking the thick pile of letter sheets in kerosene. I was obliged to make a fair copy for my uncle, and my father kept the oily, smelly original. After a couple of years' teasing, he induced me to translate the letter into English, for the benefit of a friend who did not know Yiddish; for the benefit of the present narrative, which was not thought of thirteen years ago. I can hardly refrain from moralizing as I turn to the leaves of my childish manuscript, grateful at last for the calamity of the overturned lamp.

Our route lay over the German border, with Hamburg for our port. On the way to the frontier we stopped for a farewell visit in Vilna, where my mother had a brother. Vilna is slighted in my description. I find special mention of only two things, the horse-cars and the bookstores.

On a gray wet morning in early April we set out for the frontier. This was the real beginning of our journey, and all my faculties of observation were alert. I took note of everything,—the weather, the trains, the bustle of railroad stations, our fellow passengers, and the family mood at every stage of our progress.

The bags and bundles which composed our travelling outfit were much more bulky than valuable. A trifling sum of money, the steamer ticket, and the foreign passport were the magic agents by means of which we hoped to span the five thousand miles of earth and water between us and my father. The passport was supposed to pass us over the frontier without any trouble, but on account of the prevalence of cholera in some parts of the country, the poorer sort of travellers, such as emigrants, were subjected, at this time, to more than ordinary supervision and regulation.

At Versbolovo, the last station on the Russian side, we met the first of our troubles. A German physician and several gendarmes boarded the train and put us through a searching examination as to our health, destination, and financial resources. As a result of the inquisition we were informed that we would not be allowed to cross the frontier unless we exchanged our third-class steamer ticket for

second-class, which would require two hundred rubles more
than we possessed. Our passport was taken from us, and we
were to be turned back on our journey.

My letter describes the situation:—

We were homeless, houseless, and friendless in a strange
place. We had hardly money enough to last us through
the voyage for which we had hoped and waited for three
long years. We had suffered much that the reunion we
longed for might come about; we had prepared ourselves
to suffer more in order to bring it about, and had parted
with those we loved, with places that were dear to us in
spite of what we passed through in them, never again to
see them, as we were convinced—all for the same dear
end. With strong hopes and high spirits that hid the sad
parting, we had started on our long journey. And now
we were checked so unexpectedly but surely, the blow
coming from where we little expected it, being, as we
believed, safe in that quarter. When my mother had recovered enough to speak, she began to argue with the
gendarme, telling him our story and begging him to be
kind. The children were frightened and all but I cried. I
was only wondering what would happen.

Moved by our distress, the German officers gave us the
best advice they could. We were to get out at the station of
Kibart, on the Russian side, and apply to one Herr Schidorsky, who might help us on our way.

The letter goes on:—

We are in Kibart, at the depot. The least important
particular, even, of that place, I noticed and remembered.
How the porter—he was an ugly, grinning man—carried
in our things and put them away in the southern corner of
the big room, on the floor; how we sat down on a settee
near them, a yellow settee; how the glass roof let in so
much light that we had to shade our eyes because the car
had been dark and we had been crying; how there were
only a few people besides ourselves there, and how I began to count them and stopped when I noticed a sign
over the head of the fifth person—a little woman with a

red nose and a pimple on it—and tried to read the German, with the aid of the Russian translation below. I noticed all this and remembered it, as if there were nothing else in the world for me to think of.

The letter dwells gratefully on the kindness of Herr Schidorsky, who became the agent of our salvation. He procured my mother a pass to Eidtkuhnen, the German frontier station, where his older brother, as chairman of a well-known emigrant aid association, arranged for our admission into Germany. During the negotiations, which took several days, the good man of Kibart entertained us in his own house, shabby emigrants though we were. The Schidorsky brothers were Jews, but it is not on that account that their name has been lovingly remembered for fifteen years in my family.

On the German side our course joined that of many other emigrant groups, on their way to Hamburg and other ports. We were a clumsy enough crowd, with wide, unsophisticated eyes, with awkward bundles hugged in our arms, and our hearts set on America.

The letter to my uncle faithfully describes every stage of our bustling progress. Here is a sample scene of many that I recorded:—

There was a terrible confusion in the baggage-room where we were directed to go. Boxes, baskets, bags, valises, and great, shapeless things belonging to no particular class, were thrown about by porters and other men, who sorted them and put tickets on all but those containing provisions, while others were opened and examined in haste. At last our turn came, and our things, along with those of all other American-bound travellers, were taken away to be steamed and smoked and other such processes gone through. We were told to wait till notice should be given us of something else to be done.

The phrases "we were told to do this" and "told to do that" occur again and again in my narrative, and the most effective handling of the facts could give no more vivid picture of the proceedings. We emigrants were herded at the stations, packed in the cars, and driven from place to place like cattle.

At the expected hour we all tried to find room in a car indicated by the conductor. We tried, but could only find enough space on the floor for our baggage, on which we made-believe sitting comfortably. For now we were obliged to exchange the comparative comforts of a third-class passenger train for the certain discomforts of a fourth-class one. There were only four narrow benches in the whole car, and about twice as many people were already seated on these as they were probably supposed to accommodate. All other space, to the last inch, was crowded by passengers or their luggage. It was very hot and close and altogether uncomfortable, and still at every new station fresh passengers came crowding in, and actually made room, spare as it was, for themselves. It became so terrible that all glared madly at the conductor as he allowed more people to come into that prison, and trembled at the announcement of every station. I cannot see even now how the officers could allow such a thing; it was really dangerous.

The following is my attempt to describe a flying glimpse of a metropolis:—

Towards evening we came into Berlin. I grow dizzy even now when I think of our whirling through that city. It seemed we were going faster and faster all the time, but it was only the whirl of trains passing in opposite directions and close to us that made it seem so. The sight of crowds of people such as we had never seen before, hurrying to and fro, in and out of great depots that danced past us, helped to make it more so. Strange sights, splendid buildings, shops, people, and animals, all mingled in one great, confused mass of a disposition to continually move in a great hurry, wildly, with no other aim but to make one's head go round and round, in following its dreadful motions. Round and round went my head. It was nothing but trains, depots, crowds,—crowds, depots, trains,—again and again, with no beginning, no end, only a mad dance! Faster and faster we go, faster still, and the noise increases with the speed. Bells, whistles, hammers, locomotives shrieking madly, men's voices, peddlers' cries, horses' hoofs, dogs' barkings—all united in doing their best to drown every other sound but their own, and made such a deafening uproar in the attempt that nothing could keep it out.

The plight of the bewildered emigrant on the way to foreign parts is always pitiful enough, but for us who came from plague-ridden Russia the terrors of the way were doubled.

In a great lonely field, opposite a solitary house within a large yard, our train pulled up at last, and a conductor commanded the passengers to make haste and get out. He need not have told us to hurry; we were glad enough to be free again after such a long imprisonment in the uncomfortable car. All rushed to the door. We breathed more freely in the open field, but the conductor did not wait for us to enjoy our freedom. He hurried us into the one large room which made up the house, and then into the yard. Here a great many men and women, dressed in white, received us, the women attending to the women and girls of the passengers, and the men to the others.

This was another scene of bewildering confusion, parents losing their children, and little ones crying; baggage being thrown together in one corner of the yard, heedless of contents, which suffered in consequence; those white-clad Germans shouting commands, always accompanied with "Quick! Quick!"—the confused passengers obeying all orders like meek children, only questioning now and then what was going to be done with them.

And no wonder if in some minds stories arose of people being captured by robbers, murderers, and the like. Here we had been taken to a lonely place where only that house was to be seen; our things were taken away, our friends separated from us; a man came to inspect us, as if to ascertain our full value; strange-looking people driving us about like dumb animals, helpless and unresisting; children we could not see crying in a way that suggested

terrible things; ourselves driven into a little room where a
great kettle was boiling on a little stove; our clothes taken
off, our bodies rubbed with a slippery substance that might
be any bad thing; a shower of warm water let down on us
without warning; again driven to another little room
where we sit, wrapped in woollen blankets till large,
coarse bags are brought in, their contents turned out, and
we see only a cloud of steam, and hear the women's orders to dress ourselves,—"Quick! Quick!"—or else we'll
miss—something we cannot hear. We are forced to pick
out our clothes from among all the others, with the steam
blinding us; we choke, cough, entreat the women to give
us time; they persist, "Quick! Quick!—or you'll miss the
train!"—Oh, so we really won't be murdered! They are
only making us ready for the continuing of our journey,
cleaning us of all suspicions of dangerous sickness. Thank
God!

In Polotzk, if the cholera broke out, as it did once or
twice in every generation, we made no such fuss as did
these Germans. Those who died of the sickness were buried,
and those who lived ran to the synagogues to pray. We
travellers felt hurt at the way the Germans treated us. My
mother nearly died of cholera once, but she was given a
new name, a lucky one, which saved her; and that was
when she was a small girl. None of us were sick now, yet
hear how we were treated! Those gendarmes and nurses
always shouted their commands at us from a distance, as
fearful of our touch as if we had been lepers.

We arrived in Hamburg early one morning, after a long
night in the crowded cars. We were marched up to a strange
vehicle, long and narrow and high, drawn by two horses
and commanded by a mute driver. We were piled up on
this wagon, our baggage was thrown after us, and we
started on a sight-seeing tour across the city of Hamburg.
The sights I faithfully enumerate for the benefit of my
uncle include little-carts drawn by dogs, and big cars that
run of themselves, later identified as electric cars.

The humorous side of our adventures did not escape me.

Again and again I come across a laugh in the long pages of the historic epistle. The description of the ride through Hamburg ends with this:—

The sight-seeing was not all on our side. I noticed many people stopping to look at us as if amused, though most passed by us as though used to such sights. We did make a queer appearance all in a long row, up above people's heads. In fact, we looked like a flock of giant fowls roosting, only wide awake.

The smiles and shivers fairly crowded each other in some parts of our career.

Suddenly, when everything interesting seemed at an end, we all recollected how long it was since we had started on our funny ride. Hours, we thought, and still the horses ran. Now we rode through quieter streets where there were fewer shops and more wooden houses. Still the horses seemed to have but just started. I looked over our perch again. Something made me think of a description I had read of criminals being carried on long journeys in uncomfortable things—like this? Well, it was strange— this long, long drive, the conveyance, no word of explanation; and all, though going different ways, being packed off together. We were strangers; the driver knew it. He might take us anywhere—how could we tell? I was frightened again as in Berlin. The faces around me confessed the same.

Yes, we are frightened. We are very still. Some Polish women over there have fallen asleep, and the rest of us look such a picture of woe, and yet so funny, it is a sight to see and remember.

Our mysterious ride came to an end on the outskirts of the city, where we were once more lined up, cross-questioned, disinfected, labelled, and pigeonholed. This was one of the occasions when we suspected that we were the victims of a conspiracy to extort money from us; for here, as at every repetition of the purifying operations we had undergone, a fee was levied on us, so much per head. My

mother, indeed, seeing her tiny hoard melting away, had
long since sold some articles from our baggage to a fellow
passenger richer than she, but even so she did not have
enough money to pay the fee demanded of her in Hamburg.
Her statement was not accepted, and we all suffered the
last indignity of having our persons searched.

This last place of detention turned out to be a prison.
"Quarantine" they called it, and there was a great deal of
it—two weeks of it. Two weeks within high brick walls,
several hundred of us herded in half a dozen compartments,
—numbered compartments,—sleeping in rows, like sick
people in a hospital; with roll-call morning and night, and
short rations three times a day; with never a sign of the
free world beyond our barred windows; with anxiety and
longing and homesickness in our hearts, and in our ears
the unfamiliar voice of the invisible ocean, which drew and
repelled us at the same time. The fortnight in quarantine
was not an episode; it was an epoch, divisible into eras,
periods, events.

The greatest event was the arrival of some ship to take
some of the waiting passengers. When the gates were
opened and the lucky ones said good-bye, those left behind felt hopeless of ever seeing the gates open for them.
It was both pleasant and painful, for the strangers grew to
be fast friends in a day, and really rejoiced in each other's
fortune; but the regretful envy could not be helped either.

Our turn came at last. We were conducted through the
gate of departure, and after some hours of bewildering
manœuvres, described in great detail in the report to my
uncle, we found ourselves—we five frightened pilgrims from
Polotzk—on the deck of a great big steamship afloat on
the strange big waters of the ocean.

For sixteen days the ship was our world. My letter dwells
solemnly on the details of the life at sea, as if afraid to
cheat my uncle of the smallest circumstance. It does not
shrink from describing the torments of seasickness; it notes

every change in the weather. A rough night is described, when the ship pitched and rolled so that people were thrown from their berths; days and nights when we crawled through dense fogs, our foghorn drawing answering warnings from invisible ships. The perils of the sea were not minimized in the imaginations of us inexperienced voyagers. The captain and his officers ate their dinners, smoked their pipes and slept soundly in their turns, while we frightened emigrants turned our faces to the wall and awaited our watery graves.

All this while the seasickness lasted. Then came happy hours on deck, with fugitive sunshine, birds atop the crested waves, band music and dancing and fun. I explored the ship, made friends with officers and crew, or pursued my thoughts in quiet nooks. It was my first experience of the ocean, and I was profoundly moved.

> Oh, what solemn thoughts I had! How deeply I felt the greatness, the power of the scene! The immeasurable distance from horizon to horizon; the huge billows forever changing their shapes—now only a wavy and rolling plain, now a chain of great mountains, coming and going farther away; then a town in the distance, perhaps, with spires and towers and buildings of gigantic dimensions; and mostly a vast mass of uncertain shapes, knocking against each other in fury, and seething and foaming in their anger; the gray sky, with its mountains of gloomy clouds, flying, moving with the waves, as it seemed, very near them; the absence of any object besides the one ship; and the deep, solemn groans of the sea, sounding as if all the voices of the world had been turned into sighs and then gathered into that one mournful sound—so deeply did I feel the presence of these things, that the feeling became one of awe, both painful and sweet, and stirring and warming, and deep and calm and grand.
>
> I would imagine myself all alone on the ocean, and Robinson Crusoe was very real to me. I was alone sometimes. I was aware of no human presence; I was conscious only of sea and sky and something I did not understand. And as I listened to its solemn voice, I felt as if I had

found a friend, and knew that I loved the ocean. It seemed as if it were within as well as without, part of myself; and I wondered how I had lived without it, and if I could ever part with it.

And so suffering, fearing, brooding, rejoicing, we crept nearer and ᴀrer to the coveted shore, until on a glorious May moɪ. ᴀg, six weeks after our departure from Polotzk, our eyes beheld the Promised Land, and my father received us in his arms.

My Country,
from
THE PROMISED LAND (1912)

The public school has done its best for us foreigners, and for the country, when it has made us into good Americans. I am glad it is mine to tell how the miracle was wrought in one case. You should be glad to hear of it, you born Americans; for it is the story of the growth of your country; of the flocking of your brothers and sisters from the far ends of the earth to the flag you love; of the recruiting of your armies of workers, thinkers, and leaders. And you will be glad to hear of it, my comrades in adoption; for it is a rehearsal of your own experience, the thrill and wonder of which your own hearts have felt.

How long would you say, wise reader, it takes to make an American? By the middle of my second year in school I had reached the sixth grade. When, after the Christmas holidays, we began to study the life of Washington, running through a summary of the Revolution, and the early days of the Republic, it seemed to me that all my reading and study had been idle until then. The reader, the arithmetic, the song book, that had so fascinated me until now, became suddenly sober exercise books, tools wherewith to hew a way to the source of inspiration. When the teacher read to us out of a big book with many bookmarks in it, I sat rigid with attention in my little chair, my hands tightly clasped on the edge of my desk; and I painfully held my breath, to prevent sighs of disappointment escaping, as I saw the teacher skip the parts between bookmarks. When the class read, and it came my turn, my voice shook and the book trembled in my hands. I could not pronounce the name of George Washington without a pause. Never had I prayed, never had I chanted the songs of David, never had I called upon the Most Holy, in such utter reverence and worship as I repeated the simple sentences of my child's story of the patriot. I gazed with adoration at the portraits of George and Martha Washington, till I could see them with my eyes shut. And whereas formerly my self-consciousness had bordered on conceit, and I thought myself an uncommon person, parading my schoolbooks through the streets, and swelling with pride when a teacher detained me in conversation, now I grew humble all at once, seeing how insignificant I was beside the Great.

As I read about the noble boy who would not tell a lie to save himself from punishment, I was for the first time truly repentant of my sins. Formerly I had fasted and prayed and made sacrifice on the Day of Atonement, but it was more than half play, in mimicry of my elders. I had no real horror of sin, and I knew so many ways of escaping punishment. I am sure my family, my neighbors, my teachers in Polotzk—all my world, in fact—strove together, by example and precept, to teach me goodness. Saintliness had a new incarnation in about every third person I knew. I did respect the saints, but I could not help seeing that most of them were a little bit stupid, and that mischief was much more fun than piety. Goodness, as I had known it, was respectable, but not necessarily admirable. The people I really admired, like my Uncle Solomon, and Cousin Rachel, were those who preached the least and laughed the most. My sister Frieda was perfectly good, but she did not think the less of me because I played tricks. What I loved in my friends was not inimitable. One could be downright

good if one really wanted to. One could be learned if one
had books and teachers. One could sing funny songs and
tell anecdotes if one travelled about and picked up such
things, like one's uncles and cousins. But a human being
strictly good, perfectly wise, and unfailingly valiant, all at
the same time, I had never heard or dreamed of. This wonderful George Washington was as inimitable as he was ir-
reproachable. Even if I had never, never told a lie, I could
not compare myself to George Washington; for I was not
brave—I was afraid to go out when snowballs whizzed—
and I could never be the First President of the United
States.

So I was forced to revise my own estimate of myself. But
the twin of my new-born humility, paradoxical as it may
seem, was a sense of dignity I had never known before.
For if I found that I was a person of small consequence, I
discovered at the same time that I was more nobly related
than I had ever supposed. I had relatives and friends who
were notable people by the old standards,—I had never
been ashamed of my family,—but this George Washington,
who died long before I was born, was like a king in greatness, and he and I were Fellow Citizens. There was a great
deal about Fellow Citizens in the patriotic literature we
read at this time; and I knew from my father how he was
a Citizen, through the process of naturalization, and how
I also was a citizen, by virtue of my relation to him. Undoubtedly I was a Fellow Citizen, and George Washington
was another. It thrilled me to realize what sudden greatness
had fallen on me; and at the same time it sobered me, as
with a sense of responsibility. I strove to conduct myself
as befitted a Fellow Citizen.

Before books came into my life, I was given to stargazing
and daydreaming. When books were given me, I fell upon
them as a glutton pounces on his meat after a period of
enforced starvation. I lived with my nose in a book, and
took no notice of the alternations of the sun and stars. But
now, after the advent of George Washington and the Ameri-

can Revolution, I began to dream again. I stayed on the common after school instead of hurrying home to read. I hung on fence rails, my pet book forgotten under my arm, and gazed off to the yellow-streaked February sunset, and beyond, and beyond. I was no longer the central figure of my dreams; the dry weeds in the lane crackled beneath the tread of Heroes.

What more could America give a child? Ah, much more! As I read how the patriots planned the Revolution, and the women gave their sons to die in battle, and the heroes led to victory, and the rejoicing people set up the Republic, it dawned on me gradually what was meant by *my country*. The people all desiring noble things, and striving for them together defying their oppressors, giving their lives for each other—all this it was that made *my country*. It was not a thing that I *understood;* I could not go home and tell Frieda about it, as I told her other things I learned at school. But I knew one could say "my country" and *feel* it, as one felt "God" or "myself." My teacher, my schoolmates, Miss Dillingham George Washington himself could not mean more tha when they said "my country," after I had felt it. For the Country was for all the Citizens, ar *I was a Citizen.* And when we stood up to sing "America," I shouted the words with all my might. I was in very earnest proclaiming to the world my love for my new-found country.

> "I love thy rocks and rills,
> Thy woods and templed hills."

Boston Harbor, Crescent Beach, Chelsea Square—all was hallowed ground to me. As the day approached when the school was to hold exercises in honor of Washington's Birthday, the halls resounded at all hours with the strains of patriotic songs; and I, who was a model of the attentive pupil, more than once lost my place in the lesson as I strained to hear, through closed doors, some neighboring

class rehearsing "The Star-Spangled Banner." If the doors
happened to open, and the chorus broke out unveiled—

"O! say, does that Star-Spangled Banner yet wave
  O'er the land of the free, and the home of the
  brave?"—

delicious tremors ran up and down my spine, and I was
faint with suppressed enthusiasm.

Where had been my country until now? What flag had I
loved? What heroes had I worshipped? The very names of
these things had been unknown to me. Well I knew that
Polotzk was not my country. It was *goluth*—exile. On
many occasions in the year we prayed to God to lead us out
of exile. The beautiful Passover service closed with the
words, "Next year, may we be in Jerusalem." On childish
lips, indeed, those words were no conscious aspiration; we
repeated the Hebrew syllables after our elders, but without
their hope and longing. Still not a child among us was too
young to feel in his own flesh the lash of the oppressor. We
knew what it was to be Jews in exile, from the spiteful treatment we suffered at the hands of the smallest urchin who
crossed himself; and thence we knew that Israel had good
reason to pray for deliverance. But the story of the Exodus
was not history to me in the sense that the story of the
American Revolution was. It was more like a glorious
myth, a belief in which had the effect of cutting me off from
the actual world, by linking me with a world of phantoms.
Those moments of exaltation which the contemplation of
the Biblical past afforded us, allowing us to call ourselves
the children of princes, served but to tinge with a more
poignant sense of disinheritance the long humdrum stretches
of our life. In very truth we were a people without a country.
Surrounded by mocking foes and detractors, it was difficult
for me to realize the persons of my people's heroes or the
events in which they moved. Except in moments of abstrac-
tion from the world around me, I scarcely understood that

Jerusalem was an actual spot on the earth, where once the Kings of the Bible, real people, like my neighbors in Polotzk, ruled in puissant majesty. For the conditions of our civil life did not permit us to cultivate a spirit of nationalism. The freedom of worship that was grudgingly granted within the narrow limits of the Pale by no means included the right to set up openly any ideal of a Hebrew State, any hero other than the Czar. What we children picked up of our ancient political history was confused with the miraculous story of the Creation, with the supernatural legends and hazy associations of Bible lore. As to our future, we Jews in Polotzk had no national expectations; only a lifeworn dreamer here and there hoped to die in Palestine. If Fetchke and I sang, with my father, first making sure of our audience, "Zion, Zion, Holy Zion, not forever is it lost," we did not really picture to ourselves Judæa restored.

So it came to pass that we did not know what *my country* could mean to a man. And as we had no country, so we had no flag to love. It was by no far-fetched symbolism that the banner of the House of Romanoff became the emblem of our latter-day bondage in our eyes. Even a child would know how to hate the flag that we were forced, on pain of severe penalties, to hoist above our housetops, in celebration of the advent of one of our oppressors. And as it was with country and flag, so it was with heroes of war. We hated the uniform of the soldier, to the last brass button. On the person of a Gentile, it was the symbol of tyranny; on the person of a Jew, it was the emblem of shame.

So a little Jewish girl in Polotzk was apt to grow up hungry-minded and empty-hearted; and if, still in her outreaching youth, she was set down in a land of outspoken patriotism, she was likely to love her new country with a great love, and to embrace its heroes in a great worship. Naturalization, with us Russian Jews, may mean more than the adoption of the immigrant by America. It may mean the adoption of America by the immigrant.

On the day of the Washington celebration I recited a poem that I had composed in my enthusiasm. But "composed" is not the word. The process of putting on paper the sentiments that seethed in my soul was really very discomposing. I dug the words out of my heart, squeezed the rhymes out of my brain, forced the missing syllables out of their hiding-places in the dictionary. May I never again know such travail of the spirit as I endured during the fevered days when I was engaged on the poem. It was not as if I wanted to say that snow was white or grass was green. I could do that without a dictionary. It was a question now of the loftiest sentiments, of the most abstract truths, the names of which were very new in my vocabulary. It was necessary to use polysyllables, and plenty of them; and where to find rhymes for such words as "tyranny," "freedom," and "justice," when you had less than two years' acquaintance with English! The name I wished to celebrate was the most difficult of all. Nothing but "Washington" rhymed with "Washington." It was a most ambitious undertaking, but my heart could find no rest till it had proclaimed itself to the world; so I wrestled with my difficulties, and spared not ink, till inspiration perched on my penpoint, and my soul gave up its best.

When I had done, I was myself impressed with the length, gravity, and nobility of my poem. My father was overcome with emotion as he read it. His hands trembled as he held the paper to the light, and the mist gathered in his eyes. My teacher, Miss Dwight, was plainly astonished at my performance, and said many kind things, and asked many questions; all of which I took very solemnly, like one who had been in the clouds and returned to earth with a sign upon him. When Miss Dwight asked me to read my poem to the class on the day of celebration, I readily consented. It was not in me to refuse a chance to tell my schoolmates what I thought of George Washington.

I was not a heroic figure when I stood up in front of the class to pronounce the praises of the Father of his Country.

Thin, pale, and hollow, with a shadow of short black curls on my brow, and the staring look of prominent eyes, I must have looked more frightened than imposing. My dress added no grace to my appearance. "Plaids" were in fashion, and my frock was of a red-and green "plaid" that had a ghastly effect on my complexion. I hated it when I thought of it, but on the great day I did not know I had any dress on. Heels clapped together, and hands glued to my sides, I lifted up my voice in praise of George Washington. It was not much of a voice; like my hollow cheeks, it suggested consumption. My pronunciation was faulty, my declamation flat. But I had the courage of my convictions. I was face to face with twoscore Fellow Citizens, in clean blouses and extra frills. I must tell them what George Washington had done for their country—for *our* country—for me.

I can laugh now at the impossible metres, the grandiose phrases, the verbose repetitions of my poem. Years ago I must have laughed at it, when I threw my only copy into the wastebasket. The copy I am now turning over was loaned me by Miss Dwight, who faithfully preserved it all these years, for the sake, no doubt, of what I strove to express when I laboriously hitched together those dozen and more ungraceful stanzas. But to the forty Fellow Citizens sitting in rows in front of me it was no laughing matter. Even the bad boys sat in attitudes of attention, hypnotized by the solemnity of my demeanor. If they got any inkling of what the hail of big words was about, it must have been through occult suggestion. I fixed their eighty eyes with my single stare, and gave it to them, stanza after stanza, with such emphasis as the lameness of the line permitted.

> He whose courage, will, amazing bravery,
>   Did free his land from a despot's rule,
> From man's greatest evil, almost slavery,
>   And all that's taught in tyranny's school,
>
>   Who gave his land its liberty,
>   Who was he?

'T was he who e'er will be our pride,
   Immortal Washington,
Who always did in truth confide.
   We hail our Washington!

The best of the verses were no better than these, but the children listened. They had to. Presently I gave them news, declaring that Washington

Wrote the famous Constitution; sacred's the hand
That this blessed guide to man had given, which says,
  "One
And all of mankind are alike, excepting none."

This was received in respectful silence, possibly because the other Fellow Citizens were as hazy about historical facts as I at this point. "Hurrah for Washington!" they understood, and "Three cheers for the Red, White, and Blue!" was only to be expected on that occasion. But there ran a special note through my poem—a thought that only Israel Rubinstein or Beckie Aronovitch could have fully understood, besides myself. For I made myself the spokesman of the "luckless sons of Abraham," saying—

Then we weary Hebrew children at last found rest
In the land where reigned Freedom, and like a nest
To homeless birds your land proved to us, and therefore
Will we gratefully sing your praise evermore.

The boys and girls who had never been turned away from any door because of their father's religion sat as if fascinated in their places. But they woke up and applauded heartily when I was done, following the example of Miss Dwight, who wore the happy face which meant that one of her pupils had done well.

The recitation was repeated, by request, before several other classes, and the applause was equally prolonged at each repetition. After the exercises I was surrounded, praised, questioned, and made much of, by teachers as well as pupils. Plainly I had not poured my praise of George Washington into deaf ears. The teachers asked me if anybody had helped me with the poem. The girls invariably asked, "Mary Antin, how could you think of all those words?" None of them thought of the dictionary!

If I had been satisfied with my poem in the first place, the applause with which it was received by my teachers and schoolmates convinced me that I had produced a very fine thing indeed. So the person, whoever it was,—perhaps my father—who suggested that my tribute to Washington ought to be printed, did not find me difficult to persuade. When I had achieved an absolutely perfect copy of my verses, at the expense of a dozen sheets of blue-ruled note paper, I crossed the Mystic River to Boston and boldly invaded Newspaper Row.

It never occurred to me to send my manuscript by mail. In fact, it has never been my way to send or delegate where I could go myself. Consciously or unconsciously, I have always acted on the motto of a wise man who was one of the dearest friends that Boston kept for me until I came. "Personal presence moves the world," said the great Dr. Hale; and I went in person to beard the editor in his armchair.

From the ferry slip to the offices of the "Boston Transcript" the way was long, strange, and full of perils; but I kept resolutely on up Hanover Street, being familiar with that part of my route, till I came to a puzzling corner. There I stopped, utterly bewildered by the tangle of streets, the roar of traffic, the giddy swarm of pedestrians. With the precious manuscript tightly clasped, I balanced myself on the curbstone, afraid to plunge into the boiling vortex of the crossing. Every time I made a start, a clanging street car snatched up the way. I could not even pick out my street; the unobtrusive street signs were lost to my unpractised sight, in the glaring confusion of store signs and advertisements. If I accosted a pedestrian to ask the way, I had to speak several times before I was heard. Jews, hurrying by with bearded chins on their bosoms and eyes intent, shrugged their shoulders at the name "Transcript," and shrugged till they were out of sight. Italians sauntering behind their fruit carts answered my inquiry with a lift of the head that made their earrings gleam, and a wave of the hand that referred me to all four points of the compass at once. I was trying to catch the eye of the tall policeman who stood grandly in the middle of the crossing, a stout pillar around which the waves of traffic broke, when deliverance bellowed in my ear.

"Herald, Globe, Record, *Tra-avel-er!* Eh? Whatcher want, sis?" The tall newsboy had to stoop to me. "Transcript? Sure!" And in half a twinkling he had picked me out a paper from his bundle. When I explained to him, he good-naturedly tucked the paper in again, piloted me across, unravelled the end of Washington Street for me, and with much pointing out of landmarks, headed me for my destination, my nose seeking the spire of the Old South Church.

I found the "Transcript" building a waste of corridors tunnelled by a maze of staircases. On the glazed-glass doors were many signs with the names or nicknames of many persons: "City Editor"; "Beggars and Peddlers not Allowed." The nameless world not included in these categories was warned off, forbidden to be or do: "Private— No Admittance"; "Don't Knock." And the various inhospitable legends on the doors and walls were punctuated by frequent cuspidors on the floor. There was no sign anywhere of the welcome which I, as an author, expected to find in the home of a newspaper.

I was descending from the top story to the street for the seventh time, trying to decide what kind of editor a patriotic poem belonged to, when an untidy boy carrying broad paper streamers and whistling shrilly, in defiance of an express prohibition on the wall, bustled through the corridor and left a door ajar. I slipped in behind him, and found myself in a room full of editors.

I was a little surprised at the appearance of the editors.
I had imagined my editor would look like Mr. Jones, the
principal of my school, whose coat was always buttoned,
and whose finger nails were beautiful. These people were in
shirt sleeves, and they smoked, and they didn't politely turn
in their revolving chairs when I came in, and ask, "What
can I do for you?"

The room was noisy with typewriters, and nobody heard
my "Please, can you tell me." At last one of the machines
stopped, and the operator thought he heard something in the
pause. He looked up through his own smoke. I guess he
thought he saw something, for he stared. It troubled me a
little to have him stare so. I realized suddenly that the hand
in which I carried my manuscript was moist, and I was
afraid it would make marks on the paper. I held out the
manuscript to the editor, explaining that it was a poem
about George Washington, and would he please print it in
the "Transcript."

There was something queer about that particular editor.
The way he stared and smiled made me feel about eleven
inches high, and my voice kept growing smaller and smaller
as I neared the end of my speech.

At last he spoke, laying down his pipe, and sitting back
at his ease.

"So you have brought us a poem, my child?"

"It's about George Washington," I repeated impressively.
"Don't you want to read it?"

"I should be delighted, my dear, but the fact is—"

He did not take my paper. He stood up and called across
the room.

"Say, Jack! here is a young lady who has brought us a
poem—about George Washington.—Wrote it yourself, my
dear?—Wrote it all herself. What shall we do with her?"

Mr. Jack came over, and another man. My editor made
me repeat my business and they all looked interested, but
nobody took my paper from me. They put their hands into
their pockets, and my hand kept growing clammier all the

time. The three seemed to be consulting, but I could not understand what they said, or why Mr. Jack laughed.

A fourth man, who had been writing busily at a desk near by, broke in on the consultation.

"That's enough, boys," he said, "that's enough. Take the young lady to Mr. Hurd."

Mr. Hurd, it was found, was away on a vacation, and of several other editors in several offices, to whom I was referred, none proved to be the proper editor to take charge of a poem about George Washington. At last an elderly editor suggested that as Mr. Hurd would be away for some time, I would do well to give up the "Transcript" and try the "Herald," across the way.

A little tired by my wanderings, and bewildered by the complexity of the editorial system, but still confident about my mission, I picked my way across Washington Street and found the "Herald" offices. Here I had instant good luck. The first editor I addressed took my paper and invited me to a seat. He read my poem much more quickly than I could myself, and said it was very nice, and asked me some questions, and made notes on a slip of paper which he pinned to my manuscript. He said he would have my piece printed very soon, and would send me a copy of the issue in which it appeared. As I was going, I could not help giving the editor my hand, although I had not experienced any handshaking in Newspaper Row. I felt that as author and editor we were on a very pleasant footing, and I gave him my hand in token of comradeship.

I had regained my full stature and something over, during this cordial interview, and when I stepped out into the street and saw the crowd intently studying the bulletin board I swelled out of all proportion. For I told myself that I, Mary Antin, was one of the inspired brotherhood who made newspapers so interesting. I did not know whether my poem would be put upon the bulletin board; but at any rate, it would be in the paper, with my name at the bottom, like my story about "Snow" in Miss Dillingham's school journal. And all these people in the streets, and more, thousands of people—all Boston!—would read my poem, and learn my name, and wonder who I was. I smiled to myself in delicious amusement when a man deliberately put me out of his path, as I dreamed my way through the jostling crowd; if he only *knew* whom he was treating so unceremoniously!

When the paper with my poem in it arrived, the whole house pounced upon it at once. I was surprised to find that my verses were not all over the front page. The poem was a little hard to find, if anything, being tucked away in the middle of the voluminous sheet. But when we found it, it looked wonderful, just like ... poetry, not at all as if somebody we knew had written it. It occupied a gratifying amount of space, and was introduced by a flattering biographical sketch of the author—the *author!*—the material for which the friendly editor had artfully drawn from me during that happy interview. And my name, as I had prophesied, was at the bottom!

When the excitement in the house had subsided, my father took all the change out of the cash drawer and went to buy up the "Herald." He did not count the pennies. He just bought "Heralds," all he could lay his hands on, and distributed them gratis to all our friends, relatives, and acquaintances; to all who could read, and to some who could not. For weeks he carried a clipping from the "Herald" in his breast pocket, and few were the occasions when he did not manage to introduce it into the conversation. He treasured that clipping as for years he had treasured the letters I wrote him from Polotzk.

Although my father bought up most of the issue containing my poem, a few hundred copies were left to circulate among the general public, enough to spread the flame of my patriotic ardor and to enkindle a thousand sluggish hearts. Really, there was something more solemn than vanity in my satisfaction. Pleased as I was with my notoriety—and nobody but I knew how exceedingly pleased—I had a sober feeling about it all. I enjoyed being praised and admired and admired and envied; but what gave a divine flavor to my happiness was the idea that I had publicly borne testimony to the goodness of my exalted hero, to the greatness of my adopted country. I did not discount the homage of Arlington Street, because I did not properly rate the intelligence of its population. I took the admiration of my schoolmates without a grain of salt; it was just so much honey to me. I could not know that what made me great in the eyes of my neighbors was that "there was a piece about me in the paper"; it mattered very little to them what the "piece" was about. I thought they really admired my sentiments. On the street, in the schoolyard, I was pointed out. The people said, "That's Mary Antin. She had her name in the paper." *I* thought they said, "This is she who loves her country and worships George Washington."

To repeat, I was well aware that I was something of a celebrity, and took all possible satisfaction in the fact; yet I gave my schoolmates no occasion to call me "stuckup." My vanity did not express itself in strutting or wagging the head. I played tag and puss-in-the-corner in the schoolyard, and did everything that was comradelike. But in the schoolroom I conducted myself gravely, as befitted one who was preparing for the noble career of a poet.

I am forgetting Lizzie McDee. I am trying to give the impression that I behaved with at least outward modesty during my schoolgirl triumphs, whereas Lizzie could testify that she knew Mary Antin as a vain, boastful, curly-headed little Jew. For I had a special style of deportment for Lizzie. If there was any girl in the school besides me who could keep near the top of the class all the year through, and give bright answers when the principal or the school committee popped sudden questions, and write rhymes that almost always rhymed, *I* was determined that that ambitious person should not soar unduly in her own estimation. So I took care to show Lizzie all my poetry, and when she showed me hers I did not admire it too warmly. Lizzie, as I have already said, was in a Sunday-school mood even on week days; her verses all had morals. My poems were about the crystal snow, and the ocean blue, and sweet spring, and fleecy clouds; when I tried to drag in a moral it kicked so that the music of my lines went out in a groan. So I had a sweet revenge when Lizzie, one day, volunteered to bolster up the eloquence of Mr. Jones, the principal, who was lecturing the class for bad behavior, by comparing the bad boy in the schoolroom to the rotten apple that spoils the barrelful. The groans, coughs, a-hem's, feet shufflings, and paper pellets that filled the room as Saint Elizabeth sat down, even in the principal's presence, were sweet balm to my smart of envy; I didn't care if I didn't know how to moralize.

When my teacher had visitors I was aware that I was the show pupil of the class. I was always made to recite, my compositions were passed around, and often I was called up on the platform—oh, climax of exaltation!—to be interviewed by the distinguished strangers; while the class took advantage of the teacher's distraction, to hold forbidden intercourse on matters not prescribed in the curriculum. When I returned to my seat, after such public audience with the great, I looked to see if Lizzie McDee was taking notice; and Lizzie, who was a generous soul, her Sunday-school airs notwithstanding, generally smiled, and I forgave her her rhymes.

Not but what I paid a price for my honors. With all my self-possession I had a certain capacity for shyness. Even when I arose to recite before the customary audience of my class I suffered from incipient stage fright, and my voice trembled over the first few words. When visitors were in the room I was even more troubled; and when I was made the special object of their attention my triumph was marred by acute distress. If I was called up to speak to the visitors, forty pairs of eyes pricked me in the back as I went. I stumbled in the aisle, and knocked down things that were not at all in my way; and my awkwardness increasing my embarrassment I would gladly have changed places with Lizzie or the bad boy in the back row; anything, only to be less conspicuous. When I found myself shaking hands with an august School-Committeeman, or a teacher from New York, the remnants of my self-possession vanished in awe; and it was in a very husky voice that I repeated, as I was asked, my name, lineage, and personal history. On the whole, I do not think that the School-Committeeman found a very forward creature in the solemn-faced little girl with the tight curls and the terrible red-and-green "plaid."

These awful audiences did not always end 'ith the handshaking. Sometimes the great personages as 1 me to write to them, and exchanged addresses with me. Some of these correspondences continued through years, and were the source of much pleasure, on one side at least. And Arlington Street took notice when I received letters with important-looking or aristocratic-looking letterheads. Lizzie McDee also took notice. *I* saw to that.

JAMES OPPENHEIM (1882–1932), in his first poems, *Monday Morning and Other Poems* (1909), reflected the influence of Walt Whitman, though the former's verse was experimental, imitative, and inconsistent. *Songs for the New Age* (1914) fostered its own sound, Biblical and yet modern, and searched and analyzed man's soul and man's problems. As Louis Untermeyer put it, "The old Isaiah note, with a new introspection, rises out of such poems as 'The Slave' and 'Tasting the Earth.'" His later volumes were *War and Laughter* (1916), *The Book of Self* (1917), *The Solitary* (1919), *The Mystic Warrior* (1921), *Golden Bird* (1923), and *The Sea* (1923).

The Slave
from
SONGS FOR THE NEW AGE

They set the slave free, striking off his chains . . .
Then he was as much of a slave as ever.

He was still chained to servility,
He was still manacled to indolence and sloth,
He was still bound by fear and superstition,
By ignorance, suspicion, and savagery . . .
His slavery was not in the chains,
But in himself . . .

They can only set free men free. . .
And there is no need of that:
Free men set themselves free.

Tasting the Earth
from
SONGS FOR THE NEW AGE

In a dark hour, tasting the Earth.

As I lay on my couch in the muffled night, and the rain
    lashed my window,
And my forsaken heart would give me no rest, no pause
    and no peace,
Though I turned my face far from the wailing of my
    bereavement . . .
Then I said: I will eat of this sorrow to its last shred,
I will take it unto me utterly,
I will see if I be not strong enough to contain it . . .
What do I fear? Discomfort?
How can it hurt me, this bitterness?

The miracle, then!

Turning toward it, and giving up to it,
I found it deeper than my own self. . .
O dark great mother-globe so close beneath me . . .
It was she with her inexhaustible grief,
Ages of blood-drenched jungles, and the smoking of craters,
    and the roar of tempests,
And moan of the forsaken seas,
It was she with the hills beginning to walk in the shapes of
    the dark-hearted animals,
It was she risen, dashing away tears and praying to dumb
    skies, in the pomp-crumbling tragedy of man . . .
It was she, container of all griefs, and the buried dust of
    broken hearts,
Cry of the christs and the   vers and the child-stripped
    mothers,
And ambition gone down to defeat, and the battle over-
    b   ,
And the dreams that have no waking . . .

My heart became her ancient heart:
On the food of the strong I fed, on dark strange life itself:
Wisdom-giving and sombre with the unremitting love of
    ages . . .

There was dank soil in my mouth,
And bitter sea on my lips,
In a dark hour, tasting the Earth.

ABRAHAM CAHAN (1860–1951), who was the longtime
editor of the *Forward,* was also the author of *Yekl* (1896),
The Imported Bridegroom and Other Stories (1898), and
The Rise of David Levinsky (1917). From his own experience, Cahan had one of his early characters give the reason for the changes so evident in the New World: "America

has done it all." For David Levinsky, who read Talmud in the Old Country, the lesson was quickly told, that is, "that's no business in America." The greenhorn learned that if you were a Jew and you came to New York and you tried to bend your religion to the new surroundings, it broke. David's answer was to become a freethinker and an enormous success. But at the end, as he admitted, "I cannot escape from my old self." In Isaac Rosenfeld's words, Cahan was writing an American novel par excellence in the very center of the Jewish genre.

I Discover America
from
THE RISE OF DAVID LEVINSKY

Two weeks later I was one of a multitude of steerage passengers on a Bremen steamship on my way to New York. Who can depict the feeling of desolation, homesickness, uncertainty, and anxiety with which an emigrant makes his first voyage across the ocean? I proved to be a good sailor, but the sea frightened me. The thumping of the engines was drumming a ghastly accompaniment to the awesome whisper of the waves. I felt in the embrace of a vast, uncanny force. And echoing through it all were the heart-lashing words:

"Are you crazy? You forget your place, young man!"

When Columbus was crossing the Atlantic, on his first great voyage, his men doubted whether they would ever reach land. So does many an America-bound emigrant to this day. Such, at least, was the feeling that was lurking in my heart while the Bremen steamer was carrying me to New York. Day after day passes and all you see about you is an unbroken waste of water, an unrelieved, a hopeless monotony of water. You know that a change will come, but this knowledge is confined to your brain. Your senses are skeptical.

In my devotions, which I performed three times a day,

without counting, a benediction before every meal and
every drink of water, grace after every meal and a prayer
before going to sleep, I would mentally plead for the safety
of the ship and for a speedy sight of land. My scanty luggage included a pair of phylacteries and a plump little
prayer-book, with the Book of Psalms at the end. The prayers I knew by heart, but I now often said psalms, in addition, particularly when the sea looked angry and the pitch-
ing or rolling was unusually violent. I would read all kinds
of psalms, but my favorite among them was the 104th, generally referred to by our people as "Bless the Lord, O my
soul," its opening words in the original Hebrew. It is a poem
on the power and wisdom of God as manifested in the
wonders of nature, some of its verses dealing with the sea.
It is said by the faithful every Saturday afternoon during the
fall and winter; so I could have recited it from memory; but
I preferred to read it in my prayer-book. For it seemed as
though the familiar words had changed their identity and
meaning, especially those concerned with the sea. Their
divine inspiration was now something visible and audible.
It was not I who was reading them. It was as though the
waves and the clouds, the whole far-flung scene of restlessness and mystery, were whispering to me:

"Thou who coverest thyself with light as with a garment,
who stretchest out the heavens like a curtain: who layeth
the beams of his chambers in the waters: who maketh the
clouds his chariot: who walketh upon the wings of the
wind. . . . So is this great and wide sea wherein are things
creeping innumerable, both small and great beasts. There
go the ships: there is that leviathan whom thou hast made
to play therein. . . ."

The relentless presence of Matilda in my mind worried
me immeasurably, for to think of a woman who is a stranger
to you is a sin, and so there was the danger of the vessel
coming to grief on my account. And, as though to spite me,
the closing verse of Psalm 104 reads, "Let the sinners be
consumed out of the earth and let the wicked be no more."

I strained every nerve to keep Matilda out of my thoughts, but without avail.

When the discoverers of America saw land at last they fell on their knees and a hymn of thanksgiving burst from their souls. The scene, which is one of the most thrilling in history, repeats itself in the heart of every immigrant as he comes in sight of the American shores. I am at a loss to convey the peculiar state of mind that the experience created in me.

When the ship reached Sandy Hook I was literally overcome with the beauty of the landscape.

The immigrant's arrival in his new home is like a second birth to him. Imagine a new-born babe in possession of a fully developed intellect. Would it ever forget its entry into the world? Neither does the immigrant ever forget his entry into a country which is, to him, a new world in the profoundest sense of the term and in which he expects to pass the rest of his life. I conjure up the gorgeousness of the spectacle as it appeared to me on that clear June morning: the magnificent verdure of Staten Island, the tender blue of sea and sky, the dignified bustle of passing craft—above all, those floating, squatting, multitudinously windowed palaces which I subsequently learned to call ferries. It was all so utterly unlike anything I had ever seen or dreamed of before. It unfolded itself like a divine revelation. I was in a trance or in something closely resembling one.

"This, then, is America!" I exclaimed, mutely. The notion of something enchanted which the name had always evoked in me now seemed fully borne out.

In my ecstasy I could not help thinking of Psalm 104, and, opening my little prayer-book, I glanced over those of its verses that speak of hills and rocks, of grass and trees and birds.

My transport of admiration, however, only added to my sense of helplessness and awe. Here, on shipboard, I was sure of my shelter and food, at least. How was I going to procure my sustenance on those magic shores? I wished the remaining hour could be prolonged indefinitely.

Psalm 104 spoke reassuringly to me. It reminded me of the way God took care of man and beast: "Thou openest thine hand and they are filled with good." But then the very next verse warned me that "Thou hidest thy face, they are troubled: thou takest away their breath, they die." So I was praying God not to hide His face from me, but to open His hand to me; to remember that my mother had been murdered by Gentiles and that I was going to a strange land. When I reached the words, "I will sing unto the Lord as long as I liv : I will sing praise to my God while I have my being," I uttered them in a fervent whisper.

My unhappy love never ceased to harrow me. The stern image of Matilda blended with the hostile glamour of America.

One of my fellow-passengers was a young Yiddish-speaking tailor named Gitelson. He was about twenty-four years old, yet his forelock was gray, just his forelock, the rest of his hair being a fine, glossy brown. His own cap had been blown into the sea and the one he had obtained from the steerage steward was too small for him, so that gray tuft of his was always out like a plume. We had not been acquainted more than a few hours, in fact, for he had been seasick throughout the voyage and this was the first day he had been up and about. But then I had seen him on the day of our sailing and subsequently, many times, as he wretchedly lay in his berth. He was literally in tatters. He clung to me like a lover, but we spoke very little. Our hearts were too full for words.

As I thus stood at the railing, prayer-book in hand, he took a look at the page. The most ignorant "man of the earth" among our people can read holy tongue (Hebrew), though he may not understand the meaning of the words. This was the case with Gitelson.

"Saying, 'Bless the Lord, O my soul'?" he asked, reverently. "Why this chapter of all others?"

"Because— Why, just listen." With ~~which~~ I took to translating the Hebrew text into Yiddish for him.

He listened with devout mien. I was not sure that he understood it even in his native tongue, but, whether he did or not, his beaming, wistful look and the deep sigh he emitted indicated that he was in a state similar to mine.

When I say that my first view of New York Bay struck me as something not of this earth it is not a mere figure of speech. I vividly recall the feeling, for example, with which I greeted the first cat I saw on American soil. It was on the Hoboken pier, while the steerage passengers were being marched to the ferry. A large, black, well-fed feline stood in a corner, eying the crowd of new-comers. The sight of it gave me a thrill of joy. "Look! there is a cat!" I said to Gitelson. And in my heart I added, "Just like those at home!" For the moment the little animal made America real to me. At the same time it seemed unreal itself. I was tempted to feel its fur to ascertain whether it was actually the kind of creature I took it for.

We were ferried over to Castle Garden. One of the things that caught my eye as I entered the vast rotunda was an iron staircase rising diagonally against one of the inner walls. A uniformed man, with some papers in his hands, ascended it with brisk, resounding step till he disappeared through a door not many inches from the ceiling. It may seem odd, but I can never think of my arrival in this country without hearing the ringing footfalls of this official and beholding the yellow eyes of the black cat which stared at us at the Hoboken pier.

The harsh manner of the immigration officers was a grievous surprise to me. As contrasted with the officials of my despotic country, those of a republic had been portrayed in my mind as paragons of refinement and cordiality. My anticipations were rudely belied. "They are not a bit better than Cossacks," I remarked to Gitelson. But they neither looked nor spoke like Cossacks, so their gruff voices were part of the uncanny scheme of things that surrounded me. These unfriendly voices flavored all America with a spirit of icy inhospitality that sent a chill through my very soul.

The stringent immigration laws that were passed some years later had not yet come into existence. We had no difficulty in being admitted to the United States, and when I was I was loath to leave the Garden.

Many of the other immigrants were met by relatives, friends. There were cries of joy, tears, embraces, kisses. All of which intensified my sense of loneliness and dread of the New World. The agencies which two Jewish charity organizations now maintain at the Immigrant Station had not yet been established. Gitelson, who like myself had no friends in New York, never left my side. He was even more timid than I. It seemed as though he were holding on to me for dear life. This had the effect of putting me on my mettle.

"Cheer up, old man!" I said, with bravado. "America is not the place to be a ninny in. Come, pull yourself together."

In truth, I addressed these exhortations as much to myself as to him; and so far, at least, as I was concerned, my words had the desired effect.

I led the way out of the big Immigrant Station. As we reached the park outside we were pounced down upon by two evil-looking men, representatives of boarding-houses for immigrants. They pulled us so roughly and their general appearance and manner were so uninviting that we struggled and protested until they let us go—not without some parting curses. Then I led the way across Battery Park and under the Elevated railway to State Street. A train hurtling and panting along overhead produced a bewildering, a daunting effect on me. The active life of the great strange city made me feel like one abandoned in the midst of a jungle. Where were we to go? What were we to do? But the presence of Gitelson continued to act as a spur on me. I mustered courage to approach a policeman, something

I should never have been bold enough to do at home. As a
matter of fact, I scarcely had an idea what his function was.
To me he looked like some uniformed nobleman—an impression that in itself was enough to intimidate me. With
his coat of blue cloth, starched linen collar, and white
gloves, he reminded me of anything but the policemen of
my town. I addressed him in Yiddish, making it as near
an approach to German as I knew how, but my efforts were
lost on him. He shook his head. With a witheringly dignified grimace he then pointed his club in the direction of
Broadway and strutted off majestically.

"He's not better than a Cossack, either," was my verdict.

At this moment a voice hailed us in Yiddish. Facing
about, we beheld a middle-aged man with huge, round,
perpendicular nostrils and a huge, round, deep dimple in
his chin that looked like a third nostril. Prosperity was
written all over his smooth-shaven face and broad-shouldered, stocky figure. He was literally aglow with diamonds
and self-satisfaction. But he was unmistakably one of our
people. It was like coming across a human being in the
jungle. Moreover, his very diamonds somehow told a tale
of former want, of a time when he had landed, an impe-
cunious immigrant like myself; and this made him a living
source of encouragement to me.

"God Himself has sent you to us," I began, acting as the
spokesman; but he gave no heed to me. His eyes were
eagerly fixed on Gitelson and his tatters.

"You're a tailor, aren't you?" he questioned him.

My steerage companion nodded. "I'm a ladies' tailor,
but I have worked on men's clothing, too," he said.

"A ladies' tailor?" the well-dressed stranger echoed, with
ill-concealed delight. "Very well; come along. I have work
for you."

That he should have been able to read Gitelson's trade
in his face and figure scarcely surprised me. In my native
place it seemed to be a matter of course that one could tell

a tailor by his general appearance and walk. Besides, had I not divined the occupation of my fellow-passenger the moment I saw him on deck?

As I learned subsequently, the man who accosted us on State Street was a cloak contractor, and his presence in the neighborhood of Castle Garden was anything but a matter of chance. He came there quite often, in fact, his purpose being to angle for cheap labor among the newly arrived immigrants.

We paused near Bowling Green. The contractor and my fellow-passenger were absorbed in a conversation full of sartorial technicalities which were Greek to me, but which brought a gleam of joy into Gitelson's eye. My former companion seemed to have become oblivious of my existence.

As we resumed our walk up Broadway the bejeweled man turned to me.

"And what was your occupation? You have no trade, have you?"

"I read Talmud," I said, confusedly.

"I see, but that's no business in America," he declared. "Any relatives here?"

"No."

"Well, don't worry. You will be all right. If a fellow isn't lazy nor a fool he has no reason to be sorry he came to America. It'll be all right."

"All right" he said in English, and I conjectured what it meant from the context. In the course of the minute or two which he bestowed upon me he uttered it so many times that the phrase engraved itself upon my memory. It was the first bit of English I ever acquired.

The well-dressed, trim-looking crowds of lower Broadway impressed me as a multitude of counts, barons, princes. I was puzzled by their preoccupied faces and hurried step. It seemed to comport ill with their baronial dress and general high-born appearance.

In a vague way all this helped to confirm my conception

of America as a unique country, unlike the rest of the world.

When we reached the General Post-Office, at the end of the Third Avenue surface line, our guide bade us stop.

"Walk straight ahead," he said to me, waving his hand toward Park Row. "Just keep walking until you see a lot of Jewish people. It isn't far from here." With which he slipped a silver quarter into my hand and made Gitelson bid me good-by.

The two then boarded a big red horse-car.

I was left with a sickening sense of having been tricked, cast off, and abandoned. I stood watching the receding public vehicle, as though its scarlet hue were my last gleam of hope in the world. When it finally disappeared from view my heart sank within me. I may safely say that the half-hour that followed is one of the worst I experienced in all the thirty-odd years of my life in this country.

The big, round nostrils of the contractor and the gray forelock of my young steerage-fellow haunted my brain as hideous symbols of treachery.

With twenty-nine cents in my pocket (four cents was all that was left of the sum which I had received from Matilda and her mother) I set forth in the direction of East Broadway.

Ten minutes' walk brought me to the heart of the Jewish East Side. The streets swarmed with Yiddish-speaking immigrants. The sign-boards were in English and Yiddish, some of them in Russian. The scurry and hustle of the people were not merely overwhelmingly greater, both in volume and intensity, than in my native town. It was of another sort. The swing and step of the pedestrians, the voices and manner of the street peddlers, and a hundred and one other things seemed to testify to far more self-confidence and energy, to larger ambitions and wider scopes, than did the appearance of the crowds in my birthplace.

The great thing was that these people were better dressed

than the inhabitants of my town. The poorest-looking man wore a hat (instead of a cap), a stiff collar and a necktie, and the poorest woman wore a hat or a bonnet.

The appearance of a newly arrived immigrant was still a novel spectacle on the East Side. Many of the passers-by paused to look at me with wistful smiles of curiosity.

"There goes a green one!" some of them exclaimed.

The sight of me obviously evoked reminiscences in them of the days when they had been "green ones" like myself. It was a second birth that they were witnessing, an experience which they had once gone through themselves and which was one of the greatest events in their lives.

"Green one" or "greenhorn" is one of the many English words and phrases which my mother-tongue has appropriated in England and America. Thanks to the many millions of letters that pass annually between the Jews of Russia and their relatives in the United States, a number of these words have by now come to be generally known among our people at home as well as here. In the eighties, however, one who had not visited any English-speaking country was utterly unfamiliar with them. And so I had never heard of "green one" before. Still, "green," in the sense of color, is Yiddish as well as English, so I understood the phrase at once, and as a contemptuous quizzical appellation for a newly arrived, inexperienced immigrant it stung me cruelly. As I went along I heard it again and again. Some of the passers-by would call me "greenhorn" in a tone of blighting gaiety, but these were an exception. For the most part it was "green one" and in a spirit of sympathetic interest. It hurt me, all the same. Even those glances that offered me a cordial welcome and good wishes had something self-complacent and condescending in them. "Poor fellow! he is a green one," these people seemed to say. "We are not, of course. We are Americanized."

For my first meal in the New World I bought a three-cent wedge of coarse rye bread, off a huge round loaf, on a stand on Essex Street. I was too strict in my religious observances to eat it without first performing ablutions and offering a brief prayer. So I approached a bewigged old woman who stood in the doorway of a small grocery-store to let me wash my hands and eat my meal in her place. She looked old-fashioned enough, yet when she heard my request she said, with a laugh:

"You're a green one, I see."

"Suppose I am," I resented. "Do the yellow ones or black ones all eat without washing? Can't a fellow be a good Jew in America?"

"Yes, of course he can, but—well, wait till you see for yourself."

However, she asked me to come in, gave me some water and an old apron to serve me for a towel, and when I was ready to eat my bread she placed a glass of milk before me, explaining that she was not going to charge me for it.

"In America people are not foolish enough to be content with dry bread," she said, sententiously.

While I ate she questioned me about my antecedents. I remember how she impressed me as a strong, clever woman of few words as long as she catechised me, and how disappointed I was when she began to talk of herself. The astute, knowing mien gradually faded out of her face and I had before me a gushing, boastful old bore.

My intention was to take a long stroll, as much in the hope of coming upon some windfall as for the purpose of taking a look at the great American city. Many of the letters that came from the United States to my birthplace before I sailed had contained a warning not to imagine that America was a "land of gold" and that treasure might be had in the streets of New York for the picking. But these warnings only had the effect of lending vividness to my image of an American street as a thoroughfare strewn with nuggets of the precious metal. Symbolically speaking, this was the idea one had of the "land of Columbus." It was a continuation of the widespread effect produced by stories of Cortes

and Pizarro in the sixteenth century, confirmed by the successes of some Russian emigrants of my time.

I asked the grocery-woman to let me leave my bundle
with her, and, after considerable hesitation, she allowed
me to put it among some empty barrels in her cellar.

I went wandering over the Ghetto. Instead of stumbling
upon nuggets of gold, I found signs of poverty. In one place
I came across a poor family who—as I learned upon inquiry—had been dispossessed for non-payment of rent. A
mother and her two little boys were watching their pile of
furniture and other household goods on the sidewalk while
the passers-by were dropping coins into a saucer placed on
one of the chairs to enable the family to move into new
quarters.

What puzzled me was the nature of the furniture. For in
my birthplace chairs and a couch like those I now saw on
the sidewalk would be a sign of prosperity. But then anything was to be expected of a country where the poorest
devil wore a hat and a starched collar.

I walked on.

The exclamation "A green one" or "A greenhorn" continued. If I did not hear it, I saw it in the eyes of the people
who passed me.

When it grew dark and I was much in need of rest I had
a street peddler direct me to a synagogue. I expected to
spend the night there. What could have been more natural?

At the house of God I found a handful of men in prayer.
It was a large, spacious room and the smallness of their
number gave it an air of desolation. I joined in the devotions with great fervor. My soul was sobbing to Heaven to
take care of me in the strange country.

The service over, several of the worshipers took up some
Talmud folio or other holy book and proceeded to read
them aloud in the familiar singsong. The strange surroundings suddenly began to look like home to me.

One of the readers, an elderly man with a pinched face
and forked little beard, paused to look me over.

"A green one?" he asked, genially.

He told me that the synagogue was crowded on Saturdays, while on week-days people in America had no time to say their prayers at home, much less to visit a house of worship.

"It isn't Russia," he said, with a sigh. "Judaism has not much of a chance here."

When he heard that I intended to stay at the synagogue overnight he smiled ruefully.

"One does not sleep in an American synagogue," he said. "It is not Russia." Then, scanning me once more, he added, with an air of compassionate perplexity: "Where will you sleep, poor child? I wish I could take you to my house, but —well, America is not Russia. There is no pity here, no hospitality. My wife would raise a rumpus if I brought you along. I should never hear the last of it."

With a deep sigh and nodding his head plaintively he returned to his book, swaying back and forth. But he was apparently more interested in the subject he had broached. "When we were at home," he resumed, "she, too, was a different woman. She did not make life a burden to me as she does here. Have you no money at all?"

I showed him the quarter I had received from the cloak contractor.

"Poor fellow! Is that all you have? There are places where you can get a night's lodging for fifteen cents, but what are you going to do afterward? I am simply ashamed of myself."

" 'Hospitality,' " he quoted from the Talmud, " 'is one of the things which the giver enjoys in this world and the fruit of which he relishes in the world to come.' To think that I cannot offer a Talmudic scholar a night's rest! Alas! America has turned me into a mound of ashes."

"You were well off in Russia, weren't you?" I inquired, in astonishment. For, indeed, I had never heard of any but poor people emigrating to America.

"I used to spend my time reading Talmud at the synagogue," was his reply.

Many of his answers seemed to fit, not the question asked, but one which was expected to follow it. You might have thought him anxious to forestall your next query in order to save time and words, had it not been so difficult for him to keep his mouth shut.

"She," he said, referring to his wife, "had a nice little business. She sold feed for horses and she rejoiced in the thought that she was married to a man of learning. True, she has a tongue. That she always had, but over there it was not so bad. She has become a different woman here. Alas! America is a topsy-turvy country."

He went on to show how the New World turned things upside down, transforming an immigrant shoemaker into a man of substance, while a former man of leisure was forced to work in a factory here. In like manner, his wife had changed for the worse, for, lo and behold! instead of supporting him while he read Talmud, as she used to do at home, she persisted in sending him out to peddle. "America is not Russia," she said. "A man must make a living here." But, alas! it was too late to begin now! He had spent the better part of his life at his holy books and was fit for nothing else now. His wife, however, would take no excuse. He must peddle or be nagged to death. And if he ventured to slip into some synagogue of an afternoon and read a page or two he would be in danger of being caught redhanded, so to say, for, indeed, she often shadowed him to make sure that he did not play truant. Alas! America was not Russia.

A thought crossed my mind that if Reb Sender were here, he, too, might have to go peddling. Poor Reb Sender! The very image of him with a basket on his arm broke my heart. America did seem to be the most cruel place on earth.

"I am telling you all this that you may see why I can't invite you to my house," explained the peddler.

rubbish that could by no means be carried to America. It was agreeable to have my Uncle Moses stroke my hair and regard me with affectionate eyes, while he told me that I would soon forget him, and asked me, so coaxingly, to write him an account of our journey. It was delicious to be notorious through the length and breadth of Polotzk; to be stopped and questioned at every shop-door, when I ran out to buy two kopecks' worth of butter; to be treated with respect by my former playmates, if ever I found time to mingle with them; to be pointed at by my enemies, as I passed them importantly on the street. And all my delight and pride and interest were steeped in a super-feeling, the sense that it was I, Mashke, *I myself,* that was moving and acting in the midst of unusual events. Now that I was sure of America, I was in no hurry to depart, and not impatient to arrive. I was willing to linger over every detail of our progress, and so cherish the flavor of the adventure.

The last night in Polotzk we slept at my uncle's house, having disposed of all our belongings, to the last three-legged stool, except such as we were taking with us. I could go straight to the room where I slept with my aunt that night, if I were suddenly set down in Polotzk. But I did not really sleep. Excitement kept me awake, and my aunt snored hideously. In the morning I was going away from Polotzk, forever and ever. I was going on a wonderful journey. I was going to America. How could I sleep?

My uncle gave out a false bulletin, with the last batch that the gossips carried away in the evening. He told them that we were not going to start till the second day. This he did in the hope of smuggling us quietly out, and so saving us the wear and tear of a public farewell. But his ruse failed of success. Half of Polotzk was at my uncle's gate in the morning, to conduct us to the railway station, and the other half was already there before we arrived.

The procession resembled both a funeral and a triumph. The women wept over us, reminding us eloquently of the perils of the sea, of the bewilderment of a foreign land, of

the torments of homesickness that awaited us. They be-
wailed my mother's lot, who had to tear herself away from
blood relations to go among strangers; who had to face
gendarmes, ticket agents, and sailors, unprotected by a
masculine escort; who had to care for four young children
in the confusion of travel, and very likely feed them trefah
or see them starve on the way. Or they praised her for a
brave pilgrim, and expressed confidence in her ability to
cope with gendarmes and ticket agents, and blessed her
with every other word, and all but carried her in their arms.

At the station the procession disbanded and became a
mob. My uncle and my tall cousins did their best to protect
us, but we wanderers were almost torn to pieces. They did
get us into a car at last, but the riot on the station platform
continued unquelled. When the warning bell rang out, it
was drowned in a confounding babel of voices,—fragments
of the oft-repeated messages, admonitions, lamentations,
blessings, farewells. "Don't forget!"—"Take care of—"
"Keep your tickets—" "Moshele—newspapers!" "Garlick
is best!" "Happy journey!" "God help you!" "Good-bye!
Good-bye!" "Remember—"

The last I saw of Polotzk was an agitated mass of people waving colored handkerchiefs and other frantic bits of
c co, madly gesticulating, falling on each other's necks,
gone wild altogether. Then the station became invisible,
and the shining tracks spun out from sky to sky. I was in
the middle of the great, great world, and the longest road
was mine.

Memory may take a rest while I copy from a con-
temporaneous document the story of the great voyage. In
accordance with my promise to my uncle, I wrote, during
my first months in America, a detailed account of our adventures between Polotzk and Boston. Ink was cheap, and
the epistle, in Yiddish, occupied me for many hot summer hours. It was a great disaster, therefore, to have a
lamp upset on my writing-table, when I was near the end,

All I did see was that the poor man could not help unburdening his mind to the first listener that presented himself.

He pursued his tale of woe. He went on complaining of his own fate, quite forgetful of mine. Instead of continuing to listen, I fell to gazing around the synagogue more or less furtively. One of the readers attracted my special attention. He was a venerable-looking man with a face which, as I now recall it, reminds me of Thackeray. Only he had a finer head than the English novelist.

At last the henpecked man discovered my inattention and fell silent. A minute later his tongue was at work again.

"You are looking at that man over there, aren't you?" he asked.

"Who is he?"

"When the Lord of the World gives one good luck he gives one good looks as well."

"Why, is he rich?"

"His son-in-law is, but then his daughter cherishes him as she does the apple of her eye, and—well, when the Lord of the World wishes to give a man happiness he gives him good children, don't you know."

He rattled on, betraying his envy of the venerable-looking man in various ways and telling me all he knew about him—that he was a widower named Even, that he had been some years in America, and that his daughter furnished him all the money he needed and a good deal more, so that "he lived like a monarch." Even would not live in his daughter's house, however, because her kitchen was not conducted according to the laws of Moses, and everything else in it was too modern. So he roomed and boarded with pious strangers, visiting her far less frequently than she visited him and never eating at her table.

"He is a very proud man," my informant said. "One must not approach him otherwise than on tiptoe."

I threw a glance at Even. His dignified singsong seemed to confirm my interlocutor's characterization of him.

"Perhaps you will ask me how his son-in-law takes it all?" the voluble Talmudist went on. "Well, his daughter is a beautiful woman and well favored." The implication was that her husband was extremely fond of her and let her use his money freely. "They are awfully rich and they live like veritable Gentiles, which is a common disease among the Jews of America. But then she observes the commandment, 'Honor thy father.' That she does."

Again he tried to read his book and again the temptation to gossip was too much for him. He returned to Even's pride, dwelling with considerable venom upon his love of approbation and vanity. "May the Uppermost not punish me for my evil words, but to see him take his roll of bills out of his pocket and pay his contribution to the synagogue one would think he was some big merchant and not a poor devil sponging on his son-in-law."

A few minutes later he told me admiringly how Even often "loaned" him a half-dollar to enable him to do some reading at the house of God.

"I tell my virago of a wife I have sold fifty cents' worth of goods," he explained to me, sadly.

After a while the man with the Thackeray face closed his book, kissed it, and rose to go. On his way out he unceremoniously paused in front of me, a silver snuff-box in his left hand, and fell to scrutinizing me. He had the appearance of a well-paid rabbi of a large, prosperous town. "He is going to say, 'A green one,'" I prophesied to myself, all but shuddering at the prospect. And, sure enough, he did, but he took his time about it, which made the next minute seem a year to me. He took snuff with tantalizing deliberation. Next he sneezed with great zest and then he resumed sizing me up. The suspense was insupportable. Another second and I might have burst out, "For mercy's sake say 'A green one,' and let us be done with it." But at that moment he uttered it of his own accord:

"A green one, I see. Where from?" And grasping my hand he added in Hebrew, "Peace be to ye."

His first questions about me were obsequiously answered by the man with the forked beard, whereupon my attention was attracted by the fact that he addressed him by his Gentile name—that is, as "Mr. Even," and not by his Hebrew name, as he would have done in our birthplace. Surely America did not seem to be much of a God-fearing country.

When Mr. Even heard of my Talmud studies he questioned me about the tractates I had recently read and even challenged me to explain an apparent discrepancy in a certain passage, for the double purpose of testing my "Talmud brains" and flaunting his own. I acquitted myself creditably, it seemed, and I felt that I was making a good impression personally as well. Anyhow, he invited me to supper in a restaurant.

On our way there I told him of my mother's violent death, vaguely hoping that it would add to his interest in me. It did—even more than I had expected. To my pleasant surprise, he proved to be familiar with the incident. It appeared that because our section lay far outside the region of pogroms, or anti-Jewish riots, the killing of my mother by a Gentile mob had attracted considerable attention. I was thrilled to find myself in the lime-light of world-wide publicity. I almost felt like a hero.

"So you are her son?" he said, pausing to look me over, as though I had suddenly become a new man. "My poor orphan boy!"

He caused me to recount the incident in every detail. In doing so I made it as appallingly vivid as I knew how. He was so absorbed and moved that he repeatedly made me stop in the middle of the sidewalk so as to look me in the face as he listened.

"Oh, but you must be hungry," he suddenly interrupted me. "Come on."

Arrived at the restaurant, he ordered supper for me. Then he withdrew, commending me to the care of the proprietress until he should return.

He had no sooner shut the door behind him than she

took to questioning me: Was I a relative of Mr. Even? If not, then why was he taking so much interest in me? She was a vivacious, well-fed young matron with cheeks of a flaming red and with the consciousness of business success all but spurting from her black eyes. From what she, assisted by one of the other customers present, told me about my benefactor I learned that his son-in-law was the owner of the tenement-house in which the restaurant was located, as well as of several other buildings. They also told me of the landlord's wife, of her devotion to her father, and of the latter's piety and dignity. It appeared, however, that in her filial reverence she would draw the line upon his desire not to spare the rod upon her children, which was really the chief reason why he was a stranger at her house.

I had been waiting about two hours and was growing uneasy, when Mr. Even came back, explaining that he had spent the time taking his own supper and finding lodgings for me.

He then took me to store after store, buying me a suit of clothes, a hat, some underclothes, handkerchiefs (the first white handkerchiefs I ever possessed), collars, shoes, and a necktie.

He spent a considerable sum on me. As we passed from block to block he kept saying, "Now you won't look green," or, "That will make you look American." At one point he added, "Not that you are a bad-looking fellow as it is, but then one must be presentable in America." At this he quoted from the Talmud an equivalent to the saying that one must do in Rome as the Romans do.

When all our purchases had been made he took me to a barber shop with bathrooms in the rear.

"Give him a hair-cut and a bath," he said to the proprietor. "Cut off his side-locks while you are at it. One may go without them and yet be a good Jew."

He disappeared again, but when I emerged from the bathroom I found him waiting for me. I stood before him, necktie and collar in hand, not knowing what to do with them, till he showed me how to put them on.

"Don't worry, David," he consoled me. "When I came here I, too, had to learn these things." When he was through with the job he took me in front of a looking-glass. "Quite an American, isn't he?" he said to the barber, beamingly. "And a good-looking fellow, too."

When I took a look at the mirror I was bewildered. I scarcely recognized myself.

I was mentally parading my "modern" make-up before Matilda. A pang of yearning clutched my heart. It was a momentary feeling. For the rest, I was all in a flutter with embarrassment and a novel relish of existence. It was as though the hair-cut and the American clothes had changed my identity. The steamer, Gitelson, and the man who had snatched him up now appeared to be something of the remote past. The day had been so crowded with novel impressions that it seemed an age.

He took me to an apartment in a poor tenement-house and introduced me to a tall, bewhiskered, morose-looking, elderly man and a smiling woman of thirty-five, explaining that he had paid them in advance for a month's board and lodging. When he said, "This is Mr. Levinsky," I felt as though I was being promoted in rank as behooved my new appearance. "Mister" struck me as something like a title of nobility. It thrilled me. But somehow it seemed ridiculous, too. Indeed, it was some time before I could think of myself as a "Mister" without being tempted to laugh.

"And here is some cash for you," he said, handing me a five-dollar bill, and some silver, in addition. "And now you must shift for yourself. That's all I can do for you. Nor, indeed, would I do more if I could. A young man like you must learn to stand on his own legs. Understand? If you do well, come to see me. Understand?"

There was an eloquent pause which said that if I did not do well I was not to molest him. Then he added, aloud:

"There is only one thing I want you to promise me. Don't neglect your religion nor your Talmud. Do you promise that, David?"

I did. There was a note of fatherly tenderness in the way this utter stranger called me David. It reminded me of Reb Sender. I wanted to say something to express my gratitude, but I felt a lump in my throat.

He advised me to invest the five dollars in dry-goods and to take up peddling. Then, wishing me good luck, he left.

My landlady, who had listened to Mr. Even's parting words with pious nods and rapturous grins, remarked that one would vainly search the world for another man like him, and proceeded to make my bed on a lounge.

The room was a kitchen. The stove was a puzzle to me. I wondered whether it was really a stove.

"Is this used for heating?" I inquired.

"Yes, for heating and cooking," she explained, with smiling cordiality. And she added, with infinite superiority, "America has no use for those big tile ovens."

When I found myself alone in the room the feeling of desolation and uncertainty which had tormented me all day seized me once again.

I went to bed and began to say my bed-prayer. I did so mechanically. My mind did not attend to the words I was murmuring. Instead, it was saying to God: "Lord of the Universe, you have been good to me so far. I went out of that grocery-store in the hope of coming upon some good piece of luck and my hope was realized. Be good to me in the future as well. I shall be more pious than ever, I promise you, even if America is a godless country."

I was excruciatingly homesick. My heart went out to my poor dead mother. Then I reflected that it was my story of her death that had led Even to spend so much money on me. It seemed as if she were taking care of me from her grave. It seemed, too, as though she had died so that I might arouse sympathy and make a good start in America.

I thought of her and of all Antomir, and my pangs of yearning for her were tinged with pangs of my unrequited love for Matilda. . . .

Episodes of a Lonely Life
from
THE RISE OF DAVID LEVINSKY

Am I happy?

There are moments when I am overwhelmed by a sense of my success and ease. I become aware that thousands of things which had formerly been forbidden fruit to me are at my command now. I distinctly recall that crushing sense of being debarred from everything, and then I feel as though the whole world were mine. One day I paused in front of an old East Side restaurant that I had often passed in my days of need and despair. The feeling of desolation and envy with which I used to peek in its windows came back to me. It gave me pangs of self-pity for my past and a thrilling sense of my present power. The prices that had once been prohibitive seemed so wretchedly low now. On another occasion I came across a Canal Street merchant of whom I used to buy goods for my push-cart. I said to myself: "There was a time when I used to implore this man for ten dollars' worth of goods, when I regarded him as all-powerful and feared him. Now he would be happy to shake hands with me."

I recalled other people whom I used to fear and before whom I used to humiliate myself because of my poverty. I thought of the time when I had already entered the cloak business, but was struggling and squirming and constantly racking my brains for some way of raising a hundred dollars; when I would cringe with a certain East Side banker and vainly beg him to extend a small note of mine, and come away in a sickening state of despair.

At this moment, as these memories were filing by me, I

felt as though now there were nobody in the world who could inspire me with awe or render me a service.

And yet in all such instances I feel a peculiar yearning for the very days when the doors of that restaurant were closed to me and when the Canal Street merchant was a magnate of commerce in my estimation. Somehow, encounters of this kind leave me dejected. The gloomiest past is dearer than the brightest present. In my case there seems to be a special reason for feeling this way. My sense of triumph is coupled with a brooding sense of emptiness and insignificance, of my lack of anything like a great, deep interest.

I am lonely. Amid the pandemonium of my six hundred sewing-machines and the jingle of gold which they pour into my lap I feel the deadly silence of solitude.

I spend at least one evening a week at the Benders'. I am fond of their children and I feel pleasantly at home at their house. I am a frequent caller at the Nodelmans', and enjoy their hospitality even more than that of the Benders. I go to the opera, to the theaters, and to concerts, and never alone. There are merry suppers, and some orgies in which I take part, but when I go home I suffer a gnawing aftermath of loneliness and desolation.

I have a fine summer home, with servants, automobiles, and horses. I share it with the Bender family and we often have visitors from the city, but, no matter how large and gay the crowd may be, the country makes me sad.

I know bachelors who are thoroughly reconciled to their solitude and even enjoy it. I am not.

No, I am not happy.

In the city I occupy a luxurious suite of rooms in a high-class hotel and keep an excellent chauffeur and valet. I give myself every comfort that money can buy. But there is one thing which I crave and which money cannot buy—happiness.

Many a pretty girl is setting her cap at me, but I know that it is only my dollars they want to marry. Nor do I care for any of them, while the woman to whom my heart is calling—Anna—is married to another man.

I dream of marrying some day. I dread to think of dying a lonely man.

Sometimes I have a spell of morbid amativeness and seem to be falling in love with woman after woman. There are periods when I can scarcely pass a woman in the street without scanning her face and figure. When I see the crowds returning from work in the cloak-and-waist district I often pause to watch the groups of girls as they walk apart from the men. Their keeping together, as if they formed a separate world full of its own interests and secrets, makes a peculiar appeal to me.

Once, in Florida, I thought I was falling in love with a rich Jewish girl whose face had a bashful expression of a peculiar type. There are different sorts of bashfulness. This girl had the bashfulness of sin, as I put it to myself. She looked as if her mind harbored illicit thoughts which she was trying to conceal. Her blushes seemed to be full of sex and her eyes full of secrets. She was not a pretty girl at all, but her "guilty look" disturbed me as long as we were stopping in the same place.

But through all these ephemeral infatuations and interests I am in love with Anna.

From time to time I decide to make a "sensible" marriage, and study this woman or that as a possible candidate, but so far nothing has come of it.

There was one woman whom I might have married if she had not been a Gentile—one of the very few who lived in the family hotel in which I had my apartments. At first I set her down for an adventuress seeking the acquaintance of rich Jews for some sinister purpose. But I was mistaken. She was a woman of high character. Moreover, she and her aged mother, with whom she lived, had settled in that hotel long before it came to be patronized by our people. She was a widow of over forty, with a good, intellectual face, well read in the better sense of the term, and no fool.

Many of our people in the hotel danced attendance upon her because she was a Gentile woman, but all of them were really fond of her. The great point was that she seemed to have a sincere liking for our people. This and the peculiar way her shoulders would shake when she laughed was, in fact, what first drew me to her. We grew chummy and I spent many an hour in her company.

In my soliloquies I often speculated and theorized on the question of proposing to her. I saw clearly that it would be a mistake. It was not the faith of my fathers that was in the way. It was that medieval prejudice against our people which makes so many marriages between Jew and Gentile a failure. It frightened me.

One evening we sat chatting in the bright lobby of the hotel, discussing human nature, and she telling me something of the good novels she had read. After a brief pause I said:

"I enjoy these talks immensely. I don't think there is another person with whom I so love to talk of human beings."

She bowed with a smile that shone of something more than mere appreciation of the compliment. And then I uttered in the simplest possible accents:

"It's really a pity that there is the chasm of race between us. Otherwise I don't see why we couldn't be happy together."

I was in an adventurous mood and ready, even eager, to marry her. But her answer was a laugh, as if she took it for a joke; and, though I seemed to sense intimacy and encouragement in that laugh, it gave me pause. I felt on the brink of a fatal blunder, and I escaped before it was too late.

"But then," I hastened to add, "real happiness in a case like this is perhaps not the rule, but the exception. That chasm continues to yawn throughout the couple's married life, I suppose."

"That's an interesting point of view," she said, a non-committal smile on her lips.

She tactfully forbore to take up the discussion, and I soon dropped the subject. We remained friends.

It was this woman who got me interested in good, modern fiction. The books she selected for me interested me greatly. Then it was that the remarks I had heard from Moissey Tevkin came to my mind. They were illuminating.

Most of the people at my hotel are German-American Jews. I know other Jews of this class. I contribute to their charity institutions. Though an atheist, I belong to one of their synagogues. Nor can I plead the special feeling which had partly accounted for my visits at the synagogue of the Sons of Antomir while I was engaged to Kaplan's daughter. I am a member of that synagogue chiefly because it is a fashionable synagogue. I often convict myself of currying favor with the German Jews. But then German-American Jews curry favor with Portuguese-American Jews, just as we all curry favor with Gentiles and as American Gentiles curry favor with the aristocracy of Europe.

I often long for a heart-to-heart talk with some of the people of my birthplace. I have tried to revive my old friendships with some of them, but they are mostly poor and my prosperity stands between us in many ways.

Sometimes when I am alone in my beautiful apartments, brooding over these things and nursing my loneliness, I say to myself:

"There are cases when success is a tragedy."

There are moments when I regret my whole career, when my very success seems to be a mistake.

I think that I was born for a life of intellectual interest. I was certainly brought up for one. The day when that accident turned my mind from college to business seems to be the most unfortunate day in my life. I think that I should be much happier as a scientist or writer, perhaps. I should then be in my natural element, and if I were doomed to loneliness I should have comforts to which I am now a stranger. That's the way I feel every time I pass the abandoned old building of the City College.

The business world contains plenty of successful men who have no brains. Why, then, should I ascribe my triumph to special ability? I should probably have made a much better college professor than a cloak-manufacturer, and should probably be a happier man, too. I know people who have made much more money than I and whom I consider my inferiors in every respect.

Many of our immigrants have distinguished themselves in science, music, or art, and these I envy far more than I do a billionaire. As an example of the successes achieved by Russian Jews in America in the last quarter of a century it is often pointed out that the man who has built the greatest sky-scrapers in the country, including the Woolworth Building, is a Russian Jew who came here a penniless boy. I cannot boast such distinction, but then I have helped build up one of the great industries of the United States, and this also is something to be proud of. But I should readily change places with the Russian Jew, a former Talmud student like myself, who is the greatest physiologist in the New World, or with the Russian Jew who holds the foremost place among American songwriters and whose soulful compositions are sung in almost every English-speaking house in the world. I love music to madness. I yearn for the world of great singers, violinists, pianists. Several of the greatest of them are of my race and country, and I have met them, but all my acquaintance with them has brought me is a sense of being looked down upon as a money-bag striving to play the Mæcenas. I had a similar experience with a sculptor, also one of our immigrants, an East Side boy who had met with sensational success in Paris and London. I had him make my bust. His demeanor toward me was all that could have been desired. We even cracked Yiddish jokes together and he hummed bits of synagogue music over his work, but I never left his studio without feeling cheap and wretched.

When I think of these things, when I am in this sort of mood, I pity myself for a victim of circumstances.

At the height of my business success I feel that if I had my life to live over again I should never think of a business career.

I don't seem to be able to get accustomed to my luxurious life. I am always more or less conscious of my good clothes, of the high quality of my office furniture, of the power I wield over the men in my pay. As I have said in another connection, I still have a lurking fear of restaurant waiters.

I can never forget the days of my misery. I cannot escape from my old self. My past and my present do not comport well. David, the poor lad swinging over a Talmud volume at the Preacher's Synagogue, seems to have more in common with my inner identity than D id Levinsky, the well-known cloak-manufacturer.

ALTER BRODY (b. 1895), born in Kartushku a-Berŏza, Russia, came to New York in 1903. His first poems were published in *The Seven Arts* in 1916–1917. *A Family Album* (1918) and *Lamentations: Four Folk-Plays of the American Jew* (1928) are interpretations of the Lower East Side he knew so well in the context of the trauma of the Old World he had left behind.

Lamentations
from
A FAMILY ALBUM

In a dingy kitchen
Facing a Ghetto backyard
An old woman is chanting Jeremiah's Lamentations,
Quaveringly,
Out of a Hebrew Bible.

The gaslight flares and falls. . . .

This night,
Two thousand years ago,
Jerusalem fell and the Temple was burned.
Tonight
This white-haired Jewess
Sits in her kitchen and chants—by the banks of the Hud-
    son—
The Lament of the Prophet.

The gaslight flares and falls. . . .

Nearby,
Locked in her room,
Her daughter lies on a bed convulsively sobbing.
Her face is dug in the pillows;
Her shoulders heave with her sobs—
The bits of a photograph lie on the dresser. . . .

Times Square
from
A FAMILY ALBUM

An August day,
The eddying roar of the Square—
Crowds, stores, theatres, tall buildings
Assaulting the senses together—
And suddenly,
The taste of an apple between my teeth
Suffuses my mouth. . . .
Where did it come from?—
Strong and sharp and deliciously sour,
The taste in my mouth—
Where?

I cross the street
And suddenly,
Crowds, stores, theatres, tall buildings,
The blare and the glare of the day
Fade. . . .
October blows through the market-place
In a town of faraway Russia—
The booths are laden with fruit. . . .
A little boy,
Snub-nosed, freckle-faced, plump,
Dressed in a newly-washed jacket,
Stolidly strolls by the booths
Clutching a coin in his fingers—

I know him,
That freckle-faced boy;
I know him.
Proudly he passes the stores of the Row,
Ignoring them all—
Until he reaches at last
The booth of the widow Rebecca:
"What do you want, little darling?"
"Here is a penny;
I want this apple."
"Take it."
The tense little fingers unclose to surrender the penny
And close on a big red apple.
And suddenly,
The taste of an apple between my teeth,
Strong and sharp and deliciously sour,
Suffuses my mouth. . . .

The toot of an automobile,
Insistent, shrill,
Jars me back to the Square.

Ghetto Twilight
from
A FAMILY ALBUM

An infinite weariness comes into the faces of the old tene-
        ments,
As they stand massed together on the block,
Tall and thoughtfully silent,
In the enveloping twilight.
Pensively,
They eye each other across the street,
Through their dim windows—
With a sad recognizing stare,
Watching the red glow fading in the distance,
At the end of the street,
Behind the black church spires;
Watching the vague sky lowering overhead,
Purple with clouds of colored smoke
From the extinguished sunset;
Watching the tired faces coming home from work,
Like dry-breasted hags
Welcoming their children to their withered arms.

ANZIA YEZIERSKA (1885–1970), born in Sukovoly, Russia,
arrived in New York in 1901. After working in various
sweatshops on Hester and Delancey Streets, she rebelled
against her family by running away. An articulate and aggressive lady, she brought together her realistic stories of
the Lower East Side in *Hungry Hearts* (1920). A brief stay
in Hollywood convinced her that she belonged in New
York. Her later books were *Salome of The Tenements*
(1922), *Children of Loneliness* (1923) and the autobiographical *Red Ribbon on a White Horse* (1950).

The Miracle

from

HUNGRY HEARTS

I did n't see the day. I did n't see the night. I did n't see
the ocean. I did n't see the sky. I only saw my lover in
America, coming nearer and nearer to me, till I could feel
his eyes bending on me so near that I got frightened and
began to tremble. My heart ached so with the joy of his
nearness that I quick drew back and turned away, and began to talk to the people that were pushing and crowding
themselves on the deck.

Nu, I got to America.

Ten hours I pushed a machine in a shirt-waist factory,
when I was yet lucky to get work. And always my head
was drying up with saving and pinching and worrying to
send home a little from the little I earned. All that my
face saw all day long was girls and machines—and nothing
else. And even when I came already home from work, I
could only talk to the girls in the working-girls' boarding-
house, or shut myself up in my dark, lonesome bedroom.
No family, no friends, nobody to get me acquainted with
nobody! The only men I saw were what passed me by in
the street and in cars.

"Is this 'lovers' land'?" was calling in my heart. "Where
are my dreams that were so real to me in the old country?"

Often in the middle of the work I felt like stopping all
the machines and crying out to the world the heaviness
that pressed on my heart. Sometimes when I walked in
the street I felt like going over to the first man I met and
cry out to him: "Oh, I'm so lonely! I'm so lonely!"

One day I read in the Jewish "Tageblatt" the advertisement from Zaretzky, the matchmaker. "What harm is it
if I try my luck?" I said to myself. "I can't die away an old
maid. Too much love burns in my heart to stand back like
a stone and only see how other people are happy. I want
to tear myself out from my deadness. I'm in a living grave.

I've got to lift myself up. I have nobody to try for me, and maybe the matchmaker will help."

As I walked up Delancey Street to Mr. Zaretzky, the street was turning with me. I did n't see the crowds. I did n't see the pushcart peddlers with their bargains. I did n't hear the noises or anything. My eyes were on the sky, praying: "Gottuniu! Send me only the little bit of luck!"

"Nu? Nu? What need you?" asked Mr. Zaretzky when I entered.

I got red with shame in the face the way he looked at me. I turned up my head. I was too proud to tell him for what I came. Before I walked in I thought to tell him everything. But when I looked on his face and saw his hard eyes, I could n't say a word. I stood like a yok unable to move my tongue. I went to the matchmaker with my heart, and I saw before me a stone. The stone was talking to me—but—but—he was a stone!

"Are you looking for a shidduch?" he asked.

"Yes," I said, proud, but crushed.

"You know I charge five dollars for the stepping in," he bargained.

It got cold by my heart. It was n't only to give him the five dollars, nearly a whole week's wages, but his thick-skinness for being only after the money. But I could n't help myself—I was like in his fists hypnotized. And I gave him the five dollars.

I let myself go to the door, but he called me back.

"Wait, wait. Come in and sit down. I did n't question you yet."

"About what?"

"I got to know how much money you got saved before I can introduce you to anybody."

"Oh—h—h! Is it only depending on the *money?*"

"Certainly. No move in this world without money," he said, taking a pinch of snuff in his black, hairy fingers and sniffing it up in his nose.

I glanced on his thick neck and greasy, red face. "And

to him people come looking for love," I said to myself, shuddering. Oh, how it burned in my heart, but still I went on, "Can't I get a man in America without money?"

He gave a look on me with his sharp eyes. Gottuniu! What a look! I thought I was sinking into the floor.

"There are plenty of *young* girls with money that are begging themselves the men to take them. So what can you expect? *Not young, not lively, and without money, too?* But, anyhow, I'll see what I can do for you."

He took out a little book from his vest-pocket and looked through the names.

"What trade do you go on your hands?" he asked, turning to me. "Sometimes a dressmaker or a hairdresser that can help make a living for a man, maybe—"

I could n't hear any more. It got black before my eyes, my voice stopped inside of me.

"If you want to listen to sense from a friend, so I have a good match for you," he said, following me to the door. "I have on my list a widower with not more than five or six children. He has a grand business, a herring-stand on Hester Street. He don't ask for no money, and he don't make an objection if the girl is in years, so long as she knows how to cook well for him."

How I got myself back to my room I don't know. But for two days and for two nights I lay still on my bed, unable to move. I looked around on my empty walls, thinking, thinking, "Where am I? Is this the world? Is this America?"

Suddenly I sprang up from bed. "What can come from pitying yourself?" I cried. "If the world kicks you down and makes nothing of you, you bounce yourself up and make something of yourself." A fire blazed up in me to rise over the world because I was downed by the world.

"Make a person of yourself," I said. "Begin to learn English. Make yourself for an American if you want to live in America. American girls don't go to matchmakers. American girls don't run after a man: if they don't get a husband they don't think the world is over; they turn their mind to something else.

"Wake up!" I said to myself. "You want love to come to you? Why don't you give it out to other people? Love the women and children, everybody in the street and the shop. Love the rag-picker and the drunkard, the bad and the ugly. All those whom the world kicks down you pick up and press to your heart with love."

As I said this I felt wells of love that choked in me all my life flowing out of me and over me. A strange, wonderful light like a lover's smile melted over me, and the sweetness of lover's arms stole around me.

The first night I went to school I felt like falling on everybody's neck and kissing them. I felt like kissing the books and the benches. It was such great happiness to learn to read and write the English words.

Because I started a few weeks after the beginning of the term, my teacher said I might stay after the class to help me catch up with my back lessons. The minute I looked on him I felt that grand feeling: "Here is a person! Here is America!" His face just shined with high thoughts. There was such a beautiful light in his eyes that it warmed my heart to steal a look on him.

At first, when it came my turn to say something in the class, I got so excited the words stuck and twisted in my mouth and I could n't give out my thoughts. But the teacher did n't see my nervousness. He only saw that I had something to say, and he helped me say it. How or what he did I don't know. I only felt his look of understanding flowing into me like draughts of air to one who is choking.

Long after I already felt free and easy to talk to him alone after the class, I looked at all the books on his desk. "Oi weh!" I said to him, "if I only knew half of what is in your books, I could n't any more sit still in the chair like you. I'd fly in the air with the joy of so much knowledge."

"Why are you so eager for learning?" he asked me.

"Because I want to make a person of myself," I answered.

"Since I got to work for low wages and I can't be young any more, I'm burning to get among people where it's not against a girl if she is in years and without money."

His hand went out to me. "I'll help you," he said. "But you must first learn to get hold of yourself."

Such a beautiful kindness went out of his heart to me with his words! His voice, and the goodness that shone from his eyes, made me want to burst out crying, but I choked back my tears till I got home. And all night long I wept on my pillow: "Fool! What is the matter with you? Why are you crying?" But I said, "I can't help it. He is so beautiful!"

My teacher was so much above me that he was n't a man to me at all. He was a God. His face lighted up the shop for me, and his voice sang itself in me everywhere I went. It was like healing medicine to the flaming fever within me to listen to his voice. And then I'd repeat to myself his words and live in them as if they were religion.

Often as I sat at the machine sewing the waists I'd forget what I was doing. I'd find myself dreaming in the air. "Ach!" I asked myself, "what was that beautifulness in his eyes that made the lowest nobody feel like a somebody? What was that about him that when his smile fell on me I felt lifted up to the sky away from all the coldness and the ugliness of the world? Gottunui!" I prayed, "if I could only always hold on to the light of high thoughts that shined from him. If I could only always hear in my heart the sound of his voice I would need nothing more in life. I would be happier than a bird in the air."

"Friend," I said to him once, "if you could but teach me how to get cold in the heart and clear in the head like you are!"

He only smiled at me and looked far away. His calmness was like the sureness of money in the bank. Then he turned and looked on me, and said: "I am not so cold in the heart and clear in the head as I make-believe. I am bound. I am a prisoner of convention."

"You make-believe—you bound?" I burst out. "You who do not have foreladies or bosses—you who do not have to sell yourself for wages—you who only work for love and truth—you a prisoner?"

"True, I do not have bosses just as you do," he said. "But still I am not free. I am bound by formal education and conventional traditions. Though you work in a shop, you are really freer than I. You are not repressed as I am by the fear and shame of feeling. You could teach me more than I could teach you. You could teach me how to be natural."

"I'm not so natural like you think," I said. "I'm afraid."

He smiled at me out of his eyes. "What are you afraid of?"

"I'm afraid of my heart," I said, trying to hold back the blood rushing to my face. "I'm burning to get calm and sensible like the born Americans. But how can I help it? My heart flies away from me like a wild bird. How can I learn to keep myself down on earth like the born Americans?"

"But I don't want you to get down on earth like the Americans. That is just the beauty and the wonder of you. We Americans are too much on earth; we need more of your power to fly. If you would only know how much you can teach us Americans. You are the promise of the centuries to come. You are the heart, the creative pulse of America to be."

I walked home on wings. My teacher said that I could help him; that I had something to give to Americans. "But how could I teach him?" I wondered; "I who had never had a chance to learn anything except what he taught me. And what had I to give to the Americans, I who am nothing but dreams and longings and hunger for love?"

When school closed down for vacation, it seemed to me all life stopped in the world. I had no more class to look forward to, no more chance of seeing my teacher. As I faced the emptiness of my long vacation, all the light went out of my eyes, and all the strength out of my arms and fingers.

For nearly a week I was like without air. There was no school. One night I came home from the shop and threw myself down on the bed. I wanted to cry, to let out the heavy weight that pressed on my heart, but I could n't cry. My tears felt like hot, burning sand in my eyes.

"Oi-i-i! I can't stand it no more, this emptiness," I groaned. "Why don't I kill myself? Why don't something happen to me? No consumption, no fever, no plague or death ever comes to save me from this terrible world. I h ive to go on suffering and choking inside myself till I grow mad."

I jumped up from the bed, threw open the window, and began fighting with the deaf-and-dumb air in the air-shaft.

"What is the matter with you?" I cried. "You are going out of your head. You are sinking back into the old ways from which you dragged yourself out with your studies. Studies! What did I get from all my studies? Nothing. Nothing. I am still in the same shop with the same shirt-waists. A lot my teacher cares for me once the class is over."

A fire burned up in me that he was already forgetting me. And I shot out a letter to him:

"You call yourself a teacher? A friend? How can you go off in the country and drop me out of your heart and out of your head like a read-over book you left on the shelf of your shut-down classroom? How can you enjoy your vacation in the country while I'm in the sweatshop? You learned me nothing. You only broke my heart. What good are all the books you ever gave me? They don't tell me how to be happy in a factory. They don't tell me how to keep alive in emptiness, or how to find something beautiful in the dirt and ugliness in which I got to waste away. I want life. I want people. I can't live inside my head as you do."

I sent the letter off in the madness in which I wrote it,

without stopping to think; but the minute after I dropped it in the mail-box my reason came again to my head. I went back tearing my hair. "What have I done? Meshugeneh!"

Walking up the stairs I saw my door open. I went in. The sky is falling to the earth! Am I dreaming? There was my teacher sitting on my trunk! My teacher come to see me? Me, in my dingy room? For a minute it got blind before my eyes, and I did n't know where I was any more.

"I had to come," he said, the light of heaven shining on me out of his eyes. "I was so desolate without you. I tried to say something to you before I left for my vacation, but the words would n't come. Since I have been away I have written you many letters, but I did not mail them, for they were like my old self from which I want to break away."

He put his cool, strong hand into mine. "You can save me," he said. "You can free me from the bondage of age-long repressions. You can lift me out of the dead grooves of sterile intellectuality. Without you I am the dry dust of hopes unrealized. You are fire and sunshine and desire. You make life changeable and beautiful and full of daily wonder."

I could n't speak. I was so on fire with his words. Then, like whirlwinds in my brain, rushed out the burning words of the matchmaker: "Not young, not lively, and without money, too!"

"You are younger than youth," he said, kissing my hands. "Every day of your unlived youth shall be relived with love, but such a love as youth could never know."

And then how it happened I don't know; but his arms were around me. "Sara Reisel, tell me, do you love me," he said, kissing me on my hair and on my eyes and on my lips.

I could only weep and tremble with joy at his touch. "The miracle!" cried my heart; "the miracle of America come true!"

2. The American Jews

MIDWAY INTO THE 1920s, about half of America's Jews
lived in New York, Chicago, and Philadelphia. Crowded
into ghettos for the most part they moved as they prospered into areas where they were unwelcome. Most were
making whatever adjustments were necessary to achieve the
promises of the American Dream. But unlike the first generation, whose tensions arose out of the necessity to survive, the second generation had to deal with the added
problems of success in the Twenties and the poverty that
affected all in the Depression of the Thirties.

Jews in the 1920s studied every subject imaginable, including Hebrew and Yiddish, joined their fellow countrymen (Landsleit), formed mutual aid societies, enjoyed
Maurice Schwartz's Yiddish Art Theatre, read the Forward, and participated exuberantly in the political process. Valuing economic survival so highly, they worked
long hours in the garment trades sweatshops, organized
unions to improve their working conditions, and learned
how the system worked and how to adjust to achieve so-

cial and economic success. Emphasizing secular education, as they once had valued Torah and Talmud, they began moving into jobs that had been closed to them; Jews now attended Columbia University as well as the College of the City of New York, and they entered the professions in numbers for the first time. Their physical survival assured, they left the ghettos; at the same time, being acculturated by the environing society they still thought it important to retain their ethnic identity. *"Beyond* was the city," Alfred Kazin remembered, but at the same time, the voice that spoke to him from his prayer book came from his bowels, grand and austere, it confirmed his Jewishness, "the fierce awareness of life to the depths, every day and in every hour: the commitment: the hunger."

In her autobiography, *Red Ribbon on a White Horse* (1950), Anzia Yezierska recalled her father's advice that "He who separates himself from people buries himself in death." In her case, a disillusioning trek to Hollywood convinced her that she should be back in New York; fire and water did not mix, neither did "godliness and the fleshpots of Mammon." Similarly on the larger scene, the immigrant generation had succeeded and failed too well, and the children had to bear the burden. The Jews were becoming people. Bending under the pressure of success, as Meyer Hirsch did in *Haunch, Paunch and Jowl,* or under the weight of poverty and despair, as in Roth's *Call It Sleep,* were the realities of the day. Some became businessmen, lawyers, and judges, and some were corrupt; Ornitz's "all-rightniks" were an example. Some went to high school and college, and some became gangsters and prostitutes. But most worked hard and maintained family and community, while the idealists, the alienated, and the radical moved into new paths. For the latter there was little concern for their Jewish identity or for Jewish values. They felt that an ocean separated them from their parents, justifying their contempt. Meanwhile self-hatred was widespread, as in

Ben Hecht's *A Jew in Love* or in Ornitz, as hostility and
the attempts to find oneself led to anarchic individualism,
interreligious marriage and corruption. Only occasionally,
as in Lewisohn's *The Island Within,* was there dramatized
a return to peoplehood.

Success and Americanization were the spurs that drove
many American Jews in the 1920s. Moses Singermann's
roots in Rumania, as a result, were lost as the family pursued its fortune from Minneapolis to Montana; in the end
he was left with an atomized family, in which Judaism had
been subordinated to the things one wanted. Similarly, in
Dahlberg's *Those Who Perish,* Eli Melamed (which means
Hebrew teacher) epitomized the Jews who hadn't made it,
and the loneliness of those who perished because they were
too anxious to please, too eager to struggle and fail. As Eli
put it, "I am being murdered, and I don't know why or for
what, and no one will help me, neither church, God nor
America." The same pessimism applied to Halper's *Sons of
the Fathers* though the breakup of the Bergmans was done
with great sensitivity. Significantly, ironically, it was in the
Temple that Saul Bergman's eldest son Milton denounced
America's participation in World War I; at Milton's birth,
Saul had exclaimed: "Thank God I came to America."

Overwhelmingly in the 1930s American Jews supported
President Roosevelt and the New Deal. Sympathetic to social change and tolerance, they worked for the return of
the health of the system they had learned about and benefited from, the system that had permitted them to become
Americans and move up and out of the ghetto. Some writers
of course, like Mike Gold, were the backbone of the Communist Party. Most, somewhere on the Left, wrote proletarian and social novels, and worked in various ways for
various causes. Samuel Ornitz, Albert Halper, Daniel
Fuchs, Edward Dahlberg, and Nelson Algren were among
the proletarian writers; Ludwig Lewisohn, one of America's
most popular writers, wrote Freudian criticism and semi-

autobiographical fiction, while Nathanael West wrote four
short novels that satirized the country's shallowness and corruption. On the legitimate stage, Clifford Odets' *Waiting for
Lefty, Awake and Sing,* and *Golden Boy* sparked the
Group Theatre's pathbreaking productions; directed by
Harold Clurman, with Luther Adler, Stella Adler, and John
Garfield, with roots in the Yiddish Theatre, as leading ac-
tors, the company's creative energy and quality ranked it
among the greatest this country has seen. It was indeed a
decade of ferment, of hope amidst despair, of new be-
ginnings.

That an affirmative view was heard more often in poetry
than in fiction is an interesting fact. Louis Untermeyer's
pride in the mission of "a race that burns, an ever fiery
sword,/To rescue tolerance and set freedom free," was a
refreshing light in a dark corridor. In the same way Robert
Nathan, known for his many novels and poems, recalled
the ironies of the "chosen people," their honey and gall.
In Stanley Kunitz's "For the Word is Flesh," however, there
is an impatience with his heritage directed at his father.
Singling out the Jewish mother for blame was still in the
future.

Between the two great wars, Americans lived through
the Roaring Twenties and the Great Depression, and began
to react to the Nazi-led holocaust. For Jews, opportunities
and acculturation characterized their rise while the appearance of success led to tensions and anxiety. While Hemingway, Fitzgerald, Faulkner, and Wolfe wrote of Michigan,
Paris, Mississippi, North Carolina and New York, the
American Jewish writers wrote of what they knew. American Jewish literature was invented by them. As Langston
Hughes wrote, much later, "The more regional or national
an art is in its origins, the more universal it may become
in the end." America's major writers, including those we
call its American Jewish writers, somehow knew this even
then.

MAXWELL BODENHEIM (1893–1954), was a Mississippi-born, self-educated poet and novelist. Living in Greenwich Village most of his life, he was as extroverted a bohemian as the characters in his novels. His poetry, collected in *Minna and Myself* (1918), *Advice* (1920), *Introducing Irony* (1922), *Bringing Jazz* (1930), and *Selected Poems 1914–1944* (1945) shows his mastery of metaphor and the sense of the grotesque. His most famous (some say infamous) novels were *Replenishing Jessica* (1925), *Georgie May* (1927), *Sixty Seconds* (1929), and *Naked on Roller Skates* (1931). Bodenheim and his third wife were found murdered in a room near the Bowery in 1954.

East Side: New York
from
ADVICE

An old Jew munches an apple
With conquering immersion.
All the thwarted longings of his life
Urge on his determined teeth.
His face is hard and pear-shaped;
His eyes are muddy capitulations;
But his mouth is incongruous.
Softly, slightly distended,
Like that of a whistling girl,
It is ingenuously haunting
And makes the rest of him a soiled, grey background.
Hopes that lie within their graves
Of submissive sternness,
Have spilled their troubled ghosts upon this mouth,
And a tortured, stoical belief
Has dwindled into tenderness upon it . . . .
He trudges off behind his push-cart
And the Ghetto walks away with him.

OLD AGE

In me is a little painted square
Bordered by old shops with gaudy awnings.
And before the shops sit smoking, open-bloused old men,
Drinking sunlight.
The old men are my thoughts;
And I come to them each evening, in a creaking cart,
And quietly unload supplies.
We fill slim pipes and chat
And inhale scents from pale flowers in the center of the
    square. ....
Strong men, tinkling women, and dripping, squealing chil-
    dren
Stroll past us, or into the shops.
They greet the shopkeepers and touch their hats or fore-
    heads to me. ....
Some evening I shall not return to my people.

SAMUEL B. ORNITZ (1890–1957), born in New York, worked as a social worker until 1920. His play *The Sock* (1919) was written under a pseudonym; his novel *Haunch, Paunch and Jowl* (1923), originally published anonymously, described how a Lower East Side Jewish boy rose from poverty to become a crooked lawyer, a conniving politician, and a corrupt judge. A Jewish atheist, assimilationist, and alleged self-hater, Ornitz also wrote *Round the World with Jocko the Great* (1925), *A Yankee Passional* (1927), and *Bride of the Sabbath* (1951). A successful motion picture writer for several decades, Ornitz was socially oriented and politically active and was named as one of the Hollywood Ten in the 1950s.

Hirsch & Freund
from
HAUNCH, PAUNCH AND JOWL

HIRSCH & FREUND
Counsellors at Law

Thus read the large gilt letters on the expansive plate-glass window of the store in which we make our offices. And a swinging yellow and black sign, high above the door, to catch the roving eyes from all points, is more to the point. It bears a one-word legend, in three languages, English, Yiddish and Russian, black gaping out of yellow:

LAWYER

Mine has been a bad night. My mood is in the throes of misgiving. Here is my office. But yesterday, I pridefully beheld it, and today, I see it shamefacedly as a pirates' ship. . . . I am in terror of the dream-stupefied. I have breathed the scents of their poppy fields.

Our pirate ship, flying its skull and bones and plague colors, lay, so to speak, at the mouth of the lagoon. Across the way is the Essex Market Courthouse. All vessels in distress, alimp, leaky, in tow, must pass our runners and steerers, pilots for the predatory crew of Hirsch & Freund, who are adept and daring with the grappling irons, and perfect ferrets for smelling out worth-while plunder.

Little groups of men and women wait in front of our office. They are the overflow of our already filled to capacity sitting room. People like to patronize a crowded shop. It is the herd instinct, the fear to be alone, act alone; the fear to try the new. . . . Deferential good mornings, stepping back and making way, raising of hats, eager, solicitous glances, servile holding out of hands, and awed whispers of "here he comes," are balm to my sick, drooping spirit. I pass through the congested sitting room. It is like being bathed with healing oils. . . . I plunge into a sea of troubles, other people's troubles, and peace comes to my soul. My brain clears. The poppy scents are dissipated. I am again Meyer Hirsch.

The little glazed door, which connects Maxie's office with mine, opens an inch. I get rid of the client who has my ear. I shut my outer door with a bang by way of signal to Maxie that the coast is clear. Immediately Maxie enters, followed by a stalwart, lumbering fellow with an inflamed face. . . . "Judge Duffy, I want you to meet my partner, Meyer Hirsch, a regular feller." . . . "Glad to know you, Mr. Hirsch." . . . A few minutes of small, awkward talk, and then His Honor departs. . . . Maxie smiles. He looks like a cat laughing in his whiskers as he remarks, "That's my fifth one. Laying the hooks and lines. . . . Well, bread on water, hey Mike? . . . Just took up Duffy's notes for two thousand. Told him not to worry about them. Pay when convenient. You know, when convenient. Won't bother me if he never pays." . . . Chuckling, Maxie makes an entry in a small black book which he has taken from his vest pocket. . . . "Charged it off to profit and loss." . . . I simply grin. Maxie's facial expression is an attempt at cuteness. It is very unbecoming. But I did not pick my partner for good looks. He is viciously clever, but loyal and above-board with me. I keep the political irons hot, fix the cops, do all the backing and filling in connection with the criminal cases. I split fees with court clerks, attendants, keepers, detectives, policemen, their superiors, saloonkeepers—anybody who will bring us cases. I take care of the boys all the way down the line from the judge on the bench to the bootblack in the criminal courts' hallway. Maxie's province is the civil courts, and his skill and subtlety as a cross-examiner along new lines have already earned him a reputation. But Maxie knows that legal knowledge only, on the part of a lawyer, even plus cleverness and preparation—entitles a lawyer to starve in New York courts. So he keeps his hand in the political grab-bag and is a note broker; only judges' notes. Like most of the judges, Judge Duffy was heavily in debt—in the beginning of his term. . . . So it was in that hurly-burly time of New York's nineties: A nomination or appointment to judgeship cost a stated sum; judgeships had their regular scale of prices. The market price for a Supreme Court place was $35,000. The average salary for the term fixed the price for the job. . . . Maxie's system was simple. All he wanted was the good will of the jurist. He did not ask any outright preference from the finicky and the fourflushers, just wanted the shade on his side. Soon the judges found it was safe to rule in his favor. For Maxie was not crude. He came into court prepared, bristling with facts, a-sparkle with decisions, and pointed like a porcupine with technicalities. First, he had won the gratitude of the judges, and then he proceeded to exact their respect for a thoroughly and cleverly prepared case—which gave them an essential sense of security. So the judge did not have to fear making a raw decision, and incur a rebuking reversal. Maxie saw to it that the case was punched full of loopholes. The judges liked him. He did not throw the full brunt upon them. He steered the case into a safe channel, tied it up in such a way that no one knew where it started or where it should land. Presently there circulated one of those quietly notorious facts that Maxie even wrote the decisions for the judges, wherein you learn how Maxie created a good many legal precedents—the secret twists of which he alone knew. . . . In time, when a big matter was broached to a judge, he feared to move unless Maxie was taken in as trial counsel. Then the Judge felt he was safe in throwing the case. . . . So, the notes bore fruits of perennial bloom. Judges became our steerers.

Steadily, with unremitting purposefulness, I was creating a political organization that I could call my own, an organization that would make me a factor in politics. I organized the pushcart peddlers into a Protective Association. In batches of four and five, sometimes as many as ten, I had them sworn in as citizens. My first move was to stop the petty police graft which extorted a quarter a day from each peddler. The peddlers began to hold up their heads. Then I pointed out that too many people were coming in as peddlers. So I had an ordinance passed making it unlawful to peddle without a license, and only citizens with pull could get licenses. All the peddlers flocked into the Protective Association, became citizens, and saw it was good business to limit the number of competitors. The Peddlers' Protective Association voted me a large yearly retainer. My principal service to them was to stop the constant, annoying and expensive interference by the police, settling squabbles over profitable spots, opening up new streets to peddlers' stands, stopping petty thievery by buying off the leaders of the gangs, who also gave the peddlers protection from marauding Irish gangs. The peddlers' vote was mine, solidly, could be counted as a unit. Big Jim Hallorhan acknowledged my good services, and I asked him a favor for the boys. I wanted to keep the good will of Shimshin and his gang, as well as the unswerving support of Boolkie and his constantly renewed ranks. There was keen competition for the pickpocket privilege of the Brooklyn Bridge terminal, where swirling, pushing crowds made pocket-picking easy and lucrative. Detectives were assigned to see that the regularly designated pickpockets operated without interference and to keep out poachers from this fine game preserve. Big Jim awarded the Brooklyn Bridge concession to my district. I divided it among four pickpockets, two from Shimshin's gang and two from Boolkie's, which gave the leaders a good income. A certain percentage of the pickings went to the guardian detectives and to the police inspector in charge of the Bridge district.

By this time the tough babies, who were quite grown up, became the gangsters' meal tickets. They were sent out on the streets. It was a police privilege for girls to solicit on certain busy highways. If you were not in right, your girl was arrested and kept from the best flesh marts. So I saw to it that my boys' girls were unmolested, collected the police tribute from them and gave it to the local inspector of police, who found it convenient to have me do his collecting. I never dealt with the girls. I saw to it that Boolkie and Shimshin took up the allotted tolls and brought them in promptly.

So it came about that I became the attorney for the flesh brokers, the procurers and resort keepers. To keep up a certain kind of police appearance, to quiet the grumblings of the press and reformers, I arranged with the pimps, procurers, girls and houses "to stand for a raid," which meant submitting to a spectacular alleged police clean-up, which for a few days filled the newspapers and the courts and was soon forgotten. The court cases were hushed up. And then business continued as usual at the old stands. As Big Jim said, New York is a nine-day town.

I talked over Allen Street with Big Jim and Little Tom, the former's cousin, who was responsible for my district. The reformers were making a fearful stew over Allen Street. It was the crudest of all bawdy-house streets. We decided that Allen Street should shift to other quarters. I knew the sentiments of my congregation and the Peddlers' Association. They did not want brothels so near their homes and

children. I thought we could make political capital by making a sensational raid on Allen Street and having it appear
that our political party without police aid broke up the vile
nuisance. Jim and Tom saw the point. They assigned the
nearby district captains to report to me with their strong-
arm men. We gave the houses two weeks' time in which to
make other arrangements, and advised them of the date of
the clean-up. I then went about stirring up the congregation and the Peddlers' Association, telling them how indignant Big Jim and Little Tom were when I laid before them
the extent of the abuse. I raised a hue and cry, a battle
slogan, "Clean up Allen Street; clean up Allen Street."
Boolkie and Shimshin, two big procurers, were my assist-
ants on the day of the clean-up. We marched into Allen
Street like virtue incarnate, drove the women from the
houses, threw furniture in the street, and in a short hour
Allen Street was no more a redlight haunt. The landlords
were quite broken-hearted, but everybody else was satisfied, the newspapers playing up and applauding the event.
I was the head and center of the publicity, and got the
lion's share of credit and esteem. Next election we swept
the district as it never was swept before. I named the candidates for the State Assembly and the City Board of Alder-
men. They were my straw men, Moritz Krulewitch and
Hermann Weisbrod. But ten years ago they were raw immigrants. Having a constitutional dislike for manual labor
—back home they were the young sons of the trader class
—and having adaptable personalities, they soon got onto
the Professional Jew game. They, ostensibly, were insurance
brokers and adjusters, notary publics and self-sacrificing
executives of the Roumanian and Polish Jewish lodges and
societies. So when the election came, their respective com-
patriots, the Roumanian and Polish Jews, joyfully voted
for Krulewitch and Weisbrod, holding it a personal honor
in having their lodge members named for official distinction. Krulewitch and Weisbrod knew how to hold their jobs.
In all their speeches they unfailingly referred to me as the

Shield of Israel in America; they busied themselves doing petty favors for their constituents, protesting against the slightest sign of anti-semitism in schools, parks, public places, newspapers, office-holders and especially in the utterances of their immediate political opponents. They would call upon me, leading sheep-like committees, and ask me as the Leader of My Oppressed People in America to end this or that discrimination. They performed their legislative duties with punctilious attention to the party's orders. In short, their conduct assured them a steady political future in New York, and a rise from poverty to riches. Hymie Rubin, who was developing into an amiable philosophical anarchist with a weakness for puns, called the progress of my office-seeking proteges, "From Wretches to Riches." Hymie could safely joke about everybody, for everybody's wife came to be his patient. Hymie began by having countless maternity cases and no fees, but this unceasing experience made him in time one of America's greatest and best paid obstetricians. When a woman attaches herself to a doctor she makes him her god.

Again we re-elected our nominee for Congress, Joseph Goodman, a high officer of a national Jewish fraternal and protective order. He held tenaciously to the Congressional job by making only one speech at each term of Congress. Goodman made his one speech and then devoted himself to his lodge and other duties. In time this speech became an East Side classic: our best heads had concocted it. It was a hair-raising recital of the horrors of Jewish persecution in Russia that splashed vitriolic denunciations upon the Tsar and his government as being officially responsible for the pogroms, and ended with an hysterical plea to the American government to sever relations with the Tsar's government until the massacres were stopped. His campaign orations gave him no troubles of composition. He simply repeated his Congressional speech. Goodman's Socialist opponent was Avrum Toledo. Avrum made the mistake an honest man always makes, tells the truth as he understands it. He ridiculed Goodman and suggested another cure for pogroms. He was nearly lynched. He must be fearless or foolish to think that he could make the Jews believe, even for a moment, that they themselves, in the slightest degree, may be responsible for pogroms. It was not so much what Avrum had said, but what we had twisted his words into, that made trouble for the Socialist Party, which, we said, was responsible for Avrum's views. . . . Avrum had said that Jewish ways made it easy for the Russian *agents-provocateur* to inflame the peasants against the Jews. That the peasants are naturally irritated and resentful when they find themselves systematiclly cheated and impoverished by the wily Jewish traders, who seem, in their simple minds, to rob them with the devil's cunning. When fired with vodka and wild reports, and religious fury, the resentment is easily fanned into hatred. He did not say that the Jews as a whole cheated the peasant and deserved his resentment, but accused the trader and money-lender classes.

He said: "Let us look with clear eyes and calm brains at the Russian pogrom question. We know the Government inspires the outrages. We know the Government uses the violence and pillaging as the means of letting off the people's steam, which otherwise might be directed against their rotten government. Is that all that concerns us? How about the people whom it is so easy to incite against our people? Have we wronged them in any way? Where is our fault, in what way do we help along the happening of pogroms! I beg for a little common sense among ourselves, a few home remedies, which will do more than all the impassioned speeches in the Halls of Congress, speeches that are used merely as bait to catch your votes. I say it will not be such a simple matter for the Tsar's government to stir up pogroms when we have won the good-will, trust and affection of our Gentile neighbors. If they have every reason to respect and love us, how then can they be made to hate and destroy us? So it is up to us to stop the abuses of the traders and money-lenders.

"We must tell our people that these traders and money-lenders, the leaders and controllers of our community, this minority of profit-takers, are the root-causes of the po-groms. Let us understand the Russian peasant's mental operations. Is it not easy to be incited against the persons who have been systematically wronging you? Stop the wrong, the first wrong, and you will end the ultimate wrong. Life is reproductive. Wrong begets wrong. Hate begets hate. Love will beget a happy family. . . . In time the Russian government, unable to instigate the peasantry, will have to come out in the open. They will have to use troops to massacre the Jews. The world will ring out in protest against such savagery. Butchery, wearing official garb, attacking a peaceful, unoffending people, will turn the world against Russia. She will be a pariah wherever there is public opinion. It will be savagery without excuse, a savagery stamped with the seal of the Russian bureaucracy, and then we can make a powerful appeal to the world's sympathy and intervention. How different it will be when the Jews come to the world with clean hands and clear consciences! No longer will the Russian government shrug its shoulders and say, smugly, 'the pogroms are the anger of the people against the abuses of the Jews.'"

There was the devil to pay. Even the Socialists turned upon Avrum. They said he was a Spanish Jew and did not feel for the Russian Jews, and was like his German ilk in his dislike and contempt for his unfortunate brethren in the Pale. . . . Scratch a Socialist—the espouser of the brotherhood of internationalism—and you will find a rabid nationalist. . . . No man can escape the prejudices and predilections of his blood nor cleanse himself of the pitch of his environment.

Avrum, college graduate, was a garment worker, a plain operator at the machine. And, now, what did it avail him to have sacrificed his personal career to become one in suffering and understanding with the slave to the needle? One indiscretion, one scratch, had angered the nationalistic people. How dare he intimate that the Russ—or Pole—Jews themselves may even in a part be responsible for the pogroms? Why, man, in other words, he was justifying—justifying pogroms!

All the explanations his friends tried to make incensed them more. They hated him for a Spaniard. . . . But Avrum smiled and plodded on in the ranks of the thin, straggly line of unionists. Before long he found it harder and harder to get a job as it became known that he was a labor agitator, a wild-eyed Socialist who could even justify pogroms. Yet Avrum carried on. If he was hurt, he did not let on; if it shook his faith in the people's ability to carry out Socialism, he showed it in an increasing demand upon educational programs for the workers. First he wanted to prepare their minds, then he wanted to prepare their hearts, after which he saw the Utopian millennium.

Sometimes he went to the extreme folly of sincerity. He tried to convert the bosses to unionism. He said an improved standard of living and working conditions would make the workers more efficient. He appealed to their interest, then he tried to touch their hearts. There was a twinkle in his eyes and a smile of self-amusement on his face, or he might have been taken for stark crazy, when he said to the bosses:—"You are keeping out the light of a great happiness from your lives. The greatest happiness is to see everyone around you happy. For how can you be happy if even one of your fellowmen is in need and distress?"

And they answered his smile and gave him the sack. . . . After a while only Philip would employ him. Philip said he did not fear his influence in his shop. No one could organize his shop. The minute a man joined the union he fired him. And there were ten greenhorns ready and eager to take his place. Philip enjoyed Avrum's talk, saying it was a fine example of the self-deluded vaporings of the dream-stupefied.

Fancy my surprise when Philip, who never took more than five minutes for lunch, and thereby gave himself a life-time of stomach trouble, called at my office and asked Maxie and me to take lunch with him in a quiet place where we could talk. At lunch Philip announced he wanted our advice on how the unions could completely stop work in all shops and for once really win a strike. . . .

Maxie taunted him, "Getting afraid of the unions? Worrying if they can win. Want to know when to hop off the fence. . . ." But soon Philip disclosed that he had a deeper purpose. He confused us for a time when he seemed to insist that he wanted the unions to paralyze all the shops for a season.

But we got an inkling when he said, "Except my shop. I want my shop to work in full blast—as a union shop, a union shop while it suits my purpose."

Maxie took him in hand with questions. He brought out that Philip wanted to expand his business, was ready for bigger, better business. He wanted to steal the best accounts in the country from the long-established German-Jewish concerns. If he could stop their production, completely, for one season, he could make an entering wedge that never could be dislodged. He had several things up his sleeve. He had standardized the difficult short stouts, he could fit any man with a ready-made suit better than a custom tailor. He could undersell his competitors. He had stolen the best styles, pippins, sure-sellers. He wanted to spring his lines on the big accounts of the country when they had to listen to him. He needed one season to convince them.

Maxie hit right at the heart of the matter. "How do you manufacturers always manage to beat the unions?"

Philip told him that when the unionized workers quit there were plenty of greenhorns to take their places. Moreover, the workers had so little money that in a few weeks' time hunger drove them back to the benches. "But," added

Philip, "our gunmen make picketing impossible. The union
might make progress in their strikes if they had a chance
to keep the scabs out of the shops. We bribe the police and
they assist our gunmen guards. They can't talk to the
workers, they don't get a chance to win them over to the
union."

"Say," remarked Philip scornfully, "doesn't it prove they
are worms, these workers? They don't know enough to put
up a fight for what they want. Why don't they get gunmen
to fight the bosses' gunmen? Gunmen are the cheapest
thing in New York. What's the price, Meyer: a black eye,
five dollars; a general beating up, ten dollars; a broken arm
or leg, twenty-five dollars; an out and out killing, fifty
dollars!

"If they won't do their own fighting, too finicky like the
respectable manufacturers, why don't they farm out the job
to a private detective agency? They don't care who pays
them. They'll hire gunmen to fight their own gunmen. That's
the cheapest thing they got to sell, human abortions—what
am I talking about—monkey abortions. When they're
killed nobody'll miss them; good riddance. Beat up the
scabs the way we maul the workers. Fight for what you
want, and the battle never goes to the finicky."

Uncle Philip's half-joking, half-earnest tirade put a
thought in my mind. I was running down a list of union
organizers. There were too many pacifists. Life-for-love's-
sake fellows. They did not understand life as unending
change in conflict. I remembered Michel Cahn. Lately he
has been spouting a new creed. . . . "All power to the
workers. Seize the industries, workers, and keep them.
They are yours, could not exist without you. You created
them. To hell with middle class parliamentarism. Act. Direct action." . . . Michel Cahn is my man. I will put my
gangs to work for him. Call off the other gangs. I will show
the dream-stupefied how to get what you want. Use the
simple method of life. Change in conflict.

"When do you want the strike?" I asked. . . . Philip

laughed. "Look at him. Mike Hirsch, Shield of Israel. Got everything fixed, already, I bet you." . . . "Pretty near," was my succinct avowal.

My emissary found Michel Cahn taking tea in the Talkers' Café. His answer was, "Let the Honorable Haunch Paunch and Jowl come here if he wants to see me." . . . Haunch Paunch and Jowl—so that's the derisive picture the radicals had drawn of me. The lean, drawn starvelings in their dream-stupefied state were jealous of my well filled out, prosperous form. It had not yet reached the terrible proportions of obesity that years in a swivel chair on the judicial bench had later given me. But I suppose I was beginning to get fat. Well, I knew how to put my pride in my pocket when it served my pocket. Anyway, I was always working for my pocket like the Big Chief of my party. So Haunch Paunch and Jowl meandered over to the Talkers' Café and sought out the ideal-proud starveling, Michel Cahn, word-spewing revolutionist.

I took Cahn by surprise. "Do you mean what you say—the struggle between capital and labor is a class war? If it is war, do you believe in the methods of war? Or, are you just a tea-drinking talker in the Talkers' Café? The union is getting nowhere. You've got an organization. The members are getting tired of paying dues, their payments are not coming in the way they should. They are backsliding, gradually; you'll lose them all unless you give them results."

"Well," he said, measuring me carefully with his eyes, trying to sense my motive, "have you come to tell me something I know, something I am saying all the time?"

"I have come to find out if you know that the unions are in a dangerous fix. What are you doing about it, besides talking? Isn't the time ripe for militant unionism, direct action, fighting the bosses with the bosses' tools?"

"Meyer," he said, slowly, running a finger up and down his glass, "I have watched you grow up. I have watched your dear uncle. I know your breed. What do you want?"

"I want a job. I want to be the union's lawyer. No fee.

Just the prestige, just the acquaintances it will get me. I
want to run your next strike, but not with your love-mum-
blers, but with you direct-actionists." . . . I held forth
temptation. . . . "Bring the strike to a successful conclu-
sion and you'll become the union's undisputed leader. The
men will follow blindly the man who wins for them the long
fought and sought points."

"And your uncle?"

"He's frank about it. He put me up to this. I can't and
don't want to humbug you on that. He sees Avrum's point.
He'll be better off with union conditions. Better conditions
will make better workers. Besides it will standardize and
regulate production. It will give him more peace, leisure,
enable him to plan ahead. But he can't do it unless he has a
strong union that will make his competitors toe the mark.
A union shop, you know, can't compete against a sweat
shop. You've got to unionize the industry. But you can't do
it by following namby-pamby methods. There's only one
way you can convince pig-headed business men, who as a
class think they know better what's best for the world than
any other class. They think their business ways are the only
ways for the world. Force and strength, and the most convincing proof—getting it done—making them do it, will
prove your point to them."

Then we began to talk in whispers.

The following day I met the secret executive committee
in the back room of a saloon on Second Avenue. A militant strike was planned. The gangs got their first jobs with
the unions to fight the bosses' gunmen. In this way gang
warfare became the crux of every New York strike. The
battle went to the strongest gangsters reinforced by policemen. Sometimes labor had control, sometimes capital; but
it was always a gang fight that decided the vital issues of
capital and labor.

Our attacks were concentrated on the shops of the biggest manufacturers, the key men of the industry, whose accounts Philip wanted to nab. They would be taken off their

guard because they would not dream of a successful strike. Until now they had found the union easy picking. Their gunmen guards, Irish and Italian guerrillas recruited by private detective agencies, and a strong police guard, were their chief reliance.

I saw the Chieftains of my party, and, thereupon, the police were suddenly needed elsewhere. At this time the garment manufacturers belonged to the silk-stockinged Republican Party, and did not count with us.

Our gangs maneuvered around the shop district in carriages pulled by swift horses. They swooped down upon the guards, who heretofore had received no resistance, and surprised them with assaults in force. Our gangs entered the workrooms with picked union men who spilled vitriol and other corroding acids on the finished and unfinished clothing. The scabs were driven out and the foremen badly beaten up. We established long picket lines, followed scabs to their homes and, if they would not listen to reason and join the union, they were severely mauled. Soon it spread around that it was dangerous to scab. The big shops were successfully tied up, and then we began to harass the smaller men. They quickly signed up with the union. But I advised against letting any shops begin manufacturing. Philip wasn't quite ready yet. Nobody would be allowed to work until he was ready to spring his lines. And he didn't intend offering his sure-sellers until there was a crying need for them.

The big manufacturers had a great deal at stake. The labor turnover was the profit of the day. They increased the number of guards and then set up a virtuous outcry in the newspapers that law and order were being threatened by the violence and destruction of the union's hired marauders. The gangs made feuds over the strike. It showed their lack of intelligence. They invaded each other's home hangouts, fired off pistols at random and occasionally slaughtered an innocent bystander, a pushcart peddler or a child. Rarely was a gangster hurt. Pickets were brutally handled

and our men broke the bones and heads of scabs. It became a battle royal, and it began to look as though the
superior numbers of the bosses would win the day. I then
hit upon the scheme of buying off the bosses' gunmen. I
worked it through the ward politicians in the gangs' home
districts. I wanted them to lay off for three weeks, by which
time the manufacturers' season would be killed. The Irish
and Italian guerrillas were under the leadership of Tanner
Jones, a young, fearless thug, and Jack the Rock, a Sicilian
bravado. Both were amenable to their politicians' request
and a handsome piece of change. Frenchie Lavelle also
helped. Jack the Rock's girls worked his place, and when
he asked the Rock to be a good fellow for a couple of
weeks, it clinched the matter.

Meanwhile there was a great hullabaloo in the newspapers. The had an axe to grind. They looked for every
chance to hit at Tammany's police administration, and
proceeded to make capital out of the reign of lawlessness
in the strike. Barney Finn was working for the strikers.
His classmate was in charge of the city desk of one of the
popular afternoon papers; and Barney interested him in the
human interest stories of the hardships of the needle
workers, and a sob sister was assigned to accompany Esther
through the homes of starving garment workers. The sob
sister turned the tide of public opinion. The sordid, semi-
starved life of the sweatshop families had a Dickensian
flavor and appeal. The vile sanitary conditions and long
hours in the shops were described tellingly. The tune of the
newspapers changed. Barney Finn emphasized Leader
Lewkowitz' point. The immigrant workers were fighting for
an American standard of living. The newspapers took up
the demand for an American standard of living, just what
that was for the average American workman nobody knew.
Sociologists were just beginning to stick their noses in the
cess-pool of industry. At any rate, our cause became the
popular one. In a month's time the manufacturers gave in
and patched up a sort of truce with the union.

Philip had gotten the accounts he wanted. He moved his showrooms to a swell Broadway office building, but continued his shop in Madison Street, which now had grown into a place that needed three large floors.

Now I was hailed as the workers' champion. The union began to flourish, and as soon as it showed signs of prosperity and success the grafters and easy-thing-boys began to edge in. They looked for the soft jobs of business agents and walking delegates.

Avrum had protested with unflagging consistency against the methods of warfare and big business in union affairs. He left the union. Cahn, flushed with victory, read him out of the organization. He said Avrum's pacifism was the worst enemy of the union's cause. It would keep the workers supine forever. Force must be met with force. Avrum said there would be no end to wrong if another wrong was used to oppose it. So Avrum said he would now devote himself to educational programs for the workers. He then began a pilgrimage that took him all over the country.

He toiled in coal mines and steel mills, always living in the wretched workmen's colonies; labored with the textile workers at the great looms of New England and the South; joined the migratory pickers and garners of fruits and grains in the East, West, Southwest and the Coast; did loathsome tasks in canneries and fisheries; became a vegetarian after three months' penance in Chicago slaughter houses; felled timber in the trackless forests of the great Northwest; grubbed in the copper and silver mines of the desert regions; saw the land and the cities, spoke with the peoples in their jargons, dialects and home-land tongues; returned once in a while to see his family and talk earnestly with Esther; and then started anew on his search for the soul and needs and desires of the American worker. Wherever he went he spoke the gospel of oneness of interests, pleaded for a combining of all crafts in one common union that would have an overwhelming moral force. He said union money should be used to found schools and universities for workers.

He was laughed at, but his sincerity in the end won a hearing. Other migratory workers took up his message, went like wandering missionaries everywhere, trying to awaken a consciousness in the workers that they had one cause that should be effectively expressed in one big union. . . . In the little office of the settlement Avrum told Esther, "I find that *there is no such thing, as yet, as an American workman.* They are to each other—Hunks, Wops, Squareheads, Kikes, Micks and Heinies. They look down upon each other from the heights of their nationalism. The American will not associate with the greasy foreigner. The Italian detests the Hungarian, and so on. Then, there is a class feeling of crafts. The mechanic holds the meaner workman as his social inferior. Everyone sees himself as a potential boss, dreams of amassing big money, employing others. The class lines are tightly drawn. But it will be different when the workers of America become a racial identity. Then they will see each other as brothers, in sympathy, comradeship and understanding, as Americans all. Meantime, we must keep at them to learn, to rise above their clannishness, and mean aspirations; stop the sporadic struggles and unite as one. When we break down the class lines, the snobbery of nationalism, replace it with a commonality of spirit, then labor in its dignity and knowledge will share equally with capital the good things of the earth."

The Allrightniks
from
HAUNCH, PAUNCH AND JOWL

So here we live in *Allrightniks* Row, Riverside Drive. The newly rich Russian, Galician, Polish and Roumanian Jews have squeezed out the German Jews and their Gentile neighbors. Great elevator apartment structures are being put up to house the clamoring *Allrightniks*. The Ghetto called anyone who was well off—one who is *all right in this world,* that is well fixed, an *Allrightnik*. We moved in the world of *Allrightniks*.

Allrightniks: plump and fat women who blandished the extremes of the latest styles in clothes, trying to outvie one another; and were never seen without a blinding array of diamonds on ears, breasts, fingers and arms . . . the men were always business men—business was their cult, hobby, pastime—their life. Did they collect in little groups of a social evening, then they discussed the fascinating details of some speculation or enterprise. They interpreted life in the terms of moneymaking. Their faces were puffed and sleekly pale; their bellies stuck out as the show windows of their prosperity. Invariably you found them chewing fat cigars; their middle fingers ablaze with many-karated solitaires: eye-openers. . . . The women played poker in the afternoon and in the evening came together to gossip and flaunt clothes and diamonds, mentioned significantly what they paid for this and that, complained of their servants, to whom they left the care of their children, and told risque stories: their talk was a hysteric din, and their laughter unrestrained . . . while, in the adjoining room, their husbands, loud-mouthed and coarse-humored, gathered to play stud poker or pinochle for high stakes. The game was not the thing: they were charmed by the gamble. Their craze for speculation expressed itself in steep gambling. Once the play began their faces set in grim lines, and they attended passionately to the fluctuations of chance with such skill and craft and bluff as they could command. . . . High-priced, vivid-hued automobiles with liveried chauffeurs helped to blazon their success. . . . Having given themselves over wholly to wealth, then show was the only sign of their existence. . . . Show. Show. . . . Even in their charity. Charity was another outlet for display. Pompous, righteous beneficing. . . . Show. . . . Even to the marrying off of their children. Spectacular matches, big money in alliances with big money, money the standard of this special aristocracy.

. . . Dollarland. . . . Gretel, after living a shutaway, dubious
rôle, now revelled in the extravaganza-life of this *Allrighi-
nik* society. . . . And *Allrightnik* religion was a bumptious
holding forth in swell temples and synagogues. . . . And
they took to their bosoms canines and griffins, aping the
so-called swell society of the *goyim.*

I am bitter and sore this evening. . . . The gang, who
came in as impoverished immigrants unused to wealth, were
made dizzy and giddy by sudden riches. . . . But I wondered about the East Side. . . . It was not the same place I
knew as a boy, a young man. . . . I had lost contact with
that world. . . . Crane said we were always swinging between extremes: a pendulum of emotion. . . . In the East
Side the radicals were making headway. Were they bringing spiritual fare for the spiritually hungry? . . . Who would
believe fifteen years ago that the Socialists would carry
one of my assembly strongholds as they did last election?
. . . Money chasers and dream chasers. . . . In the Ghetto
there was a large, growing, fanatic cult of intellectualism
. . . a fine-frenzied idealism . . . art, literature, music, social
science and politics in the pure meaning of the word—
calling the new generation . . . to me a strange generation,
so different, so alien to my understanding. . . . The new
generation, this queer stranger, seemed to be creeping
upon me . . . what is their meaning . . . what do they want
. . . where will they end . . . will the money craze get them
and dazzle them? . . .

I drowsed again, and opened my eyes because someone
was looking at me. It was Mr. Bernard Lowe, my neighbor,
come to condole with me. . . . Bernard Lowe, a sweet-faced,
aging man, gazing upon me with kindly blinking eyes . . .
Bernard Lowe . . . do you remember Berel of yesteryear,
Berel Lotvin, the harness fixer in the Ludlow Street cellar
. . . Berel——

"Sleep . . . rest . . . don't let me disturb you, my friend."
His voice is gentle and pleasing.

"Just a little catnap, a fat man's drowse," I told him,

clasping his hand. "And, how do you feel, Berel?" I asked. He responded with his ready good humor: "What a question to ask of a Christian Scientist!"

And we both laughed. Funny: Berel is a Christian Scientist and a sincere one: always ready to give his personal testimony of its healing, pacifying wonders. . . . Once he told me his story in his unaffected way. He was a man of considerable means. But Berel attributed his wealth to mere chance. Someone told him the automobiles were come to stay and multiply. He gave up the harness-fixing hole and opened a little tire repair shop in upper Broadway. It was a new industry: the firstcomer got the pioneer's big chance. But what was more to the point, Berel's good humor and dependable word won him respect and friends among the Gentiles. . . . In time he grew to be the largest distributor of tires and accessories. . . . In the heyday of his prosperity he was laid low with diabetes, commonly called the Jewish sickness. He tried every famous doctor and cure. He was given up. . . . In her despair Berel's wife called in a Christian Science healer. . . . And Berel said faith and love healed him and made him whole and well; best of all, it brought him equanimity and peace: being took on meaning. His simple exposition was very touching.

We talked of his two boys, big young men, putting in their last years in Yale. Berel did not want them to go into business. He said business soils . . . he was encouraging his lads to give themselves to art and science . . . life was something more than mere competing for money. . . .

"Life speeds on . . . just think . . . soon you'll be thinking of marrying off the boys," I said.

"I don't have to think about it at all . . . they're thinking of it themselves. . . . They used to go to church with me Sunday mornings when home . . . but now I notice they're going to Rabbi Drucker's New Temple. There's a reason. . . . You know the beautiful daughters of Sid Raleigh . . . you know our old boy friend, Sam Rakowsky . . . he has two golden beauties . . . like their mother . . . two clever girls, musicians, who detest their father's songs. . . . Funny, he doesn't mind what they think of his music. He's sending them abroad to study under the masters. Well, my boys are after the golden beauties with the golden voices. . . . Now, just to please me, they join me to church Wednesday nights. . . . Well, there's one thing I owe the lads, the right to choose their own wives and own beliefs. . . . Good evening, Meyer, mamma will be looking for me for dinner. Good evening——"

I'll not stay home tonight; I am too depressed. . . . I'll slip out and telephone Margot . . . Margot, my consolatrice. . . . I interested Al Wolff in her. He put her in a show, a show I financed. She was an excellent investment. She was to the theatregoers the pert personification of the New York pleasure girl. The critics praised her vim and originality. All the artists wanted to paint her exquisite hands and feet. Her legs were a stage classic, having the shapeliness of a Greek vase. Al starred her in a big revue called "The Chicken of the Crossways"—the crossways being Forty-second Street and Broadway. Then came the movies to tempt her with a big contract. Always she consulted her sweet daddy. She never forgot to be grateful, although she was occasionally unfaithful. The public adored her as their whimsical Margot of the Movies. . . . Margot lived in a bizarre apartment chaperoned by an ancient duenna, an aunt created for my protection. . . . I can't complain of Margot. She was always honest. She tried her best to keep her little affairs a secret from me. . . . But I knew she had love affairs lurking around the corner, and I tried not to think of this unpleasantness. . . . Sometimes when I stood over her I felt like a hulking pachyderm, gross, flesh-odorous, snorting over a white gazelle, a white gazelle with a burnished head. . . .

Again I drowsed, and I seemed to have a pleasant dream that Margot was on my knee gently pinching my ear. But it was that confounded dog who had been placed on a cushion on a table near me. His little paw had been touching my ear. . . . Gretel is humming Sid Raleigh's latest hit, a topical song he wrote for Margot. It is a hodge-podge of sentiment, mixing sunshine and rain, love and jealousy, joy and grief, laughter and tears, commonplaces for the masses, easy thoughts for the sluggish multitude. Margot had made its refrain famous, something about . . . "tell me, life, tell me, what's it all about; tell me, life, what's it all about?" . . .

Gretel calls, "Come, Meyer, come and eat. I got something you like. *Gedamfte brust und patate lahtkes.*" (Potted breast and potato pancakes.) . . . I heave my great bulk and waddle towards the dining room. . . . Again Gretel sings . . . "Tell me, life, tell me, what's it all about; tell me, life, what's it all about?" . . .

What——

It smells good.

Gedamfte brust und patate lahtkes——

A NOTE OF EXPLANATION

The subject of this autobiography died several years after the concluding episode described in the book. The grief displayed by so many persons, irrespective of creed or class, at the news of the fatal termination of his long illness is still vivid in the recollection of New Yorkers. Seldom has the memory of a public man been so definitely honored by a wide-spread sympathy as was shown on that occasion by his fellow citizens and the press.

After the death of his dearly loved wife who predeceased him by several years, a decided change was noticeable in the Judge. Always modest and charitable, these characteristics assumed a pathological form. He himself must have had some intimation of this as those who remember the contents of the opening paragraph of this work will doubtless have remarked. No man was more charitable in his judgment of his fellow men. No man was sterner with himself. Always willing to believe in the rectitude of others' motives he was unduly suspicious of his own. At times his remarks on certain events of his life surprised those who were conversant with the facts. His derogatory remarks concerning himself pained and startled us. It would be possible for me to take up many of the episodes described in this book and show how unjust the Judge had been to himself. It would be a long task and I deem an unnecessary one. The Judge's character was too well known to need a defense against even himself.

In the fulfillment of my duties as an executor of the estate of the author of Haunch, Paunch and Jowl, I discovered in a private drawer, a holographic document which on inspection proved to be this purported history of his life. It was with surprise and consternation that I turned over its pages. It was so unlike the truth and yet in many respects it was the truth. Attached to it was a note directing that it be published as shortly after his death as possible. I hesitated whether to obey it or not. Finally, I decided that his wishes should be observed by me. Having given it to the world in the performance of my duty I think it but right to offer this word of explanation.

*   *   *   *   *

LUDWIG LEWISOHN (1883–1955), born in Berlin, was brought to the New World when he was seven and reared in Charleston, South Carolina. An American, a Southerner —and a Christian in his teens—he was educated at Charleston and at Columbia University and then became a professor of German language and literature at Wisconsin and Ohio State. His opposition to World War I, and his German birth, led to his resignation from university life. In 1919 he joined *The Nation,* and subsequently became an ardent Zionist; he returned to Judaism in the 1920s. A prolific novelist, translator, essayist, and critic, Lewisohn's best-known novels are *The Island Within* (1928) and *Stephen Escott* (1930). *Upstream* (1922) and *Midchannel* (1929) are autobiographical. Among his critical and essayistic works are *Israel* (1925), *The Jew and the World* (1949) and *The American Jew* (1950).

Arthur and Elizabeth
from
THE ISLAND WITHIN

He knew that the war had loosened the taut strain of
Puritan morals. He knew it and approved it as a man and,
above all, as a scientist. But he discovered that he wanted
Elizabeth Knight excepted from this loosening, that he
resented bitterly the thought that at other parties men
would touch and handle her again and perhaps discuss
with her whether she should remain a virgin or not. . . .
He persuaded himself that he wanted to test out the situation and that for this reason alone he called her up at her
apartment only two days after the Adams party. It was in
the evening and he said that he hadn't been able to get her
out of his mind and wanted to see her. She accused him
laughingly of using a condescending tone and said that she
was tired and in her dressing-gown; she needed to sleep;
she needed a great deal of sleep. Always. But if he really
cared about it so much he should drop in after dinner on the
next day. Why not have dinner together first, he asked. He
didn't like her voice at all when she answered that she
wasn't a young lady who could be asked out hit and miss,
but a working-woman. She had a late assignment next day.
He could come if he chose. But the fact that he hadn't
liked her tone didn't help him at all. He found, on the
contrary, that he longed all the more for the morrow in
order to have the impression which blurred the image of
her in his mind obliterated. . . .

He went precisely at nine. She was lying on a chaise-
longue in her little drawing-room, smoking a cigarette out
of an enormously long holder of onyx. There was a tired
strained look about her eyes. Behind that look hovered the
look of the naughty little girl. Again she had on a black
evening frock, simpler than the one she had worn at the
party, a little shabby in fact, and again Arthur was stirred
by her pale arms and throat and by the proud yet pathetic

way she held her head as she sat up to give him her hand.

"Today was worse than I feared. I'll be dull as ditch water."

"What's the difference?" he said. "As I told you, I've been thinking about you. I simply wanted to see you again."

"You are a nice man. You'll find cigarettes over there. Have you got any patients yet?"

He laughed. "No, but Eugene called me up to tell me that a very distinguished friend of his was coming to see me."

"Wonder who it'll be. I have a hunch it'll be Prout, the author of *Hills of Morning.*"

"What makes you think so?"

"Oh; his actions the other night. I have these hunches about sexual things."

He looked into space. He had a silly sense that she was besmirching herself. "How can you have these hunches without any experience of your own?"

She insisted that that didn't seem to matter. Besides, there was experience and experience. He felt his cheeks and lips tingle; he wanted to know and dared not ask what these experiences were; he was evidently retroactively jealous of her. He tried to guide their talk in other directions, but she came back again and again to the question of the relations of men and women, especially of their physical relations and of the effects of these physical relations upon life and character. Her virginity was evidently an ache to her, an ache at least as much of the mind as of the body, and she resented this troubling wound and lack at the core of her and had cultivated a harsh, almost petulant hostility to men. She said things that seemed foolish to Arthur; she denied the bearing on life of fundamental biological facts; yet all her talk, even at its most wrong-headed, had an engaging quality, a blending of fine, precise speech with warmth. He stopped arguing. He came over and sat down beside her. Into her face came suddenly the frightened expression of a child, and he took her in his arms and kissed her. . . . He was amazed and thrilled and infinitely flattered at the intensity of her response. Her lips clung to his and her pupils dilated until her eyes looked black and she clutched her hands together around his neck. . . . Then suddenly she pushed him away with a peremptory, almost angry gesture and told him to go. He asked her when he would see her.

"I don't know," she said and her mouth quivered a little like the mouth of a child. "I don't know. But I want you to go."

Two days later, toward sunset of a spring day, she came to see him. She had on a black suit with very straight lines and a little hat that accentuated the boyishness of her profile; she was exquisitely gloved and shod. She walked about his apartment like a strange, elegant lady who had come to see it; then she lightly touched things here and there. A faint perfume of heliotrope breathed from her. She seemed ethereal and aloof and more desirable than ever. She would not even sit down, as though that would be a fatal concession, but consented to go out with him for a bite of dinner. The air was very clear and the sky edged with deep rose and fading orange and a faint tinge of green. From every tree set in the pavement here and there, from every tiny square of city-grass, came the fresh, sharp fragrance of life. Elizabeth said she wasn't hungry; she didn't care where they went. The world was so beautiful, so beautiful. That was enough. She could see the fields and ragged groves about her father's shabby parsonage; she could see herself as a little girl, hot and tired from play, hearing her mother calling her in for supper and stopping for a minute quite still, all by herself, a tiny mite of a girl in a terribly plain frock, overcome by the loveliness of earth and sky and the trees darkening against the afterglow. . . . There was something liquid in her eye as she evoked this vision of her childish self for him, and something free and noble and wistful. . . . They went to a small restaurant and she hardly touched the food, in spite of his urging, and went on talking about her childhood: how poor they had been and how her father was in his narrow way a perfect saint who had to be kept from giving his money and his clothes to any chance beggar, and how her mother, frail and burdened by poverty and children, had died early. It was an aunt, an intelligent but unlovable person, who had helped Elizabeth go to high school and then, even more half-heartedly, to college. At Barnard the girl had early been swept into the suffrage movement and had been for several years a paid agitator and organizer and had then been offered a newspaper job. "I never had a single nice thing—just plain, serviceable ones—until I bought them for myself. I love nice things." About all her talk there was something fresh and lyrical and sad. She talked dreamily as though to herself. . . .

They walked back in the direction of Arthur's apartment. The stars were out now and Arthur could feel the throbbing of his heart and he heard himself say—distinctly heard his own voice—"I love you, Elizabeth." And the intoxication of those words was like no other intoxication he had ever felt; it was an intoxication in which one saw things as clearly and as intensely and as visionarily as in a dream. . . . The world of reality was drowned for the hour in another world that was magical and mad and overwhelmingly tangible, too. . . . He was not surprised that she went back to his apartment with him, nor that she entered, nor at her white, scared face, nor at her utter yielding, nor at her straining to him, nor at her sweet ways or beauty of body. . . . Then the magic snapped. . . . She sat on the edge of the bed, wrapping a silk coverlet about her, her face haggard with pain and a touch of brooding horror. "Is that all?" She stifled a sob in her throat.

Arthur slipped into a dressing-gown. He tried to touch her, but she drew away from him. "Is that all?" There was something despairing in her level tone. He gave her a cigarette and lit it for her and took one himself. He begged her to listen to him. He told her that, from a medical point of view, a good deal of nonsense was talked in so-called radical circles about the freedom of love. He hadn't him- self the slightest respect for laws and conventions; it didn't matter what seasoned people did with their lives. But the necessity for marriage, not in law but in spirit, and for the intention of fidelity, was founded on the fact that in all but the rarest cases a woman who gave up her virginity found no pleasure in the act of love, only pain and disil- lusion, and that it required the continuous care and tender- ness of a man who loved her to induce in her that subtle psychical and physical coördination of attention and con- sent and freedom from unconscious inhibition which would gradually ripen her for love. She looked at him with wide, hurt, hostile eyes.

"But a man always——"

He nodded. "Yes, always."

She asked him to go out so that she could dress. Fifteen minutes later she appeared quite as she had come. A faintly humorous apologetic smile was on her lips.

"You must think me an awful fool."

He shook his head. "You're sweet and adorable."

She pressed his hand. "You're a nice, nice man. I'm terribly glad it was you." For the first time they kissed each other tenderly. She asked him not to bother about her for a few days. She wanted to think. She would be heard from. . . .

It was on toward the middle of September that she came to his apartment on an evening of breathless dusty heat. She threw down her hat and shook her hair, which was slightly moist.

"What weather!"

"Yes," he said, "and I suppose you've been in the heat all day." He looked at her as she drooped and cuddled into a chair, and she looked so lovely and child-like and he felt so united to her, that he said, with a sudden lifting of the heart: "You'd better marry me and throw up your

ghastly job." He was amazed when he saw her hide her
face against the back of the tall chair and suddenly cry
quietly but deeply with little hushed, continued sobs. He
took her hand and laid his own on her head. "What is it,
dearest?"

She recovered herself gradually and wiped her eyes with
a moist, funny little handkerchief and turned to him. "Why
did you say that just tonight, Arthur?"

"Because I felt it, quite simply."

"I'm glad," she said. "And yet I'm horror-stricken at the
position of woman—wholly without decency or dignity."

He sat down opposite her. "How come?" He had caught
amusing little American folk-phrases from her.

She sat up flushed, spirited, her eyes dark with indignation. "I came here tonight to beg you or, like all women,
wheedle you to give me something which I don't want, in
which I don't believe, but which—which is forced on us by
our slave status." Her face hardened. "I came to ask you
whether you wouldn't marry me, because we're going to
have a child."

A tangible substance seemed to melt in his breast. He
went to her with outstretched arms, with moist eyes. But
she protested.

"I thought, by the way, that you had taken proper precautions."

He couldn't help laughing, though he knew at once that
the note of happiness in his laugh seemed silly and sentimental to her. "I have, you know. But there are, unluckily,
no unfailing precautions. One has always to reckon with
the off-chance."

She still warded him off. "I see. But suppose you hadn't
condescended to me, could nothing have been done?"

He was angry. "You're talking nonsense, Elizabeth,
damned nonsense. I can conceive of cases in which an il-
legal operation might be morally justified. This isn't one of
them. In my sense of the word we've been married for
months. The child is mine as much as yours. It doesn't

particularly interest me, except as a social convenience, whether we go through a ceremony or not. I want the child. And since you're the child's mother and human infancy is a long process, you belong to me, too. Such are the biological and the moral facts."

She bit her lip. "It's loathsome."

He felt himself grow pale with anger. "What? Our having a child?"

"No, Arthur. I don't mean that. I mean your attitude of taking possession of me, mastering me, reducing me on account of this accident to the status of a nurse and a slave."

He put his two hands to the side of his head for a moment. Then he arose and strode up and down with his hands behind him and realized dimly beneath his stormy preoccupation of the moment that he was walking up and down, like his father, in the characteristic way of Jewish men when agitated. But that perception faded. He turned and stopped before Elizabeth.

"I swear to you, Elizabeth, I had no idea how you feminists had gotten warped and crazed on fundamentals. The use of contraceptives is the accident, the abnormality —a useful and beneficent accident and abnormality, I grant you. Motherhood is the eternally normal thing for a woman. You might as well criticize the rising of the sun and the growing of the grass. And as for your being reduced— reduced"—he couldn't help almost shouting the word— "to the status of a nurse and a slave, well, the length of human infancy is the thing that makes man human. A kitten can fend for itself at the end of a few weeks, a child in modern civilization at the end of from seventeen to twenty-five years. Certainly parenthood 'reduces' both the man and the woman to the fulfillment of certain duties. You have no more right, there's no more sense in criticizing that fact than in complaining, for instance, that we live by food. You remind me of some one who would say: it's so slavish to eat two or three times a day. Let's live on air. Such fool talk!"

Elizabeth had arisen now. She stood straight and had a haughty, girlish sternness in her posture and aspect. Something of the eternal Diana, maiden and huntress. "I shall go on with my work. Understand that. I won't be kept by a man. I shall retain my name, like most of my friends. I'll go through with this thing. I agree that it's the decent thing to do. But you will never see me become the exclusive mother-animal that you'd like to see me."

He couldn't help laughing. "Mother-animal—such verbiage. As for your going on with your work—it's much better for a pregnant woman to be active. But that can be overdone. I'll take you to a friend of mine, a gynecologist, and he'll tell you what's best for both you and the child. I——"

She went brusquely to the table for her hat and gloves. "You'll do nothing of the kind. I'll see a woman physician by and by." She stopped suddenly with outstretched hand. "Pregnant woman! Good God!"

He joined her and put his arms around her. "Elizabeth," he pleaded.

She drooped toward him for a moment and rested her head lightly on his shoulder. She smiled sadly. "You've scolded me like a husband already. I won't have it. Since I discovered this thing I'm not even sure that I love you any longer. I only feel trapped and caged. I'm sorry. But it's so."

He let her go. "I think you'll find that a readjustment will come about and with that you'll hear the voice of normal instincts. Don't be so unyielding, Elizabeth. You're so taut. A woman gets her truest self-fulfillment when she is broken by love and motherhood."

She smiled bitterly. "I had no idea you were so mid-Victorian."

He shrugged his shoulders. "I am strictly scientific and up-to-date. There are a few facts, my dearest, that have not changed, so far as we know, within historic time."

"Well, then, we'll change them now." She kissed him lightly on the forehead and went out, slim, proud, erect. . . .

Arthur put his hands against his temples. Often in other years he had a little resented his father's absorption in business. He thought that he suddenly understood the quality that marked Jewish absorption in business. Money was not success; money was security, weapon, defense, it built a home in the homeless world; it was the only reliance in the evil day. The enemy was never to be reasoned with. He might be bought off. . . . There were the learned to be taken care of and the poor and God's fools. . . . He read on and one passage concerning the happenings in England burned strangely into his mind: "There was a town in which the community consisted of only twenty souls. And they were all proselytes. All these were slain. They would not return to their former faith, but preferred to sanctify the Name by their death." He didn't, of course, care about myth or ritual or dogma. He never would. But he had always taken it for granted that even in the ages of faith the Jewish faith had had no persuasive power, that the spirit of Israel was hard, self-contained, unbending. But in that age one Christian proselyte outweighed ten thousand Jewish ones. For the Jew who became a Christian received in return security and fellowship and honor; the Christian who became a Jew received hatred, torture, death. . . . There were a few more pages.

He could read no more. And had he not read enough? . . . How still it was about him! Still as the beginning of things. The only pain in the stillness was the absence of his child's voice. He must try to save his son's heritage for him, his incomparable spiritual heritage. His son should not stand before a Gentile friend as he had stood beside Charles Dawson, and wish that he, too, could boast as ancestors tartaned clansmen who had fought at Flodden Field. His son should have too much pride to need to be proud. Too much inner security to be hurt by words or slights. His son should be incapable of feeling excluded; he must possess the knowledge that he stood by birth at the human centre of things. For if history has an ethical direction its symbol is not the clansman or the warrior, but he who passively defends an idea and thus sanctifies an ineffable Name. . . .

He made an appointment to see Elizabeth. The Adamses asked him to dine, but he said that he preferred to come in after dinner. He hardly knew whether he wanted to see Eugene and Joanna or not. He left it to chance and was received by his cousin. Eugene talked trivialities. Each knew that a subject burned between them. But Eugene had armored himself in advance. He had chosen his path with the utmost sagacity; he had reached his goal. Neither he nor Joanna ever pretended that they were not Jews; they were sincerely convinced that it mattered neither negatively nor positively. They were more than accepted. They were social and intellectual leaders in the group that was most congenial to them. If there were, in spite of all, whisperers behind their backs—well, there were vulgar and stupid people everywhere. One reckoned with that. How precisely they managed to shut out of their consciousness the needs and sufferings of their people Arthur didn't know. That was, he supposed, a matter of temperament. It was also a carefully and tacitly nursed ignorance. If once one *knew*. . . . One was careful not to know. . . . Finally, Arthur couldn't help saying, "I'm going to Rumania on a commission to investigate the condition of the Jewish communities there."

Eugene flicked the ashes from his cigarette. "Frightfully interesting. You ought to write something about your trip when you come back. I'm thinking seriously of starting a magazine. By the way, Elizabeth's novel will be our first serial. It's charming—charming." Yes, Eugene was armored. He had determined not even to admit the possibility of a discussion.

Elizabeth and Joanna came in together. Joanna couldn't be quite as icy as Eugene. In spite of her husband's frown she teased: "So you're going back to the Jews, Arthur. What a quaint thing to do!" Elizabeth took Arthur's hand and kept it for a moment in her own. Almost immediately —it had evidently been arranged—the Adamses withdrew. Elizabeth sat down on a low chair and leaned her right elbow on her knee and supported her chin in her cupped hand. She was grave and graceful, but a little wan. She asked him first when he was leaving, and he told her.

"I'm going away, too," she said. "If you don't mind on account of John, I'm going to the country with him. I want to be quiet and I think it will do him good, too. Spring is almost here."

"Eugene tells me they've asked you to stay on indefinitely."

"Oh yes. They're very sweet to me. But it's sort of cold and comfortless here. And they quarrel with me about you." She laughed a little.

"About me?"

"Yes. Isn't it funny? I hardly know how to explain it. They think you're making a plain damned fool of yourself. In addition they consider your folly dangerous. They think that any emphasizing of the Jewish question might drag them in and shake their position."

"Well, Elizabeth, and you don't agree with them?"

"Of course not. I'm my father's daughter. I understand the religious and humanitarian temperament instinctively. When I was a kid, long before I knew what suffrage was, I thought I'd like to be a missionary in China and maybe be martyred for the sake of our Lord. Only—" She hesitated.

Arthur leaned forward. "Do go on, Elizabeth, do!"

"Well, you see, we're not suited to each other in a number of ways. I know that, you poor darling. And then can you see me, with the best will in the world, trying to be a Jewess? You can't, can you?"

"No. Things like that can't be learned. I suppose they have to be resurrected out of one's inner self."

"That's it. Of course you did me one injustice."

"What's that?"

"Through your ignorance of yourself. You didn't know you were going to resurrect the Jew in you."

"You're right, Elizabeth, quite right. But really I didn't even have to resurrect the Jew. I just put away a pretense —a stubborn, hard, protective pretense. But no more."

"It's a kind of an argument, isn't it, against mixed marriages?" Her eyes were sad.

"I'm afraid it is," he answered. "One among many others."

She nodded. "You must see John. He's getting to be such a duck. What are we going to do about him?"

They went upstairs. The child was already asleep in his little bed and they moved softly. John's long black lashes were lying on his cheeks; his nose was delicately curved; a slightly careworn look was on his forehead. Arthur kissed the child gently and they went across the hall into Elizabeth's room.

"A Jewish child," he said.

She nodded. "I'll consent to anything reasonable in regard to his education. Are there Jewish boarding-schools?"

"There must be. I'll inquire by and by. There's still plenty of time for that. But you're very dear and splendid, Elizabeth."

Her eyes were moist as she answered: "My life has been hollow, too. I've come to see that recently. Maybe that has helped me to see your point of view. I think I may take a cottage in the country for good."

"Do you think you'll want to marry again, Elizabeth?"

"Can't tell. But you will, Arthur," She laughed a pathetic little laugh. "You'll marry a nice Jewish girl some day. I'll release you whenever you like."

He took her face into his hands. "It's rather a pity about us, isn't it?"

"Rather."

He kissed her and begged her to remember him to the

Adamses. He would see her and the child again to say good-by.

Having listened carefully to his son, old Jacob Levy said: "I knew det story about de old chest and de docooments. My grendmudder Braine—de von who vent to die in Cherusalem—she told it to my fadder ven he vas little. Ent I can see my fadder chust like if it vas today telling us children about it. Of course I vas de youngest ent I didn't understent so vell. But I remember. I remember a great deal, come to t'ink about it, det I t'ought I hed forgot. Vy do ve forget? De olt people in de olt chenerations didn't use to forget. Maybe in de olt country dey forget less den ve do in America. I don't know. I don't know. . . . But in de early years here I chust forgot everything ent your dear mudder —*her* mudder had already forgotten—ent so ve told you notting. It's funny, too. In our business, you know, ve come in contact wid de people det manoofacture reel Colonial antiques. Every family wid a New England name vants reel Colonial antiques ent den dey tell deir frients—some of dem, anyhow—det dey inherited de t'ings from deir ancestors. Deir proud of deir ancestors. Vell, of course, some of dem are foolish about it. But it's natural for people to be proud of deir ancestors. Vy did ve forget so? Maybe because America used to say: Dis is no place vere ancestors count. Only individooal vorth. . . . But det didn't last long. It hes changed in my time. . . . Yes, in my time. Vell, I'm glet to see my son remembering. I hear of odder young people remembering. My cheneration tried to pull down de house of Israel; maybe yours vill build it up again. . . ."

Hollsworthy Brown, D.S.M., joined Dr. Charles Dawson at luncheon in their club. Brown spoke with a perceptible British accent: "You used to know Arthur Levy at Columbia?" he asked.

"Very well. We were great friends at one time. Sort of

drifted apart later. A fine chap—quiet, thoughtful, very able."

"Well," Brown said with pursed, ironical lips, "I hear that he's abandoned his wife because she was a Christian and has become religious and has gone on a Jewish mission to the Balkans. Isn't that rather curious?"

Dawson's cool, pale eyes took in Brown with a touch of contempt. "That doesn't sound like old Arthur. Thoroughly decent chap. I'd want to know the facts from him or his wife. I wouldn't carry that sort of poisonous gossip if I were you. As to his casting in his lot with his own people —I don't know but what I like that; it's natural and thoroughly honorable to him. If all Jews did it, I for one would respect them the more. I don't think that Jews who try not to be Jews do themselves any good in the eyes of intelligent people. There's something wrong with a man who betrays his own kind. . . . I didn't always take that point of view. But I've changed my mind about a good many things during the years since the war. . . ."

Reb Moshe said to Arthur: "Don't be too enthusiastic. Jews are people. Remember that even our teacher Moses was angry at them. The Jews have always been a difficult people. Avoid two errors—a *Goyish* error and a Jewish error."

Arthur smiled. "Now you're going to tell a story."

"I am. Listen! A man came to a Polish magnate and asked him: 'What do you think of the Jews?' The answer was: 'Swine, Christ-killers, usurers, not to be trusted.' 'But what do you think of Isaac?' 'A man after my own heart. An honorable man. A kind man. He saved me from bankruptcy.' 'And what do you think of Berl?' 'I have known Berl all my life. He's one of the best.' 'And of Shmuel?' 'Shmuel is a saint as everyone knows.' The same man went to a rich and pious Jew and asked him: 'What do you think of the Jews?' The pious man answered: 'A kingdom of priests and a holy nation, the elect of the Eternal, blessed be his name.' 'And what do you think of Isaac?' 'That thief? That scoundrel? May his bones be broken. He looks at you and you are robbed!' 'And of Berl?' 'A fellow of the same kind, without truth or justice.' 'And of Shmuel?' 'Do you think I am taken in by his piety? A pretentious idiot.' " Reb Moshe hid his hands in his sleeves. "Avoid both errors." Arthur laughed. He was quite sure that he would fall into a thousand errors. He was equally sure that the sky curved over him like a tent against the outer darkness and that the earth which his foot trod was his natural habitation and his home.

MYRON BRINIG (b. 1900) was brought up in Minnesota and Montana but attended New York University and Columbia University. The son of a Jewish storekeeper in Butte, Montana, he knew firsthand the country and the merchants he wrote of. *Singermann* (1929), set in Montana, is a story of a family in which the children break away and marry Gentiles, at the same time as Moses Singermann's position as father is eaten away. *The Sisters* (1937), and *May Flavin* (1938) are his most memorable novels of the Thirties; his most recent book has been *The Looking-Glass Heart* (1958).

Joseph and Daisy
from
SINGERMANN

Early one morning Joseph lay in bed feeling a singular loneliness that was not unhappiness. He was thinking of Daisy Korner. He had taken Daisy to the ball given by the Charitable Daughters of Israel the night before at the Moose Auditorium. He had danced with Daisy many times, and he still felt her warmth, her teasing proximity in his arms. The particular scent she had used was deep in his pillow and filled him with an intense wistfulness of desire. He remembered Daisy's blue eyes, so rare, so pleasingly unfamiliar for a Singermann to see. It was strange that Joseph should suddenly have this feeling for Daisy Korner. He had known her ever since she had come to Silver Bow; she was a Roumanian like himself, and her father, Adolph Korner, was the Montana representative for a South American banana commission house. He had thought Daisy rather silly the first night he had seen her. She had been doing a cake-walk in the parlor of the Korner home, and every few minutes she would stop in her dance and burst into helpless giggles. Joseph thought these giggles quite unnecessary, and he had come away from Daisy's house with an unfavorable impression of her.

But he had gone on seeing Daisy quite regularly after that first visit. She was a puzzling girl, sometimes so happy and yielding, and at other times so hard and clever. You never quite knew about her, so you were always expecting something exciting. Joseph was not very observant of people. He could see a man day in, day out for months and be unable to tell what was the color of his hair or whether he was short or tall. It was much the same with girls. He would be close to Daisy and she would seduce him into strange, troubled thoughts. He would see that her hair was brown with golden lights; he would realize the lovely softness of her complexion and the way her red lips turned up at the corners. He would hear her laugh. And then he would leave her and try to remember the exact shade of her hair and the shape of her mouth. He would try so hard, but it didn't seem to do any good. He was angry with himself, and he felt that never before had there been such a fool in the world.

But it was not only a voluptuous delight that Daisy Korner caused him. She was shrewd. She had a fine brain for business. One evening in the week she would go over her father's books in which were long columns of figures, and she would add and subtract. No matter how insignificant a mistake had been made, Daisy would always find it. Joseph was deeply impressed by her cleverness. You would think that a girl who was so good-looking would be extravagant and careless in money matters. But Daisy always knew just how much she spent and whether the purchase had been worth while. Whenever Joseph saw her he thought how fine she would look back of the cash register in his father's store.

Joseph escorted her out to Columbia Gardens, Silver Bow's one amusement park, and wanted to spend money on her. He wanted to buy her candy and take her into the Scenic Railway, where, pressed close to her shoulder, he could watch the high mountains of the Alps and the low, lush meadows of Holland. But Daisy would refuse to go into any place that meant an expenditure of money.

"That's expensive," she would say. "What's the use of wasting money on such foolish things? Let's walk around in the fresh air." And she would inhale deep breaths of the cool air and lift her arms and cry, "Ah-h! Ah-h! This is wonderful. And it don't cost anything."

"But let me buy you a box of candy," Joseph would plead with her. "Only a twenty-five-cent box of these chocolates to take home with you." Joseph was sad to think that Daisy would not let him buy things for her. He had a wild desire to clothe her from head to foot in fine clothes and furs and frills here and there, even though his common sense told him that Daisy was wise in refusing gifts.

"It ain't necessary, Joe," she would say. "Twenty-five cents is too much for candy. Buy a bag for ten cents and that's good enough. Save your money and you'll get somewheres. Do you always want to be just a clerk in your father's store?"

"I'd like to have a store of my own," he said fiercely. "I hate to work for my father. We don't get along at all."

"Put your pennies away then," Daisy counseled him.

Daisy's thriftiness and prudence caused Joseph to forget her brown hair with the golden lights, her mouth turned up at the corners. He was fired with ambitions. He would break away from his father and open his own store; and Daisy would sit back of the cash register all day, her merry laughter chiming in with the ringing up of sales. He would have his own home to come back to every evening, and there would be Daisy with his dinner all prepared. He would talk over the day's sales with her. He would discuss with her the relative merits of different wholesale houses. Was Lindeke, Warner as reasonable on cotton underwear as Wyman, Partridge? Daisy would keep his books and go to bed with him. Did she not answer his every desire? Was she not wise and was she not beautiful?

He must marry. He must get away from his father, his younger brothers. He must start in business for himself. These desires were turning Joseph hot and cold, happy and miserable. So many young Jews of his own age had their own homes and were their own bosses that it irritated Joseph to think he had to work for a father who appreciated him so little, who threw shoes at him in a burst of temper. It was degrading, humiliating to be forced to put up with these things.

The ball given under the auspices of the Charitable Daughters of Israel brought Joseph closer to Daisy. Twice a year the Jewish ladies would sponsor the ball and charge one dollar a ticket. In this way, the Charitable Daughters collected several thousands of dollars in a year. The hungry were fed, the ragged and homeless clothed and sheltered. There is no more charitable race in the world than the Jews. They are forever thinking up new ways of collecting funds for charitable purposes. Balls are given, kaffee-klatches are held, picnics are contrived. Those who are prosperous give with a prodigal hand, but not modestly. It is a great pleasure for me to help my poor unfortunate brother who is in distress. It is more than a pleasure—it is a sensual delight. One wealthy man will say to another, "Well, I gave fifty dollars to the Consumptives' Hospital in Denver."

And the other will say, "Piker! I gave a hundred!" And the one who gave the extra fifty dollars will experience a vivid throb of pleasure. He gave fifty dollars more than So-and-So, and So-and-So ought to feel pretty small, a man like that, and with his income, too.

So it was a rich, gaudy night when the Charitable Daughters held their Semi-Annual Ball. Many marriageable daughters were there dressed in their brightest; and the young men wore their little fancy programs attached by colored strings to their buttonholes. Each program was stamped in purple with the seal of David, and inside were listed the dances. 1. Grand March. 2. Waltz. 3. Two Step. 4. Mazurka. 5. Waltz, and so on through some twenty numbers and five "extras." With the dying note of the last "extra" many a young man wrote the last X on the last pretty program that would ever dangle from a bachelor's buttonhole.

Daisy was the most conspicuous girl on that night of the ball. She wore a long velvet dress that looked as if it had been dyed in a rare old vintage wine; her arms were bare to the shoulders and her finely shaped neck was unadorned by the trinkets that would have spoiled its beauty. She would never look so well again.

It was Daisy's way to enter a ballroom late so that her entrance would be noticed by everybody, so that people would look at her and say, "That's Daisy Korner. She looks mighty nice. But where does her father get all the money for those dresses?" Daisy thrived on such remarks. She would go home and tell her mother, "I was the prettiest girl at the ball tonight. Sarah Edelstein had on a more expensive dress and Rachel Singermann wore that pair of slippers she got from the Brown Shoe Company's traveling man. But everybody looked at me."

When Daisy first came into the ballroom leaning on his arm, Joseph was somewhat embarrassed. He did not regard himself as worthy of escorting such a beautiful girl into the light and publicity of Jewish Silver Bow. But he was also proud. All the young men envied him, and he

knew that they would go home thinking, That Joseph
Singermann must have prospects or Daisy Korner wouldn't
go to a ball with him. I guess the Singermanns are doing a
good business.

Perhaps it was the strong punch, served in the alcove, that
made Joseph feel that way towards Daisy. But she went to
his senses, and after a few dances he forgot that he was such
a lucky man to have brought such a beautiful girl to the
ball. He only knew that she had agreed to give him every
waltz and nearly every extra. He was not a very graceful
dancer, but with Daisy in his arms he was lithe and expert
beyond all his fondest hopes. He moved over the dance floor
in a daze of delight, and the fragrance of the flowers, of
the powders and perfumes and silks was deep in him.
Daisy's breasts were soft against him, and she appeared to
swoon in his arms. The music seemed to disentangle itself
from the tips of her fingers and the strands of her hair.
Joseph could not remember that he had spent the day in
the store waiting on coarse, heavy muckers from underground, selling them hobnailed shoes and ribbed wool socks.
All his skin was receptive to Daisy, and languorous, sensual
words dreamed through his mind. In the early morning
hours when the punch ran more thinly through Joseph's
veins, it occurred to him that Daisy was shrewd and a sharp
bargainer. Had she not told him that she had made her
own dress? Had she not insisted on riding to Moose Hall in
a street car instead of a carriage? So Daisy became both
Romance and Sensible Reality to him, and he could not
say which was more beautiful or even whether this about
her was Romance, and this other, Sensible Reality.

So it was that the morning after the ball Joseph got out of
bed rubbing his eyes with the realization that he was in love
and that he must marry Daisy Korner. He recollected that
in all the times he and Daisy had been together, he had
never spoken of marriage, though they had talked about his
future. He remembered that she had always counseled him

to take care of his money so that he could open his own
store and be free of his father's tyranny. What had she meant
but that she would be his wife? There was no other explanation. So he certainly was a fool to have let the grass grow
under his feet when some other man would have spoken to
her right away, saying, "Daisy, let's get married."

He would speak to his father. Joseph was forever ridicul-
ing Adolph Korner's business. "A fine business for a man—
bananas!" But Joseph was determined to marry Daisy no
matter what Moses would have to say. True, she never attended services in the synagogue, but she attended the new
Reform Temple on Friday evenings. Though Moses had
nothing but contempt for "Reform" Jews, he would have to
accept Daisy. What difference, Joseph asked himself, did it
make whether you attended a temple or a synagogue? Both
were Jewish churches, both believed in the same Jehovah.
The only difference, as far as Joseph could see, was that the
congregation in the Reform Temple was made up of a
wealthier class of Jews who preferred to worship in the
chaste spaciousness of a large, airy church rather than in the
congested discomfort of the synagogue.

But Moses thought that the Jews who attended the temple
were snobs. They were, for the most part, beardless—a sinful state—for every hair of his body should be sacred to a
descendant of Moses and Abraham. Reform Jews were men
and women diluted with Protestantism. They did not wear
the characteristic *tallith* draped over their shoulders, and
they removed their hats upon entering the temple. In the
synagogue the prayer books were in Hebrew; but in the temple the prayers were printed in both Hebrew and English.
The rabbi of the temple was addressed as "Doctor" and he
was usually a graduate of an American Rabbinical School.
He knew Hebrew, but it did not flow from him in a torren-
tial flood of melody; he spoke the ancient tongue with an
American accent and somewhat apologetically. The rabbi
did not sing in the temple. Neither did the congregation.
Prayers were cold and formal and lifeless, interspersed by

the voices of the choir in the balcony. It was much the same
kind of choir that is to be found in Baptist churches. The
voices were good enough, but the Hebrew was ludicrous
since most of the singers were Christians out to earn a little
extra pin money. The whole atmosphere of the temple was
filtered, cleanly, serene. There was nothing of the struggle,
the sense of a race pursued by tragedy that is to be found
in the synagogue. In the temple, the aisles were swept and
garnished, the benches were polished until they shone. But
the synagogue was small and smelled of old prayer books,
candle-drippings, the white silk that enclosed the *Holy
Torah*, the warm, perspiring bodies of men who work with
their hands.

In the Synagogue, Moses, with his broad-brimmed black
hat pulled low over his eyes, had tramped up and down the
narrow aisles, raising his beautiful voice to the rafters, a
voice profound with an agony of lamentations and of golden
ecstasy. He had beat his breast until the sound of his fist
against his heart was heard to the very last row of benches.
Judaism was not a standpat religion as Moses lived it, not a
calm, ordered service spoken in refined accents, colorless
and imitative. His faith was of the Israelites of Saul and
David, a fight, a cry to Heaven. His faith was conflict, bitter
tears, the iron of agony. Jews were not meant to sit at the
feet of an immature youth who spoke of *The Psychology of
Anti-Semitism*. Each Jew was his own rabbi and he must
make his own prayer to God. Moses and Abraham, David
and Solomon are in my blood. Life is intense, dyed with the
crimson of blood, the purple of passion.

So Moses was contemptuous of the Reform Temple, saying that it lacked only a gilded cross and then it would be
complete.

Joseph thought of these things when he considered telling
his father of his love for Daisy. He thought of the fact that
Daisy ate ham, and he remembered a rumor about town that
she had been seen in a Christian Science church. He had

seen flesh of the pig on the Korners' table. At first the sight
of this food had revolted Joseph, so deeply ingrained in him
was a certain obedience to the orthodox belief. Worse still,
Mrs. Korner served butter with her meat dishes and she ate
bread during the Passover. Joseph had spoken to Daisy
about it.

"I love ham," Daisy said. "There's nothing wrong about
eating food that you like. It's a real American dish. It ain't
as if we was still living in the Old Country. The trouble with
Jews like your father is that they love to roll around in
misery. I hope you don't get to be like your father, that's all.
What I always say is, 'Laugh and the world laughs with
you, eat ham and enjoy yourself.' The orthodox Jews are
always crying about something. And the rabbi is so dirty.
I bet he never washes his hands when he gets through killing
a chicken."

"But ham is unclean," argued Joseph. "At least that's
what good doctors say. It makes you sick."

"Don't you ever believe it. It's just as clean as any other
kind of meat. But the main thing is that I like it. Don't you
see, Joe, it's just the way you have of looking at things. Your
father believes in old-fashioned ideas and he wouldn't change
them—not if the world came to an end. It's the way he was
brought up, narrow, strict, you know. That's the way with
those Old Country people. But me an' you, Joe, we're a new
generation."

"I think papa would kill me if he knew that I ate ham,"
Joseph said, blushing. "Of course it's wrong the way he feels
that way. I can see where you're right, Daisy. The only way
to progress is to have new ideas. Sure, I believe that."

"Your father thinks that the only way to be religious is
to act old-fashioned and go to that awful synagogue. Why,
I wouldn't mingle with those people," said Daisy contemptu-
ously. "They're not my class."

Joseph was awed by these highly original sentiments of
Daisy's. They were almost blasphemous to him, but they
seemed to have an outer edge of common sense as Daisy

delivered them. He swallowed a few times, and then, in a trembling voice, asked if it were true that she had been seen in a Christian Science church?

"It certainly is," said Daisy. "I've been reading Mary Baker Eddy's book, *Science and Health,* and it's just too beautiful. The words are like poetry. And in this book it says everything is love. A bad thought is error. The trouble with Moses Singermann is he's full of error."

"But, Daisy, maybe this book believes in Christ? You know. Maybe it ain't Jewish. I don't think it's right to read a book like that."

"I tell you, it's beautiful, Joe. And you got to read this book. It'll teach you a lot. It says when you're sick to believe, to trust in God." Daisy pronounced it "Gawd." "If you believe with pure thoughts you'll get well. I tell you this Mary Baker Eddy must be a wonderful woman. To be able to write like that must take a lot of purity. You remember when I was sick last week, Joe? I had such a bad cold, my head was all stuffed up and mama kept asking me all the time if I was crying. 'Look at Daisy, she's crying,' Mama said. It was only my cold. Tears kept running out of my eyes and my nose was red. I looked a sight. I was afraid to show my face in the street. And then a friend of mine lent me this book, *Science and Health,* and I read it clear through. A kind of soothing feeling come over me. 'God is love,' I kept repeating to myself. 'God is love.' And do you know, when I closed that book my cold was gone? Maybe you think I'm joshing you. But I ain't, as God is my judge, Joe."

"You mean to say just reading this book cured you?" asked Joseph incredulously. "It must be a wonderful book, all right."

"It's more than wonderful," said Daisy, her eyes alight with a great discovery. "It's divine. That's what it is. Divine. And it's an experience to go to the Christian Science church. The people who go there aren't just the masses. They're superior. And you know, Joseph, if you want to get anywhere in the world nowadays, you got to mingle with a better class of people—spiritual people. You don't find a high class of spiritual people in the synagogue. Sometimes, I feel sorry for your father, Joe, with his old-fashioned ideas like he has. He'll always be one of the masses."

"Well, I won't be," protested Joseph stoutly. "I'm going to have my own store one of these days and be independent."

"I wouldn't wish your father any harm, Joe. I tell you I love your father. He's a fine man, only he has these old-fashioned ideas. It would do him a lot of good to read this book by Mary Baker Eddy. It would do your mother good if she could read. A whole new world would be opened before her eyes. Education! Purity! Love! Think how much these things mean. Just stop to think. And the greatest of all is love."

"Love," repeated Joseph, and looked into Daisy's eyes. "Love certainly is a great thing. I guess I'm beginning to learn a lot about love lately," and Joseph shifted his gaze and looked embarrassed.

"You'll learn a lot more about it in *The Key to the Scriptures*," said Daisy. Tears came to her eyes. "When I think how long I was ignorant of the truth, it makes me feel sad. But it's never too late to see the light."

Joseph did not tell his father about the great light that had come into Daisy's life. He had every intention of doing so, but at the critical moment his courage failed him. Moses never would have understood about love and error. He would never pick up a book with a cross stamped on its cover.

Joseph and Daisy were married in the Singermann house on West Granite Street into which the family had recently moved. They were married by Rabbi Lachter despite Adolph Korner's objections. The banana salesman had wanted the marriage ceremony performed by the young Doctor of the Reform Temple, but Moses would not hear of the plan. Korner was overwhelmed by Moses' arguments, and Daisy said that she'd just as soon be married by one as by the other. It was all the same in the eyes of God, she said.

All the members of the Singermann family were present, including the ten-months-old Michael who squealed in his cradle. The sight of Rabbi Lachter and his rusty black *kaftan* sent the infant into hysterics as if he were remembering the *Bris* and its pain. So loud were Michael's wails and protestations that he threatened to interfere with the replies of the bride and groom. The situation was saved by Mary O'Brien, who lifted the frantic child into her arms and bore him screaming into the kitchen.

Rachel was present with her attentive young man, Sam Straller. Louis had on a red necktie and chewed Sen Sen until his breath assumed precedence over the carnations that Daisy had pinned to her bodice. Joseph had wanted American Beauty roses, but Daisy had frowned at the expense. Brother David was there and near him stood Lina Bachmann, her modest beauty in charming contrast to Daisy's elaborate assurance. Sol watched the wedding from one corner of the room, thinking it very grand but wishing that it were over so that he could go out and play football in a nearby vacant lot. Harry had a new violin tucked under his arm and he was going to be asked to play after the ceremony. Harry was musical, as were all the other Singermanns. David possessed a cornet which he could play loud and strong. He was fond of saying that a violin, now, was a sweet instrument, and pretty, too, but it took a man to play the cornet. It took lungs to blow out a Sousa's march on the cornet.

After the ceremony was over and the rabbi had received his customary fee of five dollars (and a box of cigars from Moses), Daisy changed to a severe gray suit with the jacket cut square and the skirt flaring out into the innumerable pleats that were fashionable at the time. She looked extremely smart and rather formidable. This was her "traveling suit," for she and Joseph were going through Yellowstone Park on their honeymoon. As they drove to the railroad station, Joseph complimented his bride on her clothes, feeling the material between his fingers to discover whether it was really as good as it looked. He was deeply impressed when Daisy explained that she had made the suit herself from materials purchased wholesale from The National Suit and Cloak House. "It cost me exactly twenty-five dollars all told," said Daisy proudly. "If I wanted to buy this same suit retail you know what it would cost me?" Joseph guessed, but his figure was too low. "It would cost me forty dollars," said Daisy.

She seemed very happy.

When Joseph and Daisy returned from the Park, they set up housekeeping in a flat on South Alabama Street and bought a complete set of mission furniture for the dining room. Daisy felt very wise and exclusive about the mission set. It had been purchased wholesale from Butler Brothers in Minneapolis, and the same set retailed in Silver Bow for twice the sum they had paid. Everyone who called on Daisy praised the mission set. Everyone was astounded when Daisy told them what it had cost.

"I can't believe it. I think they were giving it away to you. I never heard of such a thing," everybody said.

"It's because I concentrate," said Daisy. "I study. It takes a brain." She smiled condescendingly upon her guests. "Some people have a knack for giving parties. Some have a knack for cooking. I have a knack for buying. It's because I study what I want. Before I write to a wholesaler I make a list. Maybe this one has quality but his prices are too high. Maybe this one has been stuck with goods on his hands. I check off the houses I want and I study the catalogues and I write letters. All the time I'm thinking it over, you understand. My brain is always working. It's only after I've investigated very careful that I make my selection. It's not everybody who has that knack."

"Daisy Singermann, you're wonderful," everybody said.

"Care," said Daisy. "Care and precaution does it."

A few months after their marriage, Daisy showed signs of restlessness. It bored her to stay home and wait for Joseph to return in the evening. She was a miserable housekeeper; never had Joseph tasted such poor food as that which Daisy prepared for him; never had he lived in such ill-kept rooms.

Coming home one evening to find the beds unmade and the breakfast dishes unwashed, Joseph lost all patience and demanded to know what she had been doing all that day. Daisy, herself, had just arrived in the flat, and she explained that she had been with her father, writing business letters for him.

"Maybe you're married to your father," said Joseph sarcastically, slipping off his arm bands preparatory to washing his hands. "After a man has worked all day it ain't exactly a pleasure for him to come home to a house like this."

Daisy removed her coat and hat and seated herself on the unmade bed, emitting a long sigh. "Well, if you want to know the truth, Joe, housework just makes me sick. It's all right for women who haven't got an ounce of brains. But why should I have to cook and wash dishes? Me with my special kind of mind? I certainly didn't marry you to be your servant, so get that out of your head right away."

"I'd like to know what you did marry me for," said Joseph gloomily, throwing himself full length on the bed and burying his head in the pillow. "You're so damned ambitious, that's the trouble with you. You're so ambitious you don't care what happens to me."

"Now that ain't true," remonstrated Daisy looking as though she were about to cry. She leaned back so that her head rested on his shoulder. "Joe, darling, let's not quarrel. Always have a sunny disposition and your troubles will fade away. A bad thought is error." She pressed her lips to his forehead. "I wish you'd speak to your father about letting me be cashier in the store."

"But I have! I have!" Joseph exclaimed into the pillow.

"He's not used to women in business. He says they drive customers out of the place."

"Just the same, I want you to talk to him again," insisted Daisy. She lay beside him in the bed and took him in her arms, kissing his lips. "Don't you know, sweet, that I've always wanted to try my hand at business? Didn't I always tell you that before we were married? Of course I'm ambitious, darling, but it's for your sake as well as mine. If I leave you alone you'll always go on working for your father at thirty dollars a week. And at the end of ten years we'll be the same poor church mice we are today. Honey, are you listening?"

"Yes. Yes."

"Don't be cross, honey. Look at me. Up-se goes! Now wipe that scowl off your face. Daisy don't like her handsome boy when he scowls like that. There! Now don't you feel better, Joey? You will speak to Papa Singermann about my being cashier?"

"I'll speak to him," said Joseph indulgently. "But if I come home with a broken head you'll know the reason why."

"I'd like to see anybody break my precious's head! Now get up, darling, and wash your face with cold water and we'll go out to dinner." She took hold of one of his hands and helped him to his feet. "You've been working hard today. *That's* the reason you're so cross. But I'm going to help you from now on, so pretty soon we'll have our own business and plenty of money in the bank, and maybe—" Daisy's pause was dramatic.

"Maybe what, Daisy?"

"Can't you guess?"

"Not a baby?" and Joseph's pale face suddenly became very animated. "You're fooling, baby doll."

"Well, you can never tell, darling. And when our son grows up we'll want to give him every advantage. We'll want to give him the start in life we never had."

"Sure we will. But he ain't here yet," growled Joseph.

"Where are we going to eat tonight? No, not at that chop suey joint! Let's get some American food for a change. Let's eat at the *Butte Grill*."

"But that place is terribly expensive, Joe," said Daisy, weighing herself down with the enormous Merry Widow hat she had made herself. "And you got to give such big tips. I think that Chong Lee's is good enough. For fifty cents you get a nice meal and a five-cent tip is plenty for them Chinks."

"All right," said Joseph, looking disappointed. "We got to think of the son that ain't even here yet."

"But he will be, dear. If God is good to us."

Willy-nilly, Joseph's wife installed herself in the store, armed with Mary Baker Eddy and a box of chocolates. For the succeeding twelve months she remained at the cash register, and not all of Moses Singermann's sarcasm and fury could uproot her. Moses raged and threatened, but only force would have driven her from her place, and Moses did not believe in striking a woman, at least not this particular woman. Daisy stuck to her post and kept smiling. Insults and taunts failed to discourage her, and when depression lay heaviest on her fair head, *Science and Health* lifted her from her slough of despond. Moses might rage at her, but she could only regard him as an insect and murmur "God is love" behind her slightly trembling lips. For it was not Moses who had insulted her but a germ of error rampant in the material body. By this time, Daisy had fortified herself with the belief that error, like an ant, can be effectively stepped on.

When Moses refused to pay her a salary, Daisy paid herself a daily stipend of five dollars out of the register. This was only justice, Daisy told Joseph. She relayed the money into her stocking and from the stocking to the State Savings Bank. At the end of twelve months, there was this strange coincidence: the savings in the bank were large enough to justify leasing a store-room that had recently been vacated on the opposite side of the street. It was Daisy who consulted the landlord about rent and a lease; and it was Daisy who placed orders for merchandise.

Ever since he had arrived in America, Moses had always found Joseph at his side, son and comrade. They had quarreled often, and upon numerous occasions almost come to blows. But at critical moments, when Moses had looked to his son for support, he had not found it wanting. With Daisy's arrival as a daughter-in-law and cashier, the father had felt the son's withdrawal, but he had not brooded over it. He had not dreamed that the day would come when Joseph would leave him. And now that extraordinary occurrence was about to take place.

Even after Moses was convinced that his son was opening another store, he could not believe that the two establishments would be separate and under different ownership. When carpenters were put to work building shelves and erecting show windows in the store across the street, Moses was often there looking on with pleasure. He held the naïve belief that he and his oldest son were to be partners in the new enterprise. The new store fascinated him with its splendid possibilities. It was a larger place than the old and it was situated on a busier side of the street. Moses looked upon the new store as a manifestation of his own and his son's success in America; not for a moment did he discern the truth, that the store was the result of Daisy's indomitable will and unscrupulousness.

The new store was to open its doors on a Monday morning, and it was not until the preceding Saturday that Joseph announced to his father his final departure. Daisy had already left the cashier's desk a week before. She was busy across the street ordering everything into readiness.

Moses made out his son's salary check and gave it to him. Whereupon Joseph said, "Well, papa, I guess this is the last salary I draw from you. Monday, we open up across the street."

"It looks like you ought to do a good business over there,"

said Moses, and could not disguise the pride in his voice.

"I guess this is good-by," and Joseph held out his hand.

"I think maybe you'll want me to help you, Monday," said Moses, taking his son's hand absently.

"No, I guess not," replied Joseph. "There's Daisy and myself, and we hired five clerks."

"Anyway, it would be better for me to help you," insisted Moses. "These clerks, they ain't to be trusted. Who can tell how many *genooven* will be ready for a chance to steal a pair of socks, or a necktie, maybe."

"No, papa, I guess we won't need you."

"What do you mean, you won't need me?" asked Moses in surprise. "Do you think maybe you can get along without me?"

For a moment, Joseph felt a twinge of pity for his father; but the moment was quick to pass, obliterated by a recollection of many disagreements they had suffered. So he stamped down his pity, thinking of the way Moses had dealt with Daisy, threatening to drive her out of the store when she had come as cashier that first day.

"Papa," he said now, "I want you to realize that me and Daisy own the new store. You understand, papa? You got nothing to do with it. You'll only make trouble if you come around Monday. It'll look bad for the clerks."

Moses was perplexed. "Are you joking with me? But this ain't no time for jokes. . . . You better go home and rest yourself so you will be ready for the grand opening. Go home now and sleep tomorrow, Joseph."

The oldest son turned away. "All right. But remember what I told you. You better tend to your own business and leave us alone."

With this final warning, Joseph crossed the threshold of his father's store into the street and left Moses staring after him.

That Monday morning, Moses rose early and pottered about the kitchen making a great noise, so that Rebecca wanted to know what was the matter and couldn't he make a cup of coffee without pulling down the roof over his head? But he was restless and nervous thinking of the new store, and he was reminded of the day he had set foot in New York, and later, Minneapolis. So many curtains in his life, rising on new scenes, new adventures! Would Joseph be up now, and would there be a big crowd waiting to get into the new store?

Moses walked to his own business and carried out his show and dusted the shoes on the benches, but his eyes were on the place across the street. Customers came in and wanted things, but he waited on them absently, eager to be rid of them. At ten o'clock, when he was free, he saw that Joseph's store was open and that a crowd was milling about the door. Moses' heart grew warm and he rubbed his hands together happily. At the moment of crossing the street, he remembered Joseph on Saturday, and his feet grew a little heavy. But he must see and feel the tumult of the new business. When you had two stores in Silver Bow, that was something.

He pressed his strong figure through the crowd at the entrance and was immediately enveloped in a throng of shoppers. The noise and feel of selling and buying shouted along his veins, and his nerves were tightly drawn strings of a harp; he could hear them sound notes. Joseph had hired too few clerks, that much was plain. Here all these people had the money in their hands, begging to spend, and they could get no one to wait on them.

Moses could not resist the lure of selling. Ater a few minutes, he was waiting on several customers, showing one shoes, another underwear, rushing back to the first and then to the second, helping a third to select a necktie. His face was flushed, his beard was damp with perspiration and his necktie flapped out of his vest; but the thunder and swell of business carried him aloft to exaltation. All this time, he was vaguely aware of Joseph moving quickly about the store, of Daisy at the cash register ringing up sales and calling out directions to the clerks.

They were not aware of him until he brought money to the register. He had sold a pair of shoes and was wrapping them while waiting mechanically for his change. Daisy saw him then, and was startled, but she made the change and said nothing. After a few minutes, she leaned down from her stool and whispered something into Joseph's ear. Joseph said, "Where?" and twisted his head about in different directions. Then his attention was diverted to an impatient customer.

So all the morning Moses forgot about his own store and worked happily in the new; at lunch time he forgot that he was hungry and no one reminded him that it was time to eat. The afternoon brought new crowds of impatient shoppers; they flooded the aisles of the store, submerging the clerks, beating against the shelves and showcases; and Moses was like a cork bobbing up and down in their midst, but never lost.

By six o'clock the masses of customers were thinned out; and soon the aisles were clear except for the clerks. Almost before Moses was aware of it, the store was closed and the crowds were gone. Daisy and Joseph stood about the cashier's desk and she was counting the money, the gold pieces, the silver, the bills. She looked hard and engrossed as Moses approached her. "Is it a thousand dollars?" asked Moses.

Daisy looked up abruptly from the piles of money. "Fourteen hundred and seventy-five," she answered coldly.

"It's good business," exulted Moses. "And it ought to keep up for a few weeks . . . By golly, I'm hungry now, you know?"

"Fifty and twenty-five and twenty-five is a hundred. You should have gone to lunch," said Daisy.

"How can a man eat with business like this?" asked Moses. "The place was so packed . . . eating can wait."

"It wasn't necessary for you to work so hard, Papa Singermann," said Daisy. "We've got plenty of help. We got three extra clerks for tomorrow."

"I told him that Saturday," put in Joseph. Moses looked at his son and could not make out the boy he had known. Joseph looked wary and clever beyond touching. The goods in the shelves were his; the money in the cash register was his.

"We won't need you tomorrow," said Daisy. "Three hundred, three and twenty, three and sixty. . . . Besides, you're neglecting your own business, Papa Singermann."

"That's what I say. Why don't you stick over in your own place?" asked Joseph. There was an executive remoteness about Joseph now, a strangeness that cut him off from Singermann ways and Singermann familiarity.

Moses felt the coldness, but he tried to warm it with words. "By golly, so many shoes I never sold in my life," he said. "It must be a hundred pairs of shoes I sold . . . like hotcakes."

"How much do you want, papa, for working here today?" asked Joseph truculently.

"I think we better give papa a present of ten dollars for his help," said Daisy. She removed a ten-dollar bill off one of the piles. "Papa, it was nice of you . . . but Joe, I think those extra clerks will be all right for tomorrow, won't they? We won't need papa tomorrow."

"That's what I told him before," muttered Joseph. "Didn't you hear me say I told him that Saturday?" He busied himself replacing boxes in the shelves, and the way he touched them and looked at them, they were his and belonged to him.

Moses received the ten-dollar bill from Daisy with an abstracted air; but when he realized what it was for, he placed it on the desk. "What is this?" he asked.

"Put it in your pocket," said Daisy. "Don't let it lay around."

"And you would pay me like a common clerk?"

"Maybe you want a share of the profits?" shouted Joseph, and turned about from the shelves with a white face and blazing eyes.

Moses caught up the ten-dollar bill, crushed it in his hand, then threw it to the floor. "What is this talk?" he asked in a rage. "Do you know I'm your father?"

But Daisy was calm and removed. Moses could see her above him, cold as ice and hard. There were no Singermann ways in her and no Singermann familiarity. "Don't you know, papa, that this is our store, Joseph's and mine? And yours is across the street."

"I told him that, Saturday," snapped Joseph.

So everything about him was now strange to Moses. The neckties were colors his eyes did not know, the shoe boxes had odd labels, the suits hanging on the racks were of unfamiliar materials and designs. Joseph had stepped away into another world and old pleas and threats could not reach him. "What's yours is yours, and I hope you make much money," Moses found himself saying. "If you want we should be strangers . . . then it is so. We are strangers." The hard, pitiless lock on the door was strange to Moses and frowned at him. The show windows had an alien glimmer, and the window cards bore numerals that were difficult to read.

Moses started crossing the street and was almost run over by a passing trolley car. The motorman cursed him. When he entered the old store, he found that David was still there, brushing his hair in front of the hat-case mirror. "Well, Joe must have started out great, eh?" asked David.

"What?"

"I said, business with Joe must have been great."

"Why not?"

"You look sick, papa."

"Who says I'm sick?" shouted Moses, and glared at his son, but his eyes had a stricken look in them.

"All right. Get sore. Is it a sin to say you look sick?"

"It's a lie, that's what it is."

David placed the comb carefully between the bristles of the hairbrush. He turned away from the mirror, put on his hat and coat and walked to the door. "Good night, papa."

"David!" The boy was startled by the grief in his father's voice. "David, remember Joseph is no longer a son from mine! And that woman . . . that Christian Scientist . . . let her to roast in Hell!"

David regarded his father for a moment, then said, "Yes, papa," and walked off.

Moses turned to the desk in the rear of the store. He opened one of the drawers and removed a photograph of Joseph that had been taken when he and his father first reached Minneapolis. For a moment, Moses stared at the childish, rather sweet face. Then he opened the rear door that looked out upon a narrow, unpaved alley and threw the picture into the mud.

STANLEY KUNITZ (b. 1905), born in Worcester, Massachusetts, was educated at Harvard and later taught poetry at The New School for Social Research, Brandeis and Columbia Universities. *Intellectual Things* (1930), his first book of poems, included "For the Word is Flesh." *Selected Poems, 1928-1958* (1958), which won the Pulitzer Prize, included "Father and Son." In the earlier poem, anger and impatience came through, perhaps at his long-dead father, perhaps at his own heritage. Of the later poem, Kunitz says, "I wrote it on the eve of World War II—the landscape is Worcester. All the essentials are true, as true as dreams are." Kunitz' most recent work is *Testing Tree* (1971).

For the Word Is Flesh
from
SELECTED POEMS

O ruined father dead, long sweetly rotten
Under the dial, the time-dissolving urn,
Beware a second perishing, forgotten,
Heap fallen leaves of memory to burn
On the slippery rock, the black eroding heart,
Before the wedged frost splits it clean apart.

The nude hand drops no sacramental flower
Of blood among the tough upthrusting weeds.
Senior, in this commemorative hour,
What shall the quick commemorate, what deeds
Ephemeral, what dazzling words that flare
Like rockets from the mouth to burst in air?

Of hypochondriacs that gnawed their seasons
In search of proofs, Lessius found twenty-two
Fine arguments, Tolet gave sixty reasons
Why souls survive. And what are they to you?
And, father, what to me, who cannot blur
The mirrored brain with fantasies of Er,

Remembering such factual spikes as pierce
The supplicating palms, and by the sea
Remembering the eyes, I hear the fierce
Wild cry of Jesus on the holy tree,
Yet have of you no syllable to keep,
Only the deep rock crumbling in the deep.

Observe the wisdom of the Florentine
Who, feeling death upon him, scribbled fast
To make revision of a deathbed scene,

Gloating that he was accurate at last.
Let sons learn from their lipless fathers how
Man enters hell without a golden bough.

Father and Son
from
SELECTED POEMS

Now in the suburbs and the falling light
I followed him, and now down sandy road
Whiter than bone-dust, through the sweet
Curdle of fields, where the plums
Dropped with their load of ripeness, one by one.
Mile after mile I followed, with skimming feet,
After the secret master of my blood,
Him, steeped in the odor of ponds, whose indomitable love
Kept me in chains. Strode years; stretched into bird;
Raced through the sleeping country where I was young,
The silence unrolling before me as I came,
The night nailed like an orange to my brow.

How should I tell him my fable and the fears,
How bridge the chasm in a casual tone,
Saying, "The house, the stucco one you built,
We lost. Sister married and went from home,
And nothing comes back, it's strange, from where she goes.
I lived on a hill that had too many rooms:
Light we could make, but not enough of warmth,
And when the light failed, I climbed under the hill.
The papers are delivered every day;
I am alone and never shed a tear."

At the water's edge, where the smothering ferns lifted
Their arms, "Father!" I cried, "Return! You know
The way. I'll wipe the mudstains from your clothes;
No trace, I promise, will remain. Instruct

Your son, whirling between two wars,
In the Gemara of your gentleness,
For I would be a child to those who mourn
And brother to the foundlings of the field
And friend of innocence and all bright eyes.
O teach me how to work and keep me kind."

Among the turtles and the lilies he turned to me
The white ignorant hollow of his face.

HENRY ROTH (b. 1906), brought to New York as an infant from Russia, had many jobs in the '20s and '30s before
he wrote *Call It Sleep* (1934). Although the novel had a
good reception when it appeared it seemed to disappear soon
after; in the late 1950s, through the efforts of Alfred Kazin,
Leslie Fiedler and others, it was recognized as one of the
major novels of the twentieth century and it has maintained
that rating ever since. Though he has written very little
since the 1930s, Roth's psychological portrait of an immigrant family's problems, seen through the eyes of a seven-
year-old, is as compelling now as then.

The Cheder
from
CALL IT SLEEP

One edge shining in the vanishing sunlight, the little
white-washed house of the cheder lay before them. It was
only one story high, the windows quite close to the ground.
Its bulkier neighbors, the tall tenements that surrounded it,
seemed to puff out their littered fire-escapes in scorn. Smoke
curled from a little, black chimney in the middle of its roof,
and overhead myriads of wash-lines criss-crossed intricately,

snaring the sky in a dark net. Most of the lines were bare,
but here and there was one sagging with white and colored
wash, from which now and again a flurry of rinsings
splashed into the yard or drummed on the cheder roof.

"I hope," said his mother, as they went down the wooden
stairs that led into the yard, "that you'll prove more gifted
in the ancient tongue than I was. When I went to cheder,
my rabbi was always wagging his head at me and swearing
I had a calf's brain." And she laughed. "But I think the
reason I was such a dunce was that I could never wrench
my nose far enough away to escape his breath. Pray this
one is not so fond of onions!"

They crossed the short space of the yard and his mother
opened the cheder door. A billow of drowsy air rolled out
at them. It seemed dark inside. On their entrance, the hum
of voices ceased.

The rabbi, a man in a skull cap, who had been sitting
near the window beside one of his pupils, looked up when
he saw them and rose. Against the window, he looked
short and bulbous, oddly round beneath the square outline
of the skull-cap.

"Good day," he ambled toward them. "I'm Reb Yidel
Pankower. You wish—?" He ran large, hairy fingers
through a glossy, crinkled beard.

David's mother introduced herself and then went on to
explain her mission.

"And this is he?"

"Yes. The only one I have."

"Only one such pretty star?" He chuckled and reaching
out, caught David's cheek in a tobacco-reeking pinch. David
shied slightly.

While his mother and the rabbi were discussing the hours
and the price and the manner of David's tuition, David
scanned his future teacher more closely. He was not at all
like the teachers at school, but David had seen rabbis before and knew he wouldn't be. He appeared old and was
certainly untidy. He wore soft leather shoes like house-

slippers, that had no place for either laces or buttons. His trousers were baggy and stained, a great area of striped and crumpled shirt intervened between his belt and his bulging vest. The knot of his tie, which was nearer one ear than the other, hung away from his soiled collar. What features were visible were large and had an oily gleam. Beneath his skull cap, his black hair was closely cropped. Though full of misgivings about his future relations with the rabbi, David felt that he must accept his fate. Was it not his father's decree that he attend a cheder?

From the rabbi his eyes wandered about the room. Bare walls, the brown paint on it full of long wavering cracks. Against one wall, stood a round-bellied stove whose shape reminded him of his rabbi, except that it was heated a dull red and his rabbi's apparel was black. Against the other wall a long line of benches ran to the rabbi's table. Boys of varying ages were seated upon them, jabbering, disputing, gambling for various things, scuffling over what looked to David like a few sticks. Seated upon the bench before the rabbi's table were several others obviously waiting their turn at the book lying open in front of the rabbi's cushioned chair.

What had been, when he and his mother had entered, a low hum of voices, had now swollen to a roar. It looked as though half of the boys in the room had engaged the other half in some verbal or physical conflict. The rabbi, excusing himself to David's mother, turned toward them, and with a thunderous rap of his fist against the door, uttered a ferocious, "Shah!" The noise subsided somewhat. He swept the room with angry, glittering eyes, then softening into a smile again returned to David's mother.

At last it was arranged and the rabbi wrote down his new pupil's name and address. David gathered that he was to receive his instruction somewhere between the hours of three and six, that he was to come to the cheder shortly after three, and that the fee for his education would be twenty-five cents a week. Moreover he was to begin that afternoon. This was something of an unpleasant surprise and at first he protested, but when his mother urged him and the rabbi assured him that his first lesson would not take long, he consented, and mournfully received his mother's parting kiss.

"Sit down over there," said the rabbi curtly as soon as his mother had left. "And don't forget," he brought a crooked knuckle to his lips. "In a cheder one must be quiet."

David sat down, and the rabbi walked back to his seat beside the window. Instead of sitting down, however, he reached under his chair, and bringing out a short-thonged cat-o'-nine-tails, struck the table loudly with the butt-end and pronounced in a menacing voice: "Let there be a hush among you!" And, a scared silence instantly locking all mouths, he seated himself. He then picked up a little stick lying on the table and pointed to the book, whereupon a boy sitting next to him began droning out sounds in a strange and secret tongue.

For awhile, David listened intently to the sound of the words. It was Hebrew, he knew, the same mysterious language his mother used before the candles, the same his father used when he read from a book during the holidays —and that time before drinking wine. Not Yiddish, Hebrew. God's tongue, the rabbi had said. If you knew it, then you could talk to God. Who was He? He would learn about Him now—

The boy sitting nearest David, slid along the bench to his side. "Yuh jost stottin' cheder?"

"Yea."

"Uhh!" he groaned, indicating the rabbi with his eyes. "He's a louser! He hits!"

David regarded the rabbi with panicky eyes. He had seen boys slapped by teachers in school for disobedience, although he himself had never been struck. The thought of being flogged with that vicious scourge he had seen the rabbi produce sealed his lips. He even refused to answer when next the boy asked him whether he had any match-pictures to match, and hastily shook his head. With a shrug, the boy slid back along the bench to the place he had come from.

Presently, with the arrival of several late-comers, older boys, tongues once more began to wag and a hum of voices filled the room. When David saw that the rabbi brandished his scourge several times without wielding it, his fear abated somewhat. However, he did not venture to join in the conversation, but cautiously watched the rabbi.

The boy who had been reading when David had come in had finished, and his place was taken by a second who seemed less able to maintain the rapid drone of his predecessor. At first, when he faltered, the rabbi corrected him by uttering what was apparently the right sound, for the boy always repeated it. But gradually, as his pupil continued in his error, a harsh note of warning crept into the rabbi's voice. After awhile he began to yank the boy by the arm whenever he corrected him, then to slap him smartly on the thigh, and finally, just before the boy had finished, the rabbi cuffed him on the ear.

As time went by, David saw this procedure repeated in part or whole in the case of almost every other boy who read. There were several exceptions, and these, as far as David could observe, gained their exemption from punishment because the drone that issued from their lips was as breathless and uninterrupted as the roll of a drum. He also noticed that whenever the rabbi administered one of these manual corrections, he first dropped from his hand the little stick with which he seemed to set the pace on the page, and an instant later reached out or struck out, as the case might demand. So that, whenever he dropped the stick, whether to scratch his beard or adjust his skull-cap or fish out a half-burned cigarette from a box, the pupil before him invariably jerked up an arm or ducked his head defensively. The dropping of that little stick, seemed to have become a warning to his pupils that a blow was on the way.

The light in the windows was waning to a blank pallor. The room was warm; the stagnant air had lulled even the most restive. Drowsily, David wondered when his turn would come.

"Aha!" he heard the rabbi sarcastically exclaim. "Is it you, Hershele, scholar from the land of scholars?"

This was addressed to the boy who had just slid into the vacant place before the book. David had observed him before, a fat boy with a dull face and an open mouth. By the cowed, sullen stoop of his shoulders, it was clear that he was not one in good standing with the rabbi.

"Herry is gonna loin," giggled one of the boys at David's side.

"Perhaps, today, you can glitter a little," suggested the rabbi with a freezing smile. "Who knows, a puppet may yet be made who can fart. Come!" He picked up the stick and pointed to the page.

The boy began to read. Though a big boy, as big as any that preceded him, he read more slowly and faltered more often than any of the others. It was evident that the rabbi was restraining his impatience, for instead of actually striking his pupil, he grimaced violently when he corrected him, groaned frequently, stamped his foot under the table and gnawed his under-lip. The other students had grown quiet and were listening. From their strained silence—their faces were by now half obscured in shadow—David was sure they were expecting some catastrophe any instant. The boy fumbled on. As far as David could tell, he seemed to be making the same error over and over again, for the rabbi kept repeating the same sound. At last, the rabbi's patience gave out. He dropped the pointer; the boy ducked, but not soon enough. The speeding plane of the rabbi's palm rang against his ear like a clapper on a gong.

"You plaster dunce!" he roared, "when will you learn a byse is a byse and not a vyse. Head of filth, where are your eyes?" He shook a menacing hand at the cringing boy and picked up the pointer.

But a few moments later, again the same error and again the same correction.

"May a demon fly off with your father's father! Won't blows help you? A byse, Esau, pig! A byse! Remember, a byse, even though you die of convulsions!"

The boy whimpered and went on. He had not uttered more than a few sounds, when again he paused on the awful brink, and as if out of sheer malice, again repeated his error. The last stroke of the bastinado! The effect on the rabbi was terrific. A frightful bellow clove his beard. In a moment he had fastened the pincers of his fingers on the cheeks of his howling pupil, and wrenching the boy's head from side to side roared out.—

"A byse! A byse! A byse! All buttocks have only one eye. A byse! May your brains boil over! A byse! Creator of earth and firmament, ten thousand cheders are in this land and me you single out for torment! A byse! Most abject of God's fools! A byse!"

While he raved and dragged the boy's head from side to side with one hand, with the other he hammered the pointer with such fury against the table that David expected at any moment to see the slender stick buried in the wood. It snapped instead!

"He busted it!" the suppressed giggle went round.

Horrified himself by what he saw, David wondered what the rest could possibly be so amused about.

"I couldn't see," the boy at the table was blubbering. "I couldn't see! It's dark in here!"

"May your skull be dark!" the rabbi intoned in short frenzied yelps, "and your eyes be dark and your fate be of such dearth and darkness that you will call a poppy-seed the sun and a carroway the moon. Get up! Away! Or I'll empty my bitter heart upon you!"

Tears streaming down his cheeks, and wailing loudly, the boy slid off the bench and slunk away.

"Stay here till I give you leave to go," the rabbi called after him. "Wipe your muddy nose. Hurry, I say! If you could read as easily as your eyes can piss, you were a fine scholar indeed!"

The boy sat down, wiped his nose and eyes with his coat-sleeve and quieted to a suppressed snuffling.

Glancing at the window, the rabbi fished in his pockets, drew out a match and lit the low gas jet sticking out from the wall over head. While he watched the visibility of the open book on the table, he frugally shaved down the light to a haggard leaf. Then he seated himself again, unlocked a drawer in the table and drew out a fresh stick which looked exactly like the one he had just broken. David wondered whether the rabbi whittled a large supply of sticks for himself, knowing what would happen to them.

"Move back!" He waved the boy away who had reluctantly slipped into the place just vacated before the table. "David Schearl!" he called out, tempering the harshness of his voice. "Come here, my gold."

Qualing with fright, David drew near.

"Sit down, my child," he was still breathing hard with exertion. "Don't be alarmed." He drew out of his pocket a package of cigarette-papers and a tobacco pouch, carefully rolled a cigarette, took a few puffs, then snuffed it out and put it into an empty cigarette box. David's heart pounded with fear. "Now then," he turned the leaves of a book beside him to the last page. "Show me how blessed is your understanding." He drew David's tense shoulder down toward the table, and picking up the new stick, pointed to a large hieroglyph at the top of the page. "This is called Komitz. You see? Komitz. And this is an Aleph. Now, whenever one sees a Komitz under an Aleph, one says, Aw." His hot tobacco-laden breath swirled about David's face.

His mother's words about her rabbi flashed through his mind. He thrust them aside and riveted his gaze to the indicated letter as if he would seal it on his eyes.

"Say after me," continued the rabbi, "Komitz-Aleph— Aw!"

David repeated the sounds.

"So!" commanded the rabbi. "Once more! Komitz-Aleph-Aw!"

And after David had repeated it several times. "And this," continued the rabbi pointing to the next character, "is called Bais, and a Komitz under a Bais—Baw! Say it! Komitz-Bais-Baw!"

"Komitz-Bais—Baw!" said David.

"Well done! Again."

And so the lesson progressed with repetition upon repetition. Whether out of fear or aptitude, David went through these first steps with hardly a single error. And when he was dismissed, the rabbi pinched his cheek in praise and said:

"Go home. You have an iron head!"

· · · ·

Two months had passed since David entered the cheder. Spring had come and with the milder weather, a sense of wary contentment, a curious pause in himself as though he were waiting for some sign, some seal that would forever relieve him of watchfulness and forever insure his well-being. Sometimes he thought he had already beheld the sign—he went to cheder; he often went to the synagogue on Saturdays; he could utter God's syllables glibly. But he wasn't quite sure. Perhaps the sign would be revealed when he finally learned to translate Hebrew. At any rate, ever since he had begun attending cheder, life had leveled out miraculously, and this he attributed to his increasing nearness to God. He never thought about his father's job any longer. There was no more of that old dread of waiting for the cycle to fulfill itself. There no longer seemed to be any cycle. Nor did his mother ever appear to worry about his father's job; she too seemed reassured and at peace. And those curious secrets he had gleaned long ago from his mother's story seemed submerged within him and were met only at reminiscent street-corners among houses or in the brain. Everything unpleasant and past was like that, David decided, lost within one. All one had to do was to imagine that it wasn't there, just as the cellar in one's house could be conjured away if there were a bright yard between the hallway and the cellar-stairs. One needed only a bright yard. At times David almost believed he had found that brightness.

It was a few days before Passover. The morning had been so gay, warmer and brighter than any in the sheaf of Easter just past. Noon had been so full of promise—a leaf of Summer in the book of Spring. And all that afternoon he had waited, restless and inattentive, for the three o'clock gong to release him from school. Instead of blackboards, he had studied the sharp grids of sunlight that brindled the red wall under the fire-escapes; and behind his tall geography book, had built a sail of a blotter and pencil to catch the mild breeze that curled in through the open window. Miss Steigman had caught him, had tightly puckered her lips (the heavy fuzz above them always darkened when she did that) and screamed:

"Get out of that seat, you little loafer! This minute! This very minute! And take that seat near the door and stay there! The audacity!" She always used that word, and David always wondered what it meant. Then she had begun to belch, which was what she always did after she had been made angry.

And even in his new seat, David had been unable to sit still, had fidgeted and waited, fingered the grain of his desk, stealthily rolled the sole of his shoe over a round lead pencil, attempted to tie a hair that had fallen on his book into little knots. He had waited and waited, but now that he was free, what good was it? The air was darkening, the naked wind was spinning itself a grey conch of the dust and rubbish scooped from the gutter. The street-cleaner was pulling on his black rain-coat. The weather had cheated him, that's all! He couldn't go anywhere now. He'd get wet.

He might as well be the first one in the cheder. Disconsolately, he crossed the street.

But how did his mother know this morning it was going to rain? She had gone to the window and looked out, and then she said, the sun is up too early. Well what if it—Whee!

Before his feet a flat sheet of newspaper, driven by a gust of damp wind, whipped into the air and dipped and fluttered languidly, melting into the sky. He watched it a moment and then quickened his step. Above store windows, awnings were heaving and bellying upward, rattling. Yelling, a boy raced across the gutter, his cap flying before him.

"Wow! Look!" The shout made him turn around.

"Shame! Shame! Everybody knows your name." A chorus of boys and girls chanted emphatically. "Shame! Shame! Everybody knows your name."

Red and giggling a big girl was thrusting down the billow of her dress. Above plump, knock-kneed legs, a glimpse of scalloped, white drawers. The wind relenting, the dress finally sank. David turned round again, feeling a faint disgust, a wisp of the old horror. With what prompt spasms the mummified images in the brain started from their niches, aped former antics and lapsed. It recalled that time, way long ago. Knish and closet. Puh! And that time when two dogs were stuck together. Puh! Threw water that man. Shame! Shame!

"Sophe-e!" Above him the cry. "Sophe-e!"

"Ye-es mama-a!" from a girl across the street.

"Comm opstehs! Balt!"

"Awaa!"

"Balt or I'll give you! Nooo!"

With a rebellious shudder, the girl began crossing the street. The window slammed down.

Pushing a milk-stained, rancid baby carraige before them, squat buttocks waddled past, one arm from somewhere dragging two reeling children, each hooked by its hand to the other, each bouncing against the other and against their mother like tops, flagging and whipped. A boy ran in front of the carriage. It rammed him.

"Ow! Kencha see wea yuh goin?" He rubbed his ankle.

"Snott nuzz! Oll—balt a frosk, Oll—give!"

"Aaa! Buzjwa!"

A drop of rain spattered on his chin.

—It's gonna—

He flung his strap of books over his shoulder and broke into a quick trot.

—Before I get all wet.

Ahead of him, flying toward the shore beyond the East River, shaggy clouds trooped after their van. And across the river the white smoke of nearer stacks were flattened out and stormy as though the stacks were the funnels of a flying ship. In the gutter, wagon wheels trailed black ribbons. Curtains overhead paddled out of open windows. The air had shivered into a thousand shrill, splintered cries, wedged here and there by the sudden whoop of a boy or the impatient squawk of a mother. At the doorway to the cheder corridor, he stopped and cast one lingering glance up and down the street. The black sidewalks had cleared. Rain shook out wan tresses in the gathering dark. Against the piebald press of cloud in the craggy furrow of the west, a long flag on top of a schoolsteeple blew out stiff as a key. In the shelter of a doorway, across the gutter, a cluster of children shouted in monotone up at the sky:

"Rain, rain, go away, come again some oddeh day. Rain, rain, go away, come again some oddeh day. Rain, rain—"

He'd better go in before the rest of the rabbi's pupils came. They'd get ahead of him otherwise. He turned and trudged through the dim battered corridor. The yard was gloomy. Wash-poles creaked and swayed, pulleys jangled. In a window overhead, a bulky, bare-armed woman shrilled curses at someone behind her and hastily hauled in the bedding that straddled the sills like bulging sacks.

"And your guts be plucked!" her words rang out over the yard. "Couldn't you tell me it was raining?"

He dove through the rain, skidded over the broken flag-stones and fell against the cheder door. As he stumbled in, the rabbi, who was lighting the gas-jet, looked around.

"A black year befall you!" he growled. "Why don't you come in like a man?"

Without answering, he sidled meekly over to the bench beside the wall and sat down. What did he yell at him for? He hadn't meant to burst in that way. Gee! The growing gas-light revealed another pupil in the room whom he hadn't noticed before. It was Mendel. His neck swathed in white bandages, sickly white under the bleary yellow flicker of gas, he sat before the reading table, head propped by elbows. Mendel was nearing his bar-mitzvah but had never learned to read chumish because he had entered the cheder at a rather late age. He was lucky, so every one said, because he had a carbuncle on the back of his neck which prevented him from attending school. And so all week long, he had arrived first at the cheder. David wondered if he dared sit down beside him. The rabbi looked angry. However, he decided to venture it and crawled quietly over the bench beside Mendel. The pungent reek of medicine pried his nostrils.

—Peeuh! It stinks!

He edged away. Dull-eyed, droopy-lipped, Mendel glanced down at him and then turned to watch the rabbi. The latter drew a large blue book from a heap on the shelf and then settled himself on his pillowed chair.

"Strange darkness," he said, squinting at the rain-chipped window. "A stormy Friday."

David shivered. Beguiled by the mildness of noon, he had left the house wearing only his thin blue jersey. Now, without a fire in the round-bellied stove and without other bodies to lend their warmth to the damp room, he felt cold.

"Now", said the rabbi stroking his beard, "this is the 'Haftorah' to Jethro—something you will read at your bar mitzvah, if you live that long." He wet his thumb and fore-finger and began pinching the top of each page in such a way that the whole leaf seemed to wince from his hand and flip over as if fleeing of its own accord. David noted with surprise that unlike the rabbi's other books this one had as yet none of its corners lopped off. "It's the 'Sedrah' for that week," he continued, "and since you don't know any chumish, I'll tell you what it means after you've read it." He picked up the pointer, but instead of pointing to the page suddenly lifted his hand.

In spite of himself, Mendel contracted.

"Ach!" came the rabbi's impatient grunt. "Why do you spring like a goat? Can I hit *you?*" And with the blunt end of the pointer, he probed his ear, his swarthy face painfully rippling about his bulbous nose into the margins of his beard and skull-cap. He scraped the brown clot of wax against the table leg and pointed to the page. "Begin, Beshnos mos."

"Beshnos mos hamelech Uziyahu vaereh es adonoi," Mendel swung into the drone.

For want of anything better to do, David looked on, vieing silently with Mendel. But the pace proved too fast for him—Mendel's swift sputter of gibberish tripped his own laggard lipping. He gave up the chase and gazed vacantly at the rain-chipped window. In a house across the darkened yard, lights had been lit and blurry figures moved before them. Rain strummed on the roof, and once or twice through the steady patter, a muffled rumble filtered down, as if a heavy object were being dragged across the floor above.

—Bed on wheels. Upstairs. (his thoughts rambled absently between the confines of the drone of the voice and the drone of the rain) Gee how it's raining. It won't stop. Even if he finishes, I can't go. If he read chumish, could race him, could beat him I bet. But that's because he has to stop . . . Why do you have to read chumish? No fun . . . First you read, Adonoi elahenoo abababa, and then you say, And Moses said you mustn't, and then you read some more abababa and then you say, mustn't eat in the traife butcher store. Don't like it any way. Big brown bags hang down from the hooks. Ham. And all kinds of grey wurst with like marbles in 'em. Peeuh! And chickens without feathers in boxes, and little bunnies in that store on First Avenue by the elevated. In a wooden cage with lettuce. And rocks, they eat too, on those stands. Rocks all colors. They bust 'em open with a knife and shake out ketchup on the snot inside. Yich! and long, black, skinny snakes. Peeuh! Goyim eat everything . . .

"Veeshma es kol adonoi omair es mi eshlach." Mendel was reading swiftly this afternoon. The rabbi turned the page. Overhead that distant rumbling sound.

—Bed on wheels again . . , But how did Moses know? Who told him? God told him. Only eat kosher meat, that's how. Mustn't eat meat and then drink milk. Mama don't care except when Bertha was looking! How she used to holler on her because she mixed up the meat-knives with the milk-knives. It's a sin. . . . So God told him eat in your own meat markets . . . That time with mama in the chicken market when we went. Where all the chickens ran around— cuckacucka—when did I say? Cucka. Gee! Funny. Some place I said. And then the man with a knife went zing! Eee! Blood and wings. And threw him down. Even kosher meat when you see, you don't want to eat—

"Enough!" The rabbi tapped his pointer on the table.

Mendel stopped reading and slumped back with a puff of relief.

"Now I'll tell you a little of what you read, then what it means. Listen to me well that you may remember it. Beshnas mos hamelech." The two nails of his thumb and forefinger met. "In the year that King Uzziah died, Isaiah saw God. And God was sitting on his throne, high in heaven and in his temple—Understand?" He pointed upwards.

Mendel nodded, grimacing as he eased the bandage round his neck.

—Gee! And he saw Him. Wonder where? (David, his

interest aroused, was listening intently. This was something new.)

"Now!" resumed the rabbi. "Around Him stood the angels, God's blessed angels. How beautiful they were you yourself may imagine. And they cried: Kadosh! Kadosh! Kadosh—Holy! Holy! Holy! And the temple rang and quivered with the sound of their voices. So!" He paused, peering into Mendel's face. "Understand?"

"Yeh," said Mendel understandingly.

—And angels there were and he saw 'em. Wonder if—

"But when Isaiah saw the Almighty in his majesty and His terrible light—Woe me! he cried, What shall I do! I am lost!" The rabbi seized his skull-cap and crumpled it. "I, common man, have seen the Almighty, I, unclean one have seen him! Behold, my lips are unclean and I live in a land unclean—for the Jews at that time were sinful—"

—Clean? Light? Wonder if—? Wish I could ask him why the Jews were dirty. What did they do? Better not! Get mad. Where? (Furtively, while the rabbi still spoke, David leaned over and stole a glance at the number of the page.) On sixty-eight. After, maybe, can ask. On page sixty-eight. That blue book—Gee! it's God.

"But just when Isaiah let out this cry—I am unclean—one of the angels flew to the altar and with tongs drew out a fiery coal. Understand? With tongs. And with that coal, down he flew to Isaiah and with that coal touched his lips—Here!" The rabbi's fingers stabbed the air. "You are clean! And the instant that coal touched Isaiah's lips, then he heard God's own voice say, Whom shall I send? Who will go for us? And Isaiah spoke and—"

But a sudden blast of voices out doors interrupted him. Running feet stamped across the yard. The door burst open. A squabbling tussling band stormed the doorway, jamming it. Scuffling, laughing boisterously, they shoved each other in, yanked each other out—

"Leggo!"

"Leggo me!"

"Yuh pushed me in id, yuh lousy stinkuh!"

"Next after Davy," one flew toward the reading table.

"Moishe flopped inna puddle!"

"Hey! Don' led 'im in!"

"Next after Sammy!" Another bolted after the first.

"I come—!"

"Shah!" grated the rabbi. "Be butchered, all of you! You hear me! Not one be spared!"

The babel sank to an undertone.

"And you there, be maimed forever, shut that door."

The milling about the doorway dissolved.

"Quick! May your life be closed with it."

Someone pulled the door after him.

"And now, sweet Sammy," his voice took on a venomous, wheedling tone. *"Nex* are you? I'll give you *nex*. In your belly it will *nex*. Out of there! Wriggle!"

Sammy hastily scrambled back over the bench.

"And you too," he waved David away. "Go sit down over there." And when David hung back. "Quick! Or—!"

David sprang from the bench.

"And quiet!" he rasped. "As if your tongues had rotted." And when complete silence had been established. "Now," he said, rising. "I'll give you something to do—Yitzchuck!"

"Waauh! I didn' do nothin'!" Yitzchuck raised a terrified whine.

"Who asked you to speak? Come here!"

"Wadda yuh wan' f'om me?" Yitzchuck prepared to blubber.

"Sit here." He beckoned to the end of the bench which was nearest the reading table. "And don't speak to me in goyish. Out of there, you! And you, David, sit where you are— Simke!"

"Yea."

"Beside him. Srool! Moishe! Avrum! Yankel! Schulim!" He was gathering all the younger students into a group.

"Schmiel! And you Meyer, sit here." With a warning glance, he went over to the closet behind his chair and drew out a number of small books.

"Aaa! Phuh!" Yitzchuck spat out in a whisper. "De lousy Hagaddah again!"

They sat silent until the rabbi returned and distributed the books. Moishe, seated a short distance away from David dropped his, but then pounced upon it hastily, and for the rabbi's benefit, kissed it and looked about with an expression of idiotic piety.

"First, louse-heads," began the rabbi when he had done distributing the books, "the Four Questions of the Passover. Read them again and again. But this time let them flow from your lips like a torrent. And woe to that plaster dunce who still cannot say them in Yiddish! Blows will he scoop like sand! And when you have done that, turn the leaves to the Chad Godya. Read it over. But remember, quiet as death—Well?" Shmaike had raised his hand as though he were in school. "What do you want?"

"Can't we hear each other?"

"Mouldered brains! Do you still need to hear each other? Do then. But take care I don't hear a goyish word out of you." He went back to his chair and sat down. For a few seconds longer his fierce gaze raked the long bench, then his eyes dropped momentarily to the book before him. "I was telling you," he addressed Mendel, "how Isaiah came to see God and what happened after—"

But as if his own words had unleashed theirs, a seething of whispers began to chafe the room.

"You hea' me say it. You hea' me! Shid on you. C'mon Solly, you hea' me! Yuh did push! Mendy's god a bendige yet on—"

"Said whom shall I send?" The rabbi's words were baffling on thickening briers of sound. "Who will go for us?"

"Izzy Pissy! Cock-eye Muligan! Mah nishtanah halilaw hazeh— Wanna play me Yonk?"

—Couldn't ask him though, (David's eyes merely rested on the page) Get mad. Maybe later when I have to read. Where was it? Yea. Page sixty-eight. I'll say, on page sixty-eight in that blue book that's new, where Mendel read, you were saying that man saw God. And a light—

"How many? I god more den you. Shebchol haleylos onu ochlim-. I had a mockee on mine head too. Wuz you unner de awningh? Us all wuz. In de rain."

"And tell this people, this fallen people—"

"Yea, and I'll kickyuh innee ass! Odds! Halaylaw hazeh kulo mazo— So from t'rowin' sand on my head I god a big mockee. I seen a blitz just w'en I commed in."

—Where did he go to see Him? God? Didn't say. Wonder if the rabbi knows? Wish I could ask. Page sixty-eight. Way, way, way, maybe. Where? Gee! Some place, me too . . . When I— When I—in the street far away . . . Hello, Mr. Highwood, goodbye Mr. Highwood. Heee! Funny!

"C'mere Joey, here's room. De rebbeh wants—Fences is all slippery. Now wadda yuh cry?"

"Nor ever be healed, nor ever clean."

"A blitz, yuh dope! Hey Solly, he says—Shebchol haleylos onu ochlim— Yea, my fadder'll beat chaw big brudder. Evens!"

—Some place Isaiah saw Him, just like that. I bet! He was sitting on a chair. So he's got chairs, so he can sit. Gee! Sit Shit! Sh! Please God, I didn't mean it! Please God, somebody else said it! Please—

"So hoddy you say blitz wise guy? Moishee loozed his bean shooduh! And den after de sand I pud wawduh on duh head, so— Lousy bestia! Miss Ryan tooked it!"

"How long? I asked. Lord, how long-"

—And why did the angel do it? Why did he want to burn Isaiah's mouth with coal? He said, You're clean. But coal makes smoke and ashes. So how clean? Couldn't he just say, Your mouth is clean? Couldn't he? Why wasn't it clean, anyway? He didn't wash it, I bet. So that . . .

"A lighten', yuh dope. A blitz! Kent'cha tuck Englitch? Ha! Ha! Sheor yerokos halaylo hazeh— Dat's two on dot! I wuz shootin chalk wid it. Somm bean shooduh! My fodder'll give your fodder soch a kick—"

—With a zwank, he said it was. Zwank. Where did I see? Zwank some place. Mama? No. Like in blacksmith shop by the river. Pincers and horseshoe. Yes must be. With pincers, zwank means pincers. So why with pincers? Coal was hot. That's why. But he was a angel. Is angels afraid? Afraid to get burned? Gee! Must have been hot, real hot. How I jumped when the rabbi pushed out with his fingers when he said coal. Nearly thought it was me. Wonder if Isaiah hollered when the coal touched him. Maybe angel-coal don't burn live people. Wonder—

"Dere! Chinky shows! Id's mine! How many fences didja go? I tore it f'om a tree in duh pock, mine bean-shooduh! T'ree fences. So a lighten den, wise guy!"

"And the whole land waste and empty."

"T'ree is a lie, mine fodder says. Yea? Matbilim afilu pa'am echos halaylo hazeh—Always wear yuh hat when a lighten' gives—"

—He said dirty words, I bet. Shit, pee, fuckenbestit— Stop! You're sayin' it yourself. It's a sin again! That's why he—Gee! I didn't mean it. But your mouth don't get dirty. I don't feel no dirt. (He rolled his tongue about) Maybe inside. Way, way in, where you can't taste it. What did Isaiah say that made his mouth taste dirty? Real dirty, so he'd know it was? Maybe—

"Shebchol haleleylos onu ochlim—. De rain wedded my cockamamy! Ow! Leggo! Yuh can't cover books wit' news-paper. My teacher don' let. An aftuh she took mine bean-shooduh, she pinched me by duh teet! Lousy bestia! Bein yoshvim uvein mesubim. So wad's de nex' woid? Mine hen'-ball wend down duh sewuh! Now, I god six poinduhs!"

—You couldn't do it with a regular coal. You'd burn all up. Even hot tea if you drink—ooh! But where could you get angel-coal? Mr. Ice-man, give me a pail of angel-coal.

Hee! Hee! In a cellar is coal. But other kind, black coal, not angel coal. Only God had angel-coal. Where is God's cellar I wonder? How light it must be there. Wouldn't be scared like I once was in Brownsville. Remember?

"C'mon chick! Hey Louie! Yuh last! Wed mine feed! Look! Me! Yea! Hea! Two!"

—Angel-coal. In God's cellar is—

All the belated ones had straggled in. A hail of jabbering now rocked the cheder.

"And-not-a-tree—" As the rabbi stooped lower and lower, his voice shot up a steep ladder of menace. "Shall-be-upright in the land!" He straightened, scaling crescendo with a roar. "Noo!" His final shattering bellow mowed down the last shrill reeds of voices. "Now it's my turn!" Smiling fiercely he rose, cat-o-nine in hand, and advanced toward the silent, cowering row. "Here!" the scourge whistled down, whacked against a thigh. "Here's for you!"

"Wow!"

"And you!"

"Ouch! Waddid I—do?"

"And you for your squirming tongue!"

"Leggo! Ooh!"

"And you that your rump is on fire! Now sit still!"

"Umph! Ow!"

"And you for your grin! And you for your nickering, and you for your bickering. Catch! Catch! Hold! Dance!"

The straps flew, legs plunged. Shrill squibs of pain popped up and down the bench. No one escaped, not even David. Wearied at length, and snorting for breath, the rabbi stopped and glared at them. Suppressed curses, whimpers, sniffles soughed from one end of the bench to the other.

"Shah!"

Even these died out.

"Now! To your books! Dig your eyes into them. The four Questions. Noo! Begin! Ma nishtanaw."

"Mah nishtanaw halilaw hazeh," they bellowed, "mikawl halaylos. Sheb chol halaylos onu ochlim chametz umazoh."

"Schulim!" the rabbi's chin went down, his voice diving past it to an ominous bass. "Dumb are you?"

"Haliylaw hazeh." A new voice vigorously swelled the already lusty chorus, "kulo mazoh!"

When they had finished the four questions, repeated them and rendered them thrice into Yiddish—

"Now the chad gadyaw," commanded the rabbi. "And with one voice. Hurry!"

Hastily, they turned the pages.

"Chad godyaw, chad godyaw," they bayed raggedly, "disabin abaw bis rai zuzaw, chad godyaw, chad godyaw—"

"Your teeth fall out, Simkeh," snarled the rabbi, grinning venomously, "what are you laughing at?"

"Nuttin!" protested Simkeh in an abused voice. "I wasn't laughing!" He was though—some one had been chanting "fot God Yaw" instead of Chad-Godyaw.

"So!" said the rabbi sourly when they had finished. "And now where is the blessed understanding that remembers yesterday? Who can render this into Yiddish? Ha? Where?"

A few faltering ones raised their hands.

"But all of it!" he warned. "Not piece-meal, all of it without stuttering. Or—" He snapped the cat-o-nine. "The noodles!"

Scared, the volunteers lowered their hands.

"What? None? Not a single one." His eyes swept back and forth. "Oh, you!" With a sarcastic wave of the hand, he flung back the offers of the older, chumish students. "It's time you mastered this feat! No one!" He wagged his head at them bitterly. "May you never know where your teeth are! Hi! Hi! none strives to be a Jew any more. Woe unto you! Even a goy knows more about his filth than you know of holiness. Woe! Woe!" He glared at David accusingly. "You too? Is your head full of turds like the rest of them? Speak!"

"I know it," he confessed, but the same time feigned sullenness lest he stir the hatred of the others.

"Well! Have you ribs in your tongue? Begin! I'm waiting!"

"One kid, the only kid," cautiously he picked up the
thread, "one kid that my father bought for two zuzim. One
kid, one only kid. And a cat came and ate the kid that my
father had bought for two zuzim. One kid, one only kid.
And a dog came and bit the cat that ate the kid that my
father bought for two zuzim. One kid, one only kid." He
felt more and more as he went on as if the others were
crouching to pounce upon him should he miss one rung in
the long ladder of guilt and requital. Carefully, he climbed
past the cow and the butcher and the angel of death. "And
then the Almighty, blessed be He— (*Gee! Last. Nobody
after. Didn't know before. But sometime, mama, Gee!*)
Unbidden, the alien thoughts crowded into the gap. For
an instant he faltered. (No! No! Don't stop!) "Blessed be
He," he repeated hurriedly, "killed the angel of death, who
killed the butcher, who killed the ox, who drank the water,
that quenched the fire, that burned the stick, that beat the
dog, that bit the cat, that ate the kid, that my father bought
for two zuzim. One kid, one only kid!" Breathlessly he
came to an end, wondering if the rabbi were angry with
him for having halted in the middle.

But the rabbi was smiling. "So!" he patted his big palms
together. "This one I call my child. This is memory. This
is intellect. You may be a great rabbi yet—who knows!"
He stroked his black beard with a satisfied air and regarded
David a moment, then suddenly he reached his hand into
his pocket and drew out a battered black purse.

A murmur of incredulous astonishment rose from the
bench.

Snapping open the pronged, metal catch, the rabbi jingled
the coins inside and pinched out a copper. "Here! Because
you have a true Yiddish head. Take it!"

Automatically, David lifted his hand and closed it round
the penny. The rest gaped silently.

"Now come and read," he was peremptory again. "And the rest of you dullards, take care! Let me hear you wink and I'll tear you not into shreds, but into shreds of shreds!"

A little dazed by the windfall, David followed him to the reading bench and sat down. While the rabbi carefully rolled himself a cigarette, David gazed out of the window. The rain had stopped, though the yard was still dark. He could sense a strange quietness holding the outdoors in its grip. Behind him, the first whisper flickered up somewhere along the bench. The rabbi lit his cigarette, shut the book from which Mendel had been reading and pushed it to one side.

—Could ask him now, I bet. He gave me a penny. About Isaiah and the coal. Where? Yes. Page sixty-eight. I could ask—

Chaa! Wuuh! Thin smoke glanced off the table. The rabbi reached over for the battered book and picked up the pointer.

"Rabbi?"

"Noo?" He pinched over the leaves.

"When Mendel was reading about that—that man who you said, who—" He never finished. Twice through the yard, as though a lantern had been swung back and forth above the roof-tops, violet light rocked the opposite walls—and darkness for a moment and a clap of thunder and a rumbling like a barrel rolling down cellar stairs.

"Shma yisroel!" the rabbi ducked his head and clutched David's arm. "Woe is me!"

"Ow!" David squealed. And the pressure on his arm relaxing, giggled.

Behind him the sharp, excited voices. "Yuh seen it! Bang! Bang wot a bust it gave! I tol' yuh I seen a blitz before!"

"Shah!" The rabbi regained his composure. "Lightning before the Passover! A warm summer." And to David as if remembering, "Why did you cry out and why did you laugh?"

"You pinched me," he explained cautiously, "and then—"

"Well?"

"And then you bent down—like us when you drop the pointer, and then I thought—"

"Before God," the rabbi interrupted, "none may stand upright."

—Before God.

"But what did you think?"

"I thought it was a bed before. Upstairs. But it wasn't."

"A bed! It wasn't!" He stared at David. "Don't play the fool with me because I gave you a penny." He thrust the book before him. "Come then!" he said brusquely. "It grows late."

—Can't ask now.

"Begin! Shohain ad mawrom—"

"Shohain ad mawrom vekawdosh shmo vakawsuv ronnu zadekim ladonoi." Thought lapsed into monotone.

After a short reading, the rabbi excused him, and David slid off the bench and went over to where the rest were sitting to get his strap of books. Schloime, who held them in his lap, had risen with alacrity as he approached and proffered them to him.

"Dey wanted t' take dem, but I was holdin' 'em," he informed him. "Watcha gonna buy?"

"Nuttin."

"Aa!" And eagerly. "I know w'ea dere's orangeballs— eight fuh a cent."

"I ain' gonna ged nuttin."

"Yuh stingy louse!"

The others had swarmed about. "I told yuh, yuh wouldn' get nuttin for holdin' his books. Yaah, yuh see! Aaa, let's see duh penny. We'll go witchah. Who couldn'a said dat!"

"Shah!"

They scattered back to the bench. David eased his way through the door.

EDWARD DAHLBERG (b. 1900), Boston-born, the illegitimate son of a Kansas City barber, was committed first to a Catholic then to a Jewish orphanage. After hoboing for two years in his teens, he went to the University of California and Columbia University, was a teacher briefly, and started writing when he was 26. *Bottom Dogs* (1930), and *From Flushing to Calgary* (1932) were semiautobiographical proletarian novels. *Those Who Perish* (1934), in part about the pressures on Jews in urban society was also concerned with the impact of Nazism. Noted for his prose style, his pungent criticisms, and his political radicalism, Dahlberg's later books included *Can These Bones Live?* (1941, 1960), *Flea of Sodom* (1950), *The Sorrows of Priapus* (1957), *The Carnal Myth* (1968), and his autobiography, *Because I Was Flesh* (1963).

Eli at the Briarcliffs
from
THOSE WHO PERISH

Eli Melamed had made his third round of Woodrow Wilson Park. His face, wind-burnt and hollowed out with tiredness, he decided that he would go to see the Briarcliffs for an hour's rest. Noticing the few finger-like trees, their embryonic buds of leaves—spring buds in reverse gear, for they had been wrinkled and corrugated by the death-fumes of automobile gasoline—he felt the need to get near to something human and warmly domesticated. Already eager to be inside the Briarcliffs' apartment and to shake hands with Edgar, he thought, with renewed courage: "We Jews do not know who we are, or from whence we come. The blood of all nations and races flows through our veins—from feudal times onward, our women have been defiled by Christians, and the offspring of these acts of rapine have passed as 'pure Jews.'" He repeated this, saying to himself: "Perhaps there is the blood of French or Italians, of the Romance Language peoples in my veins; after all, I'm a Sephardic type, and my Palestinian forebears must have been in Spain during the Inquisition." All this he said with the same kind of racial reasoning and inferiority complex that prompts Jews to call a Hitler or an Ivy Lee a Jew.

As Melamed stepped under the pseudo-beachish canopy outside the apartment house entrance, a thin rain began to canter lightly against the sidewalk. Suddenly he turned back, took off his hat and stood under it for a moment, lifting up his chin and face as though he were taking a shower. Melamed wanted to get wet so that it would appear that he had run in on the Briarcliffs for refuge. The rain grew swifter, galloping against the curbs, and Melamed ducked under the canopy again. The elevator took him up to the eighth floor.

Standing in front of the Briarcliffs' door, he turned up his coat collar, unthinkingly shivered for a second, his arms and legs rippling against his suit, as though he were at large and not inside of it, and touched the bell, sotto voce. When Mrs. Briarcliff came to the door, he was wiping the back of his neck and swobbing his face with gymnastic phews and clucks. As he took hold of Mrs. Briarcliff's hand, he shut his eyes, vigorously shook it up and down, piston-like, as if he had to reach up to seize it, and greeted her in a high, off-pitch voice: "So awfully glad to see you, Jenny!" He had never called her Jenny before, and he was appalled by his over-familiarity. "Just ran in out of the rain . . . hope I'm not . . ." He stopped short here, for he heard voices inside, felt that he was intruding, and was afraid that she would give him one of those straight looks that would indicate that he was.

There was something thin-lipped about Mrs. Briarcliff's body. She was one of those women, with long sharp noses and paper-thin throats that readily crease, whom handsome men so often marry. Frequently taken for a Jewess, or suspected of being one because of her nose, she was, as a matter of fact, of old New England stock. Melamed had always been a little afraid of her, because he thought she was Jewish and was hiding it, and because he believed she knew that he thought so. In one of his nasty moments he had had fleeting pictures of her as the wooden American Indian in front of the cigar store, but as he disliked harboring any sort of unkind thoughts about other human beings, he had summarily exorcised this mental photograph of Jenny Briarcliff.

The Briarcliffs' apartment, whose fake medieval wooden panels and electric candle-bulbs made it resemble the interior of Schrafft's restaurant, was filled with people standing around a ping-pong table. Three or four people were seated in chairs behind them drinking cocktails; some were sipping from their glasses and standing. Edgar Briarcliff, who had a clean-cut Arrow collar physiognomy and the Gentile retroussé nose, which American Jews admire, was serving. His opponent was a somewhat hefty woman whose green silk dress noisily rustled against her bust. She had a squat Slavonic nose, and her name was Evelyn Syracuse Beach.

Edgar Briarcliff was cutting the ball low over the net, and Miss Evelyn Syracuse Beach was having considerable difficulty in gauging and returning the serve. While the ping-pong balls sped back and forth across the green table with the clicking precision of typewriter keys, jibes and japes constantly came from the spectators. "Say, Edgar," said a heavily begoggled, gawky Freudian, "a little less sadism in those returns—save that for the wife!" "Oh, Evelyn, put a postage stamp on that last one, and no return address," said another.

When the game was over, Edgar Briarcliff approached Eli Melamed and introduced him, and Melamed shook hands with each one. After a colored maid had brought him a cocktail, Edgar left him.

The spectators were now watching the new game. The man who was serving held the paddle upright against his stomach. His opponent was his wife, and this set in motion the stenciled marital remarks. As the server sprung the paddle so as to release the ball, the psychoanalyst called:

"Say, Burt, where did you get that umbilical serve, or what have you?" Melamed also let out a small, guttural he-heh-huh, which sounded like a slender stick being lightly run across a wooden picket fence. He had been admiring the faces around him, and listening with esthetic attentiveness and pleasure to their Aryan, fiscal names. Finally, he had gotten up enough courage to make a complete semicircular smile, showing all his white teeth, for Miss Evelyn Syracuse Beach, but she did not notice him.

The Negro maid came around again with a tray of ice-clinking glasses. Mrs. Briarcliff moved from one couple to the other, and Edgar was seated on a cushion on the floor in the next room, holding a serious theosophical discussion with Mrs. Van Cortland Dinwiddie. Shortly afterwards, Edgar came over and said, "How about a set, Mel-ah-mede?" and Melamed emotionally bubbled over this intimacy.

Melamed went toward one end of the table and picked up his paddle, and Edgar moved toward the other. Eli Melamed, who had played a good deal of ping-pong at the Phœnix Physical Culture Club of New Jersey, now for the first time felt sure of himself.

He had a short, inching, sniping serve, which Edgar was unable to pick up. Melamed won the first five points. The people standing around the table stopped talking and began to watch. Edgar corkscrewed his serve which twisted and landed in an askew cut. But Melamed coolly waited for it to hit the table and then slammed it back across the net with the speed of a football player. Melamed, whenever Edgar returned the ball, ran from one part of the rim of the table to the other, picking up the ball, and lunging in after it with quarterback alacrity and the confidence of good fleshly poundage across his shoulders. As his bow-wing collar touched his neck, he felt as if it were a strong leathern head-gear. Melamed took the next three points, and pausing for a second, examined his small feet with glowing sartorial satisfaction.

"Really, you're not the man you were," said Melamed, in

a friendly non-competitive spirit, but without looking at Edgar. As he took the ninth point Melamed accidentally caught a vague cross-section of Edgar Briarcliff's countenance, which seemed to have become plaque-like. Looking again to make certain, Melamed missed the next one. The two men changed sides. Melamed laid his paddle down to adjust his suspenders and to catch Edgar's eye, and to soften him with a warm glance. But Briarcliff did not see and was impatient to continue the game.

Melamed then turned to the guests, and parting his lips he imagined that he had smiled at them. No one returned his greetings. However, this slight movement of the lips was more of an unprinted negative in Melamed's mind than an objective salutation. Melamed sent the next three balls wildly off the table, and did not see the following one which Briarcliff lightly popped over the net. His trousers hanging in a wretched defeatist sag, his suspenders loosening again and sprawling over his suspiciously gray shirt, Melamed fumbled another shot. Troubled and unhinged by the silent, tense faces around the table, Melamed felt like an oppressed minority people engulfed by a hostile imperialistic power.

By now Melamed had entirely lost his intuitive and photographic sense of time and place, which had made him so uncannily precise in his serves and returns at the beginning of the game. When Melamed hit the ball off the table again, and both men stooped over to pick it up off the floor, Edgar said: "Too bad, old man, I know how it feels." These words of non-competitive sympathy filled Melamed with gratitude. And when they both stepped forward and bent over to get another ball, Briarcliff patted Melamed's shoulder. Melamed closed his eyes, which simmered with quiescent emotions. His face was covered with the light pink marks of happiness that a lover might have playfully put there with his teeth. He was enormously thankful that it was Edgar Briarcliff and not he who was winning. Melamed gazed at Briarcliff's aristocratic Nordic eyes, mouth, teeth, and cravat, which were of one piece, and felt this was as it should be.

After the game was ended, Briarcliff having won, Mela-med thought he had better leave. He had the same unmistakable sense of time now, the precise time for leaving, that he had had at the beginning of the game when he had served and returned each separate, atomic ping-pong ball with an historic intuition of time and place. But he wanted to slip out of the room without leaving, so that there should be no interruption, no gap, no empty and fatuous space between him and the onlooking guests.

But someone began to discuss the German situation. Everyone trailed into the next room, taking chairs or sitting on cushions on the carpeted floor. "Do you think Hitler will last?" someone asked. "I feel that the whole Nazi Youth Movement has a homosexual basis," said the bespectacled Freudian, whose snub Tyrolese nose looked as though it were pressed up against a windowpane. "The only way to approach the whole situation is psychoanalytically," he continued.

"I must tell you of a little experience I had," said Mrs. Van Cortlandt Dinwiddie, who was related to the Astors and Bismarck, and who, genealogically speaking, had a Wotan-like bust. Otherwise, she had Samoan brown eyes and resembled the Phœnician Jack of Spades. "I had dinner with Charmian London, the wife of Jack London, at the Bohemian Club in San Francisco. She told me—and incidentally, I am using this in my memoirs—that she believed that certain meteorological changes which had taken place in 1914 had so unhinged people's nerves that they brought on the World War. I have since developed this thesis as a kind of undertone in my autobiography, which I was going to call *I Have Only Myself to Blame* until I discovered that the title had already been copyrighted and used for another book. Fancy my disappointment. . . . Anyway, it is my opinion that we are compelled to interpret Fascism in terms of neurones and meteorology. I think that the Versailles Treaty had such a devastating effect upon the nervous system of the German people."

"Don't you think," interrupted Mr. Monte Lorrimer, who had stout Arabic thighs, "that it was the stomach rather than the nerves?"

"I think that the Versailles Treaty," pursued Mrs. Van Cortlandt Dinwiddie with more resolution than before, "had such an exhausting effect upon the nervous system of the German nation that it turned them into lunatics; so what we have in Germany today is an insane asylum, with the only difference that the few sane people left are strait-jacketed and kept in the protective custody of the crazy who are the wardens."

"I think that's a brilliant analysis, Mrs. Dinwiddie," exclaimed the young Freudopath. "Just think what superb endocrine portraits Modigliani could do of Hitler and Rosenberg if he were alive today. Why, the League of Nations would actually sanction intervention so that they could be committed."

"I don't think we'll ever solve the European situation until Germany is wiped off the map. They're always getting us into trouble," stated an intellectual Anglo-American in a dreary adenoidal tone.

"Now take Goering," went on the Psychoanalyst.

"No, *you* take him," popped up Melamed who had been waiting for such an opportunity. Everyone laughed and Melamed's eyes glistened. He had been anxious to be included in the conversation, not because he had anything specific to say, but because he felt unhappily isolated. A Dakota Western-pulp type, with a Semitic Tom Mix proboscis, was so tickled over this bit of repartee that he pulled out his handkerchief and began to loudly boo-hoo into it. He was as shaken up as a large fleshy woman, and Melamed fetched a glass of water from a tray, brought it to him, and sort of held his arm as he drank it down.

"Well, Goering's a drug-addict and a dangerous paranoiac," continued the psychoanalytic student. "He was in an asylum in Stockholm in 1925."

"I don't think it's paranoia, but race," uttered Edgar Briarcliff.

"You're absolutely right," supported Mrs. Briarcliff. "Edgar, it is race."

"You-you—will p-pardon me," stuttered Monmouth Hightower, turning to Melamed. "I didn't get your name."

"Oh, this is Mr. Mel-ah-mede," spoke up Edgar Briarcliff. "Terribly sorry."

"We—ell," continued Monmouth Hightower, who had a dark smutty Mediterranean complexion and was the son of a D.A.R., "I—I have the—the great—greatest fancy for pe—people—of your race. You are Hebrew, aren't you?" Melamed nodded. He was beginning to feel deeply united with these persons and to derive a jubilant æsthetic experience from their Anglican names and countenances. Seeing Monmouth Hightower in a happily weepy haze he thought his soiled maple hair was the mane of Siegfried.

"But—but I—I be—believe," said Monmouth Hightower, "that the an—antagonism between different nationalities, as—as well as the—the attraction, is chemical. Take —take intermarriage." By this time his mouth had become a nervous hoop out of which the words rolled askew. "And —and just go back to Goethe's *Elective Affinities,* and— and——"

"Well—ah, per—perhaps there's something in what you say," interrupted Melamed, also stammering, because he felt very sensitive and highkeyed at that moment, and because he believed there was a certain wonderful non-Jewish quality about Monmouth Hightower's Aryan stuttering.

"I—I don't wan—want you to mis—misunderstand me, Mr. Mel—mel—ah—ah—mede. I think your people have gifts of genius, and—and—that accounts for—for my opinion, no doubt, but don't—don't you think the Hebrew people are—are a little difficult?"

"Well—ah, per—perhaps there's a certain amount of truth in what you say," answered Melamed. "Of course, if you—you mean some of the pushing aggressive type," added Melamed, feeling that it would be in good taste to be a little anti-Semitic in order to show them how objective and impartial a Jew could be, "I must admit, I find that kind just as objectionable as you do."

"And—and don't you think—think the—the Hebrew people are a little too sensi—sensitive?" pursued Monmouth Hightower.

To prove how outside of it he was, Melamed replied: "Maybe Jews are—to borrow the information Mr. Burt Webb has been so good as to give us—as paranoiac as Goering."

"I think," stated a tallish woman, with a Hittite beak and charcoal Armenian hair, who came from the Arran Islands and who spoke as though it were high time for a little political housecleaning, "that the German-Jews are getting what's coming to them. They not only lorded it over," she sped on in a shrill and impassioned prose, "the poor Russian and Lithuanian Jews who migrated into Eastern Germany, but it was actually German-Jewish money that supported and kept in power the Czar so that he was able to carry on his pogroms. Don't you think that's right, Mr. Mel-ah-mede?" Melamed, who was still occupied tying emotional bonds with these new acquaintances, and who had not been listening attentively, attempted to shuttle back to the conversation.

"Of course, eh, but you know my mother and father were born in Palestine. But then, what you say is . . . Well, I guess it is true the German-Jews were a little impatient about becoming Germans, and no doubt they did lose their heads in the excitement."

"What's your opinion on Russia?" asked Mr. Monte Lorrimer, whose nose, which looked like the toe of Italy, seemed racially at loggerheads with his Ottoman thighs. By now everybody was directing questions at Melamed, presupposing that he as a Jew naturally knew all about Germany, Communism, and the Soviet Union.

"We—well," interrupted the Son of the D.A.R., "I'm in

fa—favor of the R—Russian Bol—Bolsheviks, but I don't like—like the Com—com—communists."

"Is—is it true," went on Monmouth Hightower, "that—that Jewish bankers financed Lenin?"

Melamed looked blank, and, weighing his words, he answered: "I—I'd be willing to look that up for you."

"What is the Communist situation in this country?" asked Mr. Lorrimer. He looked with kind eyes at Melamed as he added: "I'm really very interested and would be grateful if you'd tell me."

"Well, I can't say off-hand," asseverated Melamed, "but I'd be willing to look that up too."

"What do you think of the German Terror?" asked Miss Evelyn Syracuse Beach.

"I think it ought to stop," replied Melamed snappily and getting his bearings for a moment.

Three people simultaneously shot questions at him, after which Monmouth Hightower asked: "Mr. Me-mel-ah-ah-mede, what is your opinion of the Com-Com-Communist International?"

"Well, I don't know whether they do or don't," replied Melamed, who now was so harassed that he had become psychologically stone-deaf. And like a deaf person, who pretends he is hearing every word spoken, Melamed replied.

"I believe we should have nothing to do with the boycott," blurted forth Mrs. Briarcliff. "I think it's positively wrong and immoral for one country to attempt to interfere in the affairs of another." Melamed's voice twittered, then died. He said nothing.

There was a pause, and then Melamed said: "I guess I must be going," but as no one noticed him, he remained. Finally he said good-by, and sort of waved at every one as though he were running for a street-car, but the others were talking. He got his hat and coat, and as he started to move toward the door, Edgar Briarcliff ran up to him: "Must you be going, old man?" Whereupon those present stopped talking and looked up at him. Mr. Monte Lorrimer smiled at him, and Melamed, beaming, took a tiny step forward and then hurried back to shake hands with Mr. Lorrimer. Looking at the others, whom he did not wish to offend, he shook hands with each one, repeating each time, "So awfully glad to have met you"—falling into that Nordic Bostonese vocabulary. By the time he reached Mrs. Jenny Briarcliff, he was bubbling again with emotion. His eyes half-shut, he grasped Mrs. Briarcliff's wrist, and pressing his fingers hard against it, broke the crystal of her watch. She screamed, and Melamed was so alarmed that he bent down, picked up the pieces of glass, and handed them back to her. Looking at him in amazement, she said, with fingernails in her voice, "Thank you."

After Edgar Briarcliff had shut the door, Melamed stood outside, wondering whether to ring the bell, go in, and apologize all over again to make amends for his clumsiness. He put his finger out, pressed the elevator bell, and then went down the steps, emptily sliding from one side of his suit to the other.

Outside the rain was still thinly scribbling against the curbs. Gazing at the trees, which looked like skeletal umbrella frames without covers, he turned up his coat collar, and, reminding himself that he was without employment and alone, he no longer wondered whether the blood of the Romance Language peoples flowed through his veins.

ROBERT NATHAN (b. 1894), New York born and a descendant of Rabbi Gershon Seixas (one of the incorporators of Columbia College) was educated abroad and at Harvard. He is a bestselling novelist as well as a poet, painter, musician, and athlete. *Peter Kindred* (1919), his first novel in a prodigious flow, was followed by such well-known works as *Portrait of Jenny* (1940). *Youth Grows Old* (1923), *The*

Cedar Box (1930), *Winter Tide* (1940), and *The Green Leaf* (1950) are representative volumes of poetry; *Road of Ages* (1935) is an imaginative novel of Jewish exile in the Gobi desert; and *A Star in the Wind* (1962) describes a man's return to his faith after experiencing the emergence into being of the State of Israel.

The Chosen People
from
THE COLLECTED POEMS

These are the chosen people. He has set
Upon their brow the diadem of thorn,
The one imperishable coronet,
The crown of pain, the briar branch of scorn.
Around their shoulders He has hung His scrolls,
Dark as the desert, yellow as the light;
His is the voice of ages in their souls,
The burning bush, the pillar in the night.
These are the chosen; He has named them all.
None can escape the poison of His grace,
Or ever ease the everlasting smart.
It is for them, the honey and the gall,
To be the wakeful, the abiding race,
And guard the wells of pity of the heart.

On the Jewish Exile
from
THE COLLECTED POEMS

Ay, send them out, the dark ones, into the desert,
If there is desert enough in all the world
To hold these lonely few, these trembling goats
Who take for burden all the sins of the flesh
Into the wilderness.
    Blow bugles, Pomp.
Build armies, march with beautiful banners flying,

Young men and old with shouts and hands flung upwards.
Under the birds of death.
    Make a place for graves:
A field for bones, a meadow for all the people.
No need of flowers or grass or marble tombs;
For all will die, under the falling fire.
Who lives by the sword shall perish too by the sword.
Alas for Rome.
    The days of her life are numbered.
Only the goats in the wilderness will survive this
Burning of cities, this war, this crying of children.
Only the kids in the desert will see the morning,
And slowly making their way back over the mountains
Feed again in peace in the shattered cities,
Browse again in the weeds of the ruined gardens.

MEYER LEVIN (b. 1905), born and raised in Chicago's
West Side, saw his neighborhood change from a ghetto to
a Little Italy as he grew up. After the University of Chicago
he went to Paris and then Palestine. *Yehuda* (1931) detailed his experiences in the Holy Land. While working for
Esquire he wrote *The Old Bunch* (1937). Among his more
recent books are *Citizens* (1940), *My Father's House*
(1947), *In Search* (1950), *Compulsion* (1956), and *The
Settlers* (1972).

Sam and Lil
from
THE OLD BUNCH

    The last straw was the argument about Passover. Lil's
folks were in Rochester, where her mother was being treated,
so Sam thought they would go to his folks' for the *seder*.
Instead Lil wanted to go to Ev Goldberg's.

"I don't understand what makes you so religious all of a sudden!" Lil exclaimed sarcastically. "Why don't you grow a beard and go to *shul* while you're at it!"

"Religion has nothing to do with it," he responded patiently. "You know perfectly well, all that stuff means nothing to me. It's just the—the social side of it. I mean——"

"That's the whole point! Socially, it means something to us to go to Ev's."

"Listen, Lil," he said with hopeless restraint. "You know perfectly well that, if your own mother was having a *seder*, we would have to go there. But since your mother and father are in Rochester, my folks naturally expect us to come to them. It would be like a slap in the face not to come."

"Oh, my god, do I have to sit like a prisoner till twelve o'clock while your grandfather mumbles the whatyacall it through his beard? We were there year before last and that ought to hold them for a while!"

"It was three years ago."

"Whenever it was, once was enough! Mygod, you'd think that, with all your uncles and aunts, your family would have enough customers for their *seder* without dragging me into it!"

"That isn't the point," Sam said. "It doesn't hurt us, and it makes them feel good to see their son and their grandchild at the table."

"Listen, Sam. We're young, we're modern. For three years we were tied down to the house with the kid and everything, but now at least we can begin to go out and see people, so why do we have to get stuck with a bunch of old dodoes? I think Ev's idea is wonderful. Why not have a *seder* for young couples only! I wish I had thought of the idea myself! A *seder* is supposed to be a celebration, isn't it! Why not have a good time!"

"If you're so keen on going there, go on," Sam said. "I'll take Jackie to my folks."

Lil gave him a burning look; her hand went to her mouth, stifling a sob. "Oh, so that's it! So you want to show them what a terrible mother he's got!" She rushed into the bedroom.

Sam sank into a chair and clutched the arms, tight. Gradually, his anger eased. He decided to laugh the whole thing off. That he should quarrel about religion—he, the agnostic!

He found her lying face down on the bed, sobbing.

"I'm sorry, Lil." He stroked her hair. "I don't know what's the matter with me lately, I'm getting so nervous I get contrary on the slightest provocation." He wanted to tell her, to tell someone, about the times in court or in his office when he felt himself getting all tense in knots, as though he were a rope being twisted tighter and tighter; to tell her of the disgust and loss he felt in his daily work, in his getting out of politics, in having to curry favors from a louse like Judge Horowitz.

"It was my fault, Sammy. I aggravate you when you're tired," she said, sitting up and drawing his head to her. "I shouldn't even have mentioned Ev. We ought to go to your family this year. It's only right."

"Oh, it doesn't matter, they probably won't even notice we're missing. We can go there for the second night, anyway. They're used to having us come then."

"Of course!" she exclaimed. The second night was a *seder,* too!

"C-o-n-
S-t-a-n-t-i-n . . ."

the radio was going, as they entered. Thelma was dancing with Manny Kassell, and there was a strange couple dancing. Ev, who looked ravishing in a flowing white gown that completely concealed her condition—though there was nothing as yet to conceal—came rushing toward them.

"Oh, darling, look at me! Does it show?" she whispered quite audibly, to Lil.

"It doesn't show a bit!" Lil whispered back.

"She just wanted an excuse to wear that gown," Phil

remarked, with a loving proud sophisticated kidding glance at his wife.

"Oh, it's cute," Lil said. "It's darling."

"Oh, Jackie! Isn't he cute!" Ev swooped.

"Say hello to Aunt Ev, Jackie."

"Hi, toots," Jackie said, and they all roared.

Phil introduced them to the strangers, Mr. and Mrs. Mc-Ilwain, who were dying to see a Jewish Passover ceremony.

The maid passed around cocktails, and little caviar canapés on matzoth.

"Aren't they wonderful!" Mrs. McIlwain cried, examining the canapés. "Passover or no Passover, I think that's an awfully smart way to serve caviar."

"They're awfully cute," Lil agreed.

"Darling, you must tell me where to buy this—what do you call it?" Mrs. McIlwain said.

"Matt-zote," Ev carefully mispronounced the word, and giggled.

"Say, this don't taste like bathtub gin to me," Manny comically complained of his drink.

"That's real prescription stuff," Phil admitted. "I'm afraid you'll have to put up with it, as Ev has been using our bathtub lately."

They laughed.

"One of the saddest things about Prohibition," McIlwain said, "is we don't know good liquor when we get it. I always used my old man as a tester-in-chief. Boy, he used to sozzle the real stuff!"

They looked at him, envious of his being the son of a real drunken Irishman.

"Well, Sam, I hear you have deserted the sinking ship," Phil remarked.

"Yah, with the rest of the rats," Sam caught him up.

"Oh," Phil laughed appreciatively. "Well, I guess Big Bill is through, in this town."

"I don't know," Sam said. "He's still mayor."

"He must be kind of lonesome, in the city hall these

days." McIlwain referred to the defeat of Thompson's candidates.

"Anyway, he might as well get out," Phil said. "His pals've grabbed everything there was to be grabbed."

"I guess that's so," Sam agreed. "They've about scraped the bottom of the till."

"I hear he has presidential aspirations," McIlwain remarked.

"With him, it's a case of I do choose to run," Manny cracked.

"Will you men stop talking politics!" Ev laughed, and steered them into the dining room.

"Oh, Ev, it's just too cute for words!" Lil screamed, seeing the table. In the center was a layer cake, and atop it was a doll in a flowing robe, with a long white cotton batting beard stuck to its cherubic chin. Moses!

"Do you get it?" Thelma tittered. "What's it supposed to be?"

"Moses on the Mountain?" Mrs. McIlwain ventured.

"Uh-uh."

"I got it! If you can't eat bread, eat cake!" Manny roared.

"No fair, you knew!" Ev cried.

They all laughed, and Ev modestly said: "It was Phil's idea."

The place cards were the cleverest things! Each card was a cut-out of a biblical character, only Ev had fixed devilish little short skirts over the long gowns of the women characters, and put derby hats on the men. But the most comical thing she had done was to get pictures of movie stars and paste their faces on the biblical figures.

"Who is this supposed to be?" Lil screeched, and they all piled around a picture of Adolphe Menjou, in a silk hat, on the body of an Egyptian taskmaster who wielded a whip.

First they thought it was McIlwain because he was a gentile (get it, Egyptian) and, besides, he was an engineer; but it turned out to be Manny Kassell on account of his Menjou

mustache, and the whip was because he was a dentist. Next
to him was a picture of Lillian Gish as Queen Esther playing a harp, and naturally that was Thelma, on account of
the harp. Phil and Ev were Doug Fairbanks and Mary Pick-
ford, the perfect couple, as Samson and Delilah! Sam was
Groucho Marx as Adam, and Lil was Vilma Banky as Eve,
and Jackie was Jackie Cooper as David. Immediately, he
yelled: "Mother, I wanna slingshot!"

"Hush, Jackie, mother will buy you one tomorrow."

"Naw, I wan' it now!"

"Where on earth did you get all those pictures of the
movie stars?" Lil said, trying to ignore him.

"Oh, Phil has a friend in Lubliner and Trinz," Ev said,
"and he got them out of their advertising department,
special."

"Wanna!" Jackie tugged at Lil.

"Look, Jackie," Phil said, and picked up the favor on
Jackie's plate. It unfolded into an Indian headdress. "Nize
beby," he quoted Milt Gross.

Jackie stopped bawling and put the paper feathers on
his head. "Yay, I'm an Indian!" he yelled, happily.

"You know, Phil really has a way with children," Ev said.
"I guess he'll make a good papa after all."

The others were discovering their favors. On each plate
was a comical hat of the sort worn at New Year's parties.

"You see, good Jews always wear skull caps or some
kind of hat at the table on Passover," Ev explained to the
Gentiles.

"Don't get the idea this is a real service," Phil said. "We
just decided to do this our own way for a change."

The McIlwains put on their hats. Mr. McIlwain had
drawn a red-white-and-blue fez with a tassel on the top. His
young, round, pink-massaged face beamed good will. Sam's
hat was yellow and green, and shaped like an overseas cap.
Manny had a dunce cap! The girls had hats, too.

"You know who would appreciate this? Alvin Fox!"

Thelma exclaimed. "Remember he trained to be a rabbi and gave it up."

"I was going to ask him," Ev said, "but they just went to Europe on a late honeymoon."

"He married a Gentile girl," Thelma said to the Mc-Ilwains, beaming.

"He was ruining the business putting out those modernistic chairs," Phil laughed, "so the old man said it was cheaper to send him to Europe."

They all laughed good-naturedly.

Now the wine went around. Phil had secured some real Chianti, with the straw basket around the bottle.

"Just like a regular *seder!*" Lil cried as the maid served the first dish, consisting of hardboiled eggs cut up in salt water.

"What do you call this?" Mrs. McIlwain inquired.

"*Charokis*," Ev promptly responded, anglicizing the word beyond recognition.

"How did you ever know about all this stuff?" Lil said, awed. "My mother used to make a kind of a *seder* but I would never dream of trying it myself!"

"Kid, you'll never guess where I got the directions," Ev said. "There was a complete Passover menu in Prudence Penny's column!"

"No!"

"I'll prove it to you!" And Ev produced the clipping. "I just gave it to the girl and told her to follow it religiously."

"Religiously, that's good," Manny repeated.

"What kind of bread would you like, rye or white?" Phil jested, passing the plate of matzoth.

"I'm really going to eat this, it's good for you, I'm on a diet!" Ev said. "My gynecologist said it was the best thing."

The maid brought in a plate of hot biscuits, which most of them accepted, though the McIlwains insisted on eating matzoth.

"Isn't there supposed to be a glass of wine for some-body?" Lil prompted.

"Oh, yah! *Eli hanoveh!*" Thelma supplied.

"What's that?"

"Elijah," Phil translated.

"Yah. That's cute," Lil said. "You're supposed to fill a glass with wine, and Elijah comes and drinks it up."

"How about giving Elijah a real treat, for a change?" Phil said, and filled a glass with gin. "There you are, old boy old boy! Open the door for Elijah!"

"Who is Elijah?" Jackie said.

"He comes and drinks it up," Lil explained.

"When?"

"Right away. You can't see him. He's invisible."

"Aw." Jackie watched her face. "You're kidding me."

"It's a fact," Lil said. "He goes into every house, and drinks the wine."

"Yah? Then I bet he gets pie-eyed!" Jackie piped.

They roared.

"Isn't he the cutest thing!"

Ev leaned intimately to Phil.

"Oh, Lil, make him ask the four questions!" suggested Thelma.

"That's right, that's what he's here for!"

Philip explained to the McIlwains. "Of course we're not doing this in proper order or anything, but at a real *seder* they follow the *Haggada*, that's a sort of book of procedure, and the youngest son of the house asks the traditional four questions, and the head of the household, usually the grand-father, reads the responses."

"Surprise!" Ev said, and produced a *Haggada*, printed in both Hebrew and English. This curiosity was passed around, everybody explaining to the McIlwains that the Hebrew was read backwards instead of up and down, like Chinese. They studied the booklet respectfully.

"Oh, you know what I want to sing!" Thelma cried. "*Chad gad yo!* We always used to sing that when I was a kid!" She turned the pages. "One kid, one kid for two *zusim!*" she began. The wine was affecting her noticeably, her cheeks were flaming. *"Chad gad yo! Chad gad yo!"*

"Doesn't that come at the end of the meal?" Ev said.

"What's the difference!"

Manny began to sing with her: *"Chad gad yo! Chad gad yo!"*

The maid brought in an immense, sugar-baked ham.

Squeals and titters.

Manny picked up a curled streamer that lay near his plate and blew noisily. The red crape paper shot across the table, and dropped over Sam's ear.

"The four questions, the four questions!" Lil insisted.

"All right, you read them for Jackie, and Phil will answer them!" Ev said.

"Now, Jackie, look." Lil showed him the lines in the book. "You say what I say—ready?"

Jackie nodded eagerly.

"Why . . ."

"Why."

"Is this night . . ."

"Is 'is night."

"Different . . ."

"Diffrunt."

Sam heard his son piping and, glancing across at the book in Lil's hand, suddenly remembered the Hebrew words: *"Mah nishtanoh halaylah hazeh . . . ?"* as he had used to say them, awed, and the grave answering intonation of his grandfather.

"From all other nights?"

"Fmallothnights." Jackie stuck out his hand, for a reward.

"Because this is April 4," Phil answered, "and every other night is another night."

Their guffaws rattled the glassware.

Sam got up.

"You'll have to excuse me," he managed to mumble, as he made for the door.

Lil rushed after him. "What's the matter, are you sick?" Her first look at him was worried. Then: "Are you crazy? Disgracing me before my best friends!"

Ev rushed up to them.

"This is the end!" Lil sputtered hotly, collapsing in tears into Evelyn's arms.

In Sam's mind, these words were flashing, as though he were reading them on an electric sign, on and off, on and off: "This is where I get off. This is where I get off." . . .

When he had walked out on Lil it had been with the excited rage of righteousness, with the vibrating exhilaration in his mind that he had felt only a few times before in his life. That time when as a kid he had walked out on the meeting of the Big Ten; and that other time at Illinois when he had walked out on military drill.

Just as in those previous times, Sam had a happy sense of the amazing simplicity of his gesture: like taking off your coat when you're hot.

The joke was that the whole thing had happened over a religious question. He, the freethinker, getting excited because people were making fun of religion!

Then why had he done it?

He needed a long time by himself to get things clear, and time for being alone and thinking spread luxuriously before him. He walked around a lot in the evenings, thinking, and it began to seem to Sam that things had been wrong between himself and Lil from the very start. He remembered and reshaped little incidents, even to that first yielding of hers, on New Year's Eve, he put things together into a pattern by which she seemed to be trying to dominate him, to shoehorn him into her way of life. The flat in her father's place, the job with her father, the friends she made . . . .

For a few days, this isolation was fine. Eating supper alone bothered him a little, but he read the paper between courses. He ate fast anyway, too fast. Always had.

Without Lil to bother him, he even passed one evening reading Shakespeare's *Macbeth*, feeling it odd that he hadn't read any of Shakespeare since high school, when the forced study had made him hate the stuff. Now he was mature, and could appreciate Shakespeare, now he would get back to a lot of reading.

All his senses, reactions, seemed to be awakened, and perceptions sprang from himself as never before.

As he came up on the El platform, he tossed a quarter to the cashier and said: "Tickets."

"Sorry, but we are only selling single fares, the ticket rate has been discontinued," she parroted.

Sam saw himself one of an endless row of customers, just the people of the city, each having to drag another nickel out of his pocket for every three rides on the El. Just as a few days ago he had gagged and puked at his domestic way of life, he felt, at this moment, a catharsis of his whole experience of the public way of life, a revulsion against the system. That delusion, that he would ever fit into such a scheme of things, was part of his life with Lil, too. He grabbed his change and passed on to the platform, knowing he would never again try to play this game. Maybe he was destined to be a lonely and angry watcher at the saturnalia of Chicago, of America, but at least he would be clear with himself.

He opened his *Trib*. Walt and Skeezix were figuring out a name for the new kid. Sam felt homesick.

Informed of Mrs. Klien's death, Sam thought: Why should I let this interfere with the way I really feel about Lil? This is special pleading.

But later in the day, Mr. Klein himself phoned. His voice was small, weary, and yet unyielding. "Sam, I don't know what happened between you two kids, and the way I feel now, you can understand. But I want to ask one thing of you. Come out to the house, and only for the funeral act like nothing happened. In a time like this, you know how Lil will feel, facing all her relatives, you understand. Sam, do me this favor."

When a man put it that way, what could a fellow do?

People were streaming in and out of the house, and it was easy for him to keep away from Lil. There was plenty for him to do, too. Mr. Klein owned a family lot in the Rosevale Cemetery, "completely paid up," but now he couldn't get a burial permit without paying a twenty-five dollar "special assessment." He burned with indignation. "To make a graft out of a thing like that! Have they no shame? Is there no limit?" He wouldn't pay, he cried, with a tense, tragic rage. It was his ground. Nobody had a right to assess it. He would go to the law!

Sam went to see the officers of the cemetery association. Oh, they had a neat little racket, legal too. The assessment had been "voted." He paid it out of his own pocket, got a burial permit, and told Klein that he had secured it merely by threatening the fat slobs with suit and exposure.

Then there was another headache. The undertakers, in cahoots with the drivers, had fixed it with the drivers' union to forbid private automobiles at funerals! The men would not drive unless all the cars in the procession were the undertaker's limousines! It was outrageous, it was ghoulish, but two or three funerals had recently been broken up. Sam had a personal talk with the squat, double-chinned undertaker Elfman. A heavy watch chain, dangling a Masonic emblem, spanned his chest. Oh, sure, he was a lodge brother of Sol Klein, and he would talk to his men, in person. Finally he secured a compromise. If fifteen limousines would be hired, the drivers would allow an equal number of private cars. "Klein has plenty of bucks, it won't break him to give his wife a decent funeral!"

All morning Sam had busied himself with these haggling errands, but now the procession began, and Lil sat stiffly erect, her handkerchief to her nose, her face turned away from him. Mr. Klein sat on the other side of Lil, looking sad and righteously indignant; two red spots flared on his cheeks; oh, if they hadn't got him by the nuts because it was his wife's funeral, he would have given it to the lousy racketeers! But they had him gagged, he couldn't even raise his voice and kick, it wouldn't seem nice.

Not a word was spoken, all through the ride.

At the burial, standing near Lil, Sam was moved by his love for her; even the womanish selfishness in her was lovable. He saw a little woman, round-faced, butter-fleshed, still young and attractive, but on the whole a woman who could recede easily into the thousands one daily passed, unnoticing, as they streamed into Mandel's, into the Davis Store, Field's, as they hurried, or loitered, or gossiped. And now she was sobbing at her mother's funeral.

Jackie grasped his hand. "Hi, pop," he whispered. "Hey, it's a big funeral, ain't it?"

"Shhh."

"I bet it's biggern any gangster's funeral. I bet she had a solid silver coffin."

"Shhh."

"Hey, ma bawls all the time you ain't home."

"Listen, Jacob. I'll play you a game. See who can keep still longer, you or me."

"Oke. Gimme a dime if I win?"

"Okay."

Riding back Mr. Klein went with his sisters, and Sam and Lil were alone in the limousine. After they had gone some time in silence, Lil exclaimed: "Oh, is your heart made of stone!"

"I can't help it," Sam said sincerely. "This is the way I am."

"Hey, I win, pop! Gimme the dime!" Jacob cried. And Sam had to laugh. Lil laughed too, and Sam shelled out. She caught herself laughing, and subdued her laughter, ending it in a sigh. Sam looked at her, and her underlip quivered appealingly and defeatedly, she swayed against him, and he held her.

"Oh, Sam, I've been so lonesome," she said.

He admitted: "So have I."

"Oh, why do we act so foolish?" she said. "Nobody is worth that much! To let us quarrel over them."

He saw clearly how he was letting himself slide, slide into this again. But, oh, it wasn't so easy to break a marriage, and habit, and the habit of love, and leave the growing child. And now, riding, they felt so sweet to each other that all else seemed secondary.

In the elevator, a scented and fast-looking blonde was with them. "Know who that is?" Lil whispered as the blonde got off. "Judge Russo is keeping her."

"I didn't know they'd allow it in this building," Sam remarked.

"Oh, but he gives her a magnificent apartment!" Lil said, with a kind of respect.

Sam wanted to fondle her and laugh. The little idiot.

But, after they had been together again, the old battle of wills began. He could see her, like a little cat sidling toward a forbidden dish, making covert approaches to having him apologize to the Wares.

"I told them you had been working so hard, it was just your nerves . . . and you were brought up Orthodox . . ."

"I wish you hadn't said anything. It wasn't necessary."

"Well, since you wouldn't apologize, I thought I'd do it for you. After all," she said lightly, "you did act disgustingly."

"Why shouldn't I, before disgusting people?"

"They're among my best friends."

"Well, they're no friends of mine!"

"Oh, Sammy, let's not start it all over again just when we——"

"I'm not starting! . . ."

They caught themselves that time. But there was the time when she demanded he evict a woman in her father's apartment building on Montrose Avenue, because the woman was running a flat, and would cheapen the building. "But you don't mind about Judge Russo's girl friend, right in this building," Sam twitted her. "Oh, but that's different!" Lil cried indignantly. And when Sam laughed at her, she got sore, and then he got sore, and then . . .

The last straw was when Mr. Liebling, her father's friend, came to Sam with another case, trying to gyp a presser out of compensation for an injury, and Sam practically threw him out of the office. Lil heard about it.

"I suppose next thing you'll be throwing my father out of your office! I might have known! As soon as he helped you get your nose out of the gutter you're too swell for his kind of business!"

That ended it.

At least this time it wasn't religion, Sam reflected bitterly. It was the real trouble, at the bottom of everything. Call it what side you were on.

Phil Ware handled the case for Lil. Thelma Ryskind testified that she had seen Sam strike his wife at a bridge game, and again at the Passover service. Thelma had to be reined in a few times by Attorney Ware, as she got over-enthusiastic and wanted to re-enact the scene before Judge Russo.

Sam found himself listening to this routine case as though it were any one of a number of routine divorce cases he had himself conducted. The grounds established. The perfunctory effort of the judge to have them kiss and make up. Lucky they hadn't drawn Judge Sabbath, who'd have taken them into his chambers, given them a Y.M.C.A. lecture, and wept over them for half an hour to raise his quota of miraculous divorce court reconciliations.

Now came the real function of the divorce court. The climax of the case. The wrangle about how much.

He had known it was no use fighting about the child; and anyway, he agreed: Let Lil take the child. Visit, one day a week.

But the wrangle about how much. The furniture is mine; don't you remember the parlor set was a gift from my father? The car—the hell with it all. Let her have it all. And at least in this case they would be spared the final haggling in which the judge set the lawyer's fees. Only this morning Sam had been through it for a poor sap who worked for Western Electric. "How much do you make? Thirty a week?" The judge calmly apportions: "You can get along on fifteen, that leaves fifteen. Ten a week for the little woman and five on the lawyer's bills." The wife's lawyer kicks, but finally accepts, on condition he be paid first. It's always assumed the poor man will scrape up the dough to pay his own lawyer somewhere. . . .

Sam caught himself—his mind wandering at his own divorce!

Lil didn't want anything for herself, she announced hotly. She accepted twelve dollars a week for the child.

It had been, Sam had to admit from a professional point of view, a decent case.

ALBERT HALPER (b. 1904) grew up in Chicago, working at a variety of jobs until a personal crisis (precipitated by a stint on a night shift at the post-office) sent him to New York and on to a writing career. *Union Square* (1933), *On the Shore* (1934), *The Foundry* (1934) and *The Chute*

(1937) were his proletarian novels. *Sons of the Fathers* (1940), a novel of more objectivity and sympathy, was followed by *The Little People* (1942), *The Little Watch* (1953), and *Goodbye Union Square* (1970). Known as a proletarian writer, Halper prefers to call himself a commentator or historian of present-day society.

Ben and Milton
from
SONS OF THE FATHERS

The afternoon sun slanted through the windows of the Bergman flat. Sidney, who had been washing his hands and face in the bathroom, came into the parlor to read to his mother awhile. He stood up before her, opened his grammar and began enunciating his next day's lesson in his fresh, young voice, when Etta handed him a letter which had arrived that morning. As Sidney was the first to come home from school, he was the official letter reader to his mother, and he was very proud of it.

"It's an advertisement," he reported, opening the letter and seeing the trade-mark of a local wet-wash laundry. " 'Dear madam,' " he read, " 'do your bundles average over fifteen pounds a week, or biweekly? If so, why not take advantage of our new rates and use the enclosed post card for your convenience? The Ace-High Laundry is proud to announce that . . .' "

But Etta was not listening. She had thought the letter was from Boston. For the truth had come out about Sammy; upon enlistment, afraid he would be rejected should his parents communicate with the Canadian military authorities, he had stated that he was an orphan and that his aunt, Mrs. Etta Bergman of Chicago, was his closest relative. All the correspondence from the Canadian government regarding Sammy, relative to his insurance and other minor items, had come to Etta who at first was puzzled about the matter. But finally Ben, scanning one of the communications, saw the word guardian under Etta's name, and solved the mystery. So that was how Sammy had covered his tracks so cunningly. Etta had quickly gotten in touch with Anna, and Anna and her husband had wired the Canadian recruiting authorities, but by that time Sammy was beyond recall. He was now somewhere in Flanders with the other Canadians, seeing the active service for which he had hungered so long and oblivious to the heartaches he had left behind in Boston and Chicago.

Etta stared out the window as Sidney kept on reading the advertisement from the wet-wash laundry. Her thoughts turned from Sammy to Ben, who was chafing at his job down at the clothing factory. She was worried about him. Ben said he wanted to quit, he said he couldn't stand the major and the four snobbish lieutenants any longer. "And what will you do then?" Saul had cried last night when Ben had come home and in a loud voice had announced his decision to resign. "Do you want to fight in France like a hero?" Saul had shouted. In the end they had managed to soothe Ben, but Etta knew that her son's resentment against the major and the four lieutenants was deep and bitter and could not be held in check forever by tranquilizing words.

After reading from his grammar, Sidney went into his bedroom and played on the legs of a chair with his drum sticks for a while. He wished he had a drum. At four o'clock, Saul came home, relieved from his duties at the store by Harry and Dave who had arrived from school.

"I don't know," said Saul. "I've been thinking about Ben all day. I've been worried. I hope he doesn't quit."

Etta looked nervous. "Talk to him again tonight."

Saul drank his tea in silence. "I'll see," he said heavily.

Ben didn't come home till late that night, having worked five hours overtime. The children were already sleeping, but Saul and Etta were waiting up for him. As soon as he entered the living room his parents saw that an explosion was brewing inside him, an explosion which needed only a match to set it off. After washing up, he came into the living room and, sitting in a chair, started looking at a newspaper, pushing the sheets up before him.

"Ben," began his mother timidly, "I saved something for you. Some soup, a chicken wing and a piece of apple pie."

"I'm not hungry," he answered from behind the newspaper.

"But don't you want to eat a bite? You must be hungry."

"I ate down at the factory."

"Yes, but it's late. Maybe you'd like for a glass of milk ———"

"Don't push any food on him," Saul put in. "He isn't hungry."

In the silence which followed, Ben rustled the sheets.

"Ben," his mother said gently, "what's troubling you? We're your parents, can't you tell us?"

"I've decided to quit my job at the factory," he answered from behind the newspaper. "I can't stand it any longer."

"Yes, but I thought you and your father talked it all over last night," began Etta timidly, striving to keep the alarm out of her voice. "Didn't you promise me and your father that you'd try and not get upset any more?"

Ben suddenly lowered the newspaper, revealing his white face and blazing eyes.

"Try? Who said I didn't try? But there's a limit beyond which you can't even kick a dog around! My superiors down at the plant are swine! I hate them, I hate them! Do you know what happened this afternoon?" His voice was shaking. "The factory worked overtime last night and I was working like a dog today trying to inspect a big mountain of garments so that they could be shipped out to Fort Meyer, Virginia, and those four boy-scout lieutenants sat on their chairs all day without giving me a hand. They're inspectors as well as I am, and it's their job to work in the plant too. I've been covering up for all of them, including the major, and I've been working like a dog. But what happened today was too much!"

"Why, what happened?" asked Etta, excited. "Your face is all white!"

"What happened? The officers went out to lunch and at two o'clock, when I was getting up to leave the restaurant, one of the lieutenants pulled me aside and said: 'Listen, Bergman, we've decided to stay here a bit longer, so would you mind writing up all the reports before going home tonight? I've got the forms already signed in my pocket, so you won't even have to show the reports to me.' I felt like knocking his teeth down his throat! And all the other officers were looking at me with that little smile playing around their lips. If Pa hadn't talked to me last night, I would have quit right then and there! I went back to the plant and saw not only my own work piled up on the tables but an extra big pile of garments that the lieutenants were supposed to look at yesterday, which they had put in another room and then transferred to my tables while I was out to lunch. And they didn't come back from the restaurant, either. They stayed away all afternoon and didn't come back at all. I had to work with all my might to get the shipments out by ten tonight."

Etta looked nervous as her son's voice rose in pitch. "But maybe they won't do it any more," she said. "Maybe they had to go somewhere so they couldn't come back to the factory——"

"Go somewhere? Where could those parasites go? Besides, their job is in the plant where the government put them. Those fellows are in uniform, and they left their post during their hours of duty. I'm not even sworn in the Army, and I wouldn't do a thing like that."

"Yes, but maybe they had a reason——"

"They sure had. To let Bergman fill in for them. I'm no fool. They did it today to see how far they could push me. Now that they've succeeded in getting away with it, they pull it off whenever they want to; they'll make me work overtime three or four nights a week. Well, they won't get away with it! I'll quit! Then they'll have the government on their necks, for they're as dumb as lumps of dirt!"

"But what will you gain by that?" asked Etta nervously. "The Army will take you right away."

"I don't care! I've stood enough!"

"Shut up!" at last cried Saul, who had been holding himself back. "What are you, a boy or a man? What will you gain if you quit and get sent to the front? Do you want to cut off your nose to spite your face?"

"I don't care, I've stood enough!"

"Shut up! What do you know! Don't you think I realize what you have to stand from those swine? I know, and your mother knows! But you've got to stick it out. If you stick it out, you'll show yourself a man. Any sheep can be drafted and get himself sent to the front. But if you take part in this war, what will you be fighting for? For liberty, or for our homes? Will you be fighting invaders? No, you'll shed your blood for a quarrel that started in Europe and concerns Europe only. Do I have to tell you again that a continent that has been having wars for over two thousand years is no place for an American to lay down his life? Do I have to repeat that what Europe starts it should finish by itself? You're an American, not a European; I saw to that. I ran away from Europe, like thirty million other immigrants. I wasn't born here like you were, but I'm as much an American as anybody here. If this country was attacked, if any enemy threatened our liberty, I'd force you and Milton to enlist at once. And I myself would fight. I may be over military age, but I could shoot as good as any man. Let any enemy set foot on this soil of ours, and I'll shed every drop of my blood in the fight to keep him out. But this whole war is a fake, and a man is dishonest to himself if he fights for a fake."

"I don't care, I've stood enough!"

"You haven't. To give in is a sign of weakness. If this war ever ends, it will be people like you who will be respected when sanity returns. How many boys would have the courage to go out to Montana and stay alone in a wilderness because they felt the war was a fake? No, they went like sheep. The war was unpopular, but they went. The people of the United States voted for a man who made a solemn promise to them to keep this country out of Europe's troubles, they gave him a mandate, but he betrayed their trust. Do you think he would be reëlected if he had said that one month after his inauguration he would pull us into the war? I'm repeating all this so that you can regain your intelligence!"

"It's easy for you to say all this," cried Ben. "You haven't got a boss but stay in the store all day. You don't know what it means to be insulted by people time and time again. They don't have to speak to do it; they can insult you by a look, or a smile, or a wave of the hand. But you stay in the store and never come in contact with such things."

"I don't? Who says so? If my person is not insulted, my intelligence is insulted every day, every hour! The talk of the storekeepers and the housewives and the salesmen from the wholesalers who come in to sell me things is enough to make me vomit! It's all I can do to hold my tongue! Sometimes I feel that if I don't cry out, 'Lies, lies!' I'll burst. I say now as I said before: it's harder for an intelligent man to endure the home front than the war front. When you're in the Army you don't have to think; the officers do the thinking for you; you get to be a machine, all you have to do is to obey. But here at home, where the air is full of hypocrisy and the newspapers full of propaganda and lies, a person has to be strong not to weaken. In a time of hysteria like now, the easiest thing to do is to run with the crowd and yell yourself patriotic until you're blue in the face."

Ben's head was in his hands. "Oh, I don't know," he cried in anguish. "I'm so fed up with it."

"All right, I'm tired of talking, go ahead and quit your

job!" Saul shouted. "Go ahead and quit. Put on a uniform, get shipped over, and fight for Europe. Lay down your life for Europe so that your mother can put a gold star in our service flag."

"Saul, Saul," exclaimed Etta. "You're hollering, the neighbors will hear!"

"So what? Let them listen! Let them hear the truth for once in all this hysteria! Haven't I got feelings about the war, too? Don't I wish, also, that the Germans would lose? But I say that neither the French Empire, nor the British Empire, nor any other European empires are worth the life of a single American soldier! If Europe starts its wars, let Europe finish its wars!"

"Saul, Saul!"

The smaller children, awakened by Saul's voice, stood frightened in the doorway of their bedroom. Dressed in their nightgowns they peered fearfully into the living room.

"Saul, Saul!" Etta repeated.

"All right, I'm finished. I'll go to bed. And if that great man sitting in his chair over there wants to quit his job, let him go ahead." And a minute later, walking heavily, the grocer retired to his room.

When the younger children were put to bed again and the flat was quiet once more, Etta came into the living room where she stroked Ben's hair. Ben was still sitting with his head in his hands.

"It's late," she began timidly. "You have to go to work in the morning, boychik mine."

"All—all right," he said brokenly. "I'll go to bed."

When the flat was dark, Etta stood at the windows, looking down the deserted street. A soft April rain was falling, wetting the sidewalks. Staring out into the night, now that the excitement of the evening was over, Etta thought of Milton, of her son who was not there. He had been down at the Southern training camp for six weeks now and her heart ached because he would not be home for the Passover

holidays which started in a few days. It would be the first
time that any member of the family missed the annual Seder,
and she regarded the coming sight of his vacant chair with
dread. As she stared out into the night, she wondered how
her first-born would spend the Seder eve.

When he arrived at his destination, Milt walked up a
street in the dark, a slip of paper in his hand. Walking away
from the small-town railroad station, he found himself in a
quiet residential section, staring at the numbers on the doors.
Finally he found the right house, went up a little lane and
rang the bell. When the door was opened by a kindly,
plump, little woman in her late fifties, he stammered:

"I'm Private Bergman—from Camp Shelby—I was told
to come for Passover services to this house—"

"Oh, come in," she exclaimed with a smile. "We were
waiting for you. The Seder is ready to start."

His campaign hat held awkwardly in his hand, he followed the woman into the dining room which was brilliantly
lit with electric lights and candles. A little man with baggy
pants and a friendly face rose from the table and greeted
him.

"Mr. Flustein, I'm Private Bergman—from Camp Shelby," Milt stammered, introducing himself. "I'm one of the
soldiers parceled out to near-by Jewish homes by the
Camp—"

"No explanations," smiled Mr. Flustein. "We know all
about it. You came here to eat, didn't you?" The others
at the table laughed. "Then no explanations, please. Here,
sit next to my daughter Sedelle. The train must have been
a little late, we thought you wouldn't come. Please—sit
down."

Milt sat down, a smile breaking over his face. He knew
he was with friends. He could smell the cooking, good
Jewish cooking, coming from the kitchen. It reminded him
of home. The girl next to him, Miss Sedelle Sonya Flustein

who helped her father in his little, village drygoods store, smiled at the Jewish soldier by her side. Twenty-five years old, plain, overplump and with a sallow skin, she was none too beautiful. But she was not without her charms; her bust was attractively large and she had sprinkled on herself a perfume called Fleur d'Amour before the guest had arrived. Patting her bodice where the perfume was heaviest, she glanced at the soldier at her side. Under her stare Milt felt a bit uncomfortable, he didn't know why.

Mr. Flustein, starting the Seder, began murmuring and chanting in Hebrew. The other men present—his two unmarried brothers who were in the scrap-metal business in the next town—put on their hats. Mrs. Flustein motioned to Milt and he put his campaign hat on his head.

Hearing the rich, melodious Hebrew coming from the host's lips, Milt thought of home, of the yearly Seders his father had conducted, and he knew that his family back in Chicago were thinking about him. As the chanting rose and fell, a lump gathered in this throat. He listened to the Hebrew, not understanding a word, but feeling the historic richness of the sounds. Unlike the guttural Yiddish, a bastardized language, which, originating in the German ghettos centuries ago, had come to be the living language of a dispersed people, the words spoken by the host were like jewels. In contrast to the Yiddish tongue, the Hebrew sounded like Arabic, austere in its texture, each syllable and inflection woven into richly patterned fabric, glittering with ornamental tones. Coming under the spell of the service, the people present became conscious of their race. A feeling of the misery and the glory of their forefathers came over them. Egypt again was in their bones. Here they sat, petty merchants drudging away in small, mean towns of the South. Here they sat, part of a race which crawled the four corners of the earth like ants, grubbing to exist, submissive, segregated from the life of the community, despised—and tolerated. The two middle-aged brothers who were junk dealers stared thickly before them, thinking of the barrenness and monotony of their lives. The young soldier, due to be shipped to a foreign land, stared thoughtfully at the tablecloth, dreaming, thinking of home. Mrs. Flustein, worried lest the soup get cold, cast furtive glances toward the kitchen. Her daughter, her head slightly inclined, smelling the perfume rising from her bosom, felt her thoughts stirring as she sat next to this strange young man.

The host read from the Haggadah, turning the pages conscientiously. Unlike Saul back in Chicago, he did not skip any pages or slur over any admonitions. Ignoring the hunger of his guests, he sternly ignored his own. But finally he turned the last page of the service and a smile broke across his face.

"It's done, it's done!" exclaimed his wife happily, and, jumping up, brought in the soup.

The spell broken, the small company gave their full attention to the food. Course followed course; it seemed the meal would last forever. The two middle-aged brothers ate like gluttons. They were big, lumpy, heavy men. When their first hunger was appeased, the family asked Milt questions. What city did he come from? Were his parents living? Were they orthodox and did they have a Seder? Did he like camp life? Wasn't it nice of camp authorities to allow Jewish boys to come to Jewish homes in near-by towns? Did Milt have a girl back in Chicago? Was he . . . engaged? The last two questions were asked by Mr. Flustein, who had been prompted by the glances of his daughter. Milt was conscious that everybody was looking at him as he hesitated before answering. He was amused. He knew Jewish parents. Possessing an unmarried daughter who was not getting any younger with the passage of time, they were ready to pounce on any eligible young man like birds of prey.

"No, I'm fancy free," he said brightly. He saw their faces light up.

"You are?"

"Yes, I am."

And for the rest of the evening Mr. Flustein poured wine into his glass. Mrs. Flustein plied him with dainties, and even the two brothers talked to him affably. Meanwhile the daughter, her cheeks suffused with the evidence of her hope and emotion, glanced at him intermittently, her bosom swelling.

But at last it was time for Milt to go. It was late, after eleven, and the last train left in twenty minutes. He rose and said his farewells, thanking them for the meal. Mr. and Mrs. Flustein and the two brothers accompanied him to the door, chattering at him in English and Yiddish, Mrs. Flustein patting his hand like a mother. Mr. Flustein, at the door, whispered:

"Now that you know us, come often, come often. Maybe you won't go to France but will be in camp for the rest of the war? You're a young man far away from home and it's not good to be lonely. My daughter—well, you know—young people, they get together somehow, who knows? And she's a jewel, ach! So clever, but all the young Jewish boys in this town are gone to the war. What was I saying? Ach, she sews—my daughter—like a genius, and cooks something wonderful. And she's very healthy, never sick a day—" The daughter, staying behind, standing quietly in the hall, listened, her limbs trembling. She could hear the young man thank her parents again, could hear her father's swiftly whispering voice, first oily and confidential, then honest and simple by turns. After all, he was only trying to do his best, trying to get her off his hands. Then she could hear the guest, for the third time, saying farewell, thanking them, saying he'd be late for the train if he didn't hurry. And she knew, as she listened, that he would never come back again. Her parents and her middle-aged uncles kept talking—they didn't know—calling out good-byes to their guest as he swung along the street. But in the hallway, standing alone, the daughter knew, she knew, and something welled up in her as she rushed to be alone, when it came, with her bitter weeping.

Off down the lamp-lit street, Milt's footfalls echoed as he made his way toward the railroad station. Now that he was alone, the spirit of all the Seder eves of his life stole over him; and though he had enjoyed the evening, he suddenly felt an almost unbearable ache for home.

3. The Holocaust

IN NOVEMBER, 1932, in the midst of the Great Depression, Franklin Delano Roosevelt was elected President of the United States: A decade before, Mussolini and the Fascisti had marched on Rome; in March, 1933, Hitler and the Nazis took power in Germany; and, by 1928, just a few years after Lenin's death, Stalin had consolidated his power in the Soviet Union. On December 7, 1941, Japan attacked Pearl Harbor and President Roosevelt called it "a day that would live in infamy." But a greater infamy had been going on for years: The deliberate killing of Jews because they were Jews—the most massive pogrom and example of genocide in history—had begun, and was being carried on in Germany and Poland. Before it was over, the Holocaust took six million Jewish lives.

In America, as Nazism rose, anti-Semitic organizations and pro-Nazi organizations sprang into being. The German-American Bund under Fritz Kuhn, *The Boston Pilot, The Brooklyn Tablet,* Father Charles E. Coughlin, and the Christian Front were some of the names associated with these movements. In Irish and German neighborhoods, Jewish shopkeepers were made to feel their status as minority members in a sea of hate. Articles appeared by respectable journalists in respectable magazines like the *Atlantic Monthly* arguing that the root of anti-Semitism was in the Jews themselves—because, one article contended, they were Orientals in an occidental land. Anti-Semitic slanders and violence grew in the land.

Through it all, in spite of President Roosevelt's "Quarantine" speech in 1937 and Secretary of the Interior Ickes' denunciation of Nazism in 1938, little was done to actually curb Nazi horrors overseas. The League of Nations was paralyzed, and the Western Powers were unwilling or unable to act. Meanwhile, American neutrality was pushed by famous people, liberal and conservative, many of them members of the America First Committee: In the name of neutrality, Senator Gerald P. Nye denounced Jewish influence in Hollywood and Senator Burton Wheeler repeated the old canard about Jewish control of international finance, while Charles Lindbergh called the Jews the most dangerous of the groups pressuring the United States to enter the war. Anti-Semitism in the guise of neutrality was in full cry. Apparently most Americans were willing to sacrifice a few countries and a few million Jews for continued peace and prosperity. Only after Pearl Harbor were American attitudes altered toward Japan and Germany, but outside of the Jewish community there was little concern for Europe's Jews till late in the war, too late.

Some American Jews, like Ben Hecht, were horrified by the Holocaust. A few described the butchering graphically, as Maxwell Bodenheim did. And some, heartened by the struggle to escape to "Israel," returned to Jewishness. But for most, understandably, there was an evolution in feeling —as the effect of the Holocaust was felt and as the State of Israel was born. In consequence, and particularly because the effect took time to sink in, the literary descriptions would appear much later. Wallant's *The Pawnbroker,* Uris' *Exodus,* and Pillin's "Miseréré" were a few of those providing the pictures. Auschwitz, Dachau, and Buchenwald had existed. Millions of Jews had been killed.

Between the two wars, Jews were caught up, as were most Americans, in the drama of the frantic Twenties and the Depression Thirties. Some were very obviously trying to right the system. As always they were identified, out of proportion to their numbers, in reform movements, in contributions in all fields. Above all, they became Americans and shared the joys and the griefs of being Americans. At the same time, they spoke from their hearts, as Jews.

Late in the seventeenth century, after a vicious pogrom, John Milton cried out, "Avenge, O Lord, Thy slaughtered saints, whose bones Lie scattered on the Alpine mountains cold." Late in the twentieth century it seems that, for most Americans, Jew and Gentile, the lesson should be clear—we are still faced with ourselves and the questions of the future.

BEN HECHT (1894-1964), a Chicago-born and -bred journalist, found success with his first novel, *Erik Dorn* (1921). *The Front Page* (1928) co-authored with Charles MacArthur, was an even bigger hit, but *A Jew in Love* (1930), in which Jo Boshere (born Abe Nussbaum) was a vulturous, ugly Jew, reflected self-hatred. In 1941, however, in "My Tribe is Called Israel," he called on all Americans to defend Jewish rights all over; an ardent Zionist in these years, he wrote *A Guide to the Bedevilled* (1944) and "God is Good to a Jew." In his last years, Hecht reverted to disillusionment though his autobiography, *Child of the Century* (1954) showed his energy undiminished;

"Among the pussy-cats who write of social issues today,"
Saul Bellow wrote of *Child*, "he roars like an old-fashioned
lion."

God Is Good to a Jew
from
THE COLLECTED STORIES OF BEN HECHT

Aaron Sholomas' eyes were without light. This was because death looked out of them. In the street or sitting in a
room Aaron Sholomas looked like a man staring at the top
of his coffin.

Such a man is a troublesome one to see moving about.
The people in the neighborhood where Sholomas had come
to live avoided his mottled white beard and offered him no
greeting when he passed. They had learned that it did not
matter if they spoke, for the old refugee in the long black
coat was unaware of them.

It was a neighborhood occupied chiefly by Jews who
were a busy folk full of the activities of poverty. And since
among these is always religion, there were many houses of
worship fronting the crowded streets. They were modest
temples that raised no towers but seemed to kneel over the
curbings.

In one of these synagogues, Sholomas spent much of his
time, but even here he attracted no companion. Other old
men wearing prayer shawls looked at him, saw the gaunt
face, the shaggy eyebrows, the bony hands holding the
prayer book, saw his lips moving soundlessly as if they were
trembling rather than praying, but, though their hearts hurt
at the sight of him, none of them went beyond a silent nod
of greeting. They knew his story and there was about
Sholomas, still standing before God, a thing that squeezed
at their souls and made them unable to speak.

When he had walked out of synagogue, many of the pious
ones hid their heads in their prayer shawls and prayed

deeply for the refugee from Poland and asked God to bring him peace.

On the hot summer afternoons when Sholomas was not in the synagogue, he went to sit on a bench in the small neighborhood park. It was an arid, dusty and almost leafless park that seemed to have been coaxed into existence by the weary old men and women who came to rest in it. Here Sholomas sat in his long black coat, his black alien hat, as if he were freezing to death. No one sat down next to him. For how can you say hello to someone who doesn't know the sun is blazing?

In the evenings, Sholomas, the refugee, climbed three flights of stairs and entered a small room that had been provided for him by a family to which he was distantly related. He walked up the steps like a man in a dream and he offered no greeting to the anxious faces that opened the door of the tenement flat.

The head of this family that sheltered Sholomas was a man of seventy named Jacob Rabinowitz. He owned a small shop in which women's dresses were made. He was a robust, pink-cheeked, hearty-voiced man and would have looked well as a great captain of industry. But his heartiness had never lifted him beyond the edges of misfortune. His shop was small, his earnings were precarious, and his strong hands were twisted with fifty years of hard work.

Nevertheless, there was a sort of indomitable childish beam on his large face, and his pride as head of his tenement family was as strong as if he were presiding in a castle. He roared when he spoke, frowned autocratically on all interruption, ate lustily and was full of gurgling love for all the faces at his table. It pleased him mightily that, despite his age, it was his hands that still provided food and a roof for his own.

Jacob had a wife who was stout, ailing and preoccupied fanatically with her kitchen stove, as if she were preparing a constant feast. Her name was Sonia and she had once been called Sonia the Beauty. With all her age and girth, her head was still tilted to one side in the arrogant manner that had delighted Jacob Rabinowitz when he first saw her fifty years ago.

There was a daughter of forty, seemingly as old as her mother, and two granddaughters of thirteen and fourteen who were fragile, blue-veined children and looked as if they had escaped the robust mold of the family. There was also Jacob's brother, a dodderer of seventy-eight named Hershel.

This Hershel was a red-eyed, feeble old fraud, full of mock piety and mock wisdom and mock suffering. He spent most of his time making sad faces and looking rebukingly at his robust brother and his other active relatives. He had given up trying to earn a living in the middle years, due to many fancied diseases and to the solvency and good nature of the younger Jacob.

Other faces had been in this tenement flat, but they had died, among them a son-in-law whose dying had left Jacob undisputed king of his roost.

In these crowded rooms, there was a place for the refugee, Sholomas, because a grandson had gone into the Army. Jacob was in a continual excitement over the heroic deeds of this grandson and, though a man of great honesty, had taken to lying about his Herman.

"Mine grandson," he would boom at any guest, "is in the Second Front."

The family, knowing that Herman was in Carolina, held their tongues. Hershel alone would have dared contradict, but the Second Front and Carolina were equally confusing places to him, so he, too, was silent.

"He is fighting over there," Jacob would continue, "and getting ready to march to Berlin. We haven't heard from him for some time. Who knows? Maybe he is fighting in Germany already. Over here is his picture. Have a look at it."

Grandfather Jacob would point to the wall where hung several photographs of Herman, revealing him at ten in a white sailor suit doing a hornpipe, at fifteen still in knee

pants and holding a violin moodily under his arm, and at
nineteen in an Army overcoat with an unexpected humorous
gleam in his eyes. Under these photographs stood a bowl of
fresh flowers.

The refugee from Poland had been given the lumpy iron
bedstead that had once been Herman's and that stood beside
a back window looking out on a swarm of other tenement
back windows.

"This is a great honor for you," Jacob had boomed. "In
this bed mine Herman slept since he was a little boy. Here
is where he growed up, in this identical room. I'll betchya
lots of times when he is fighting the Germans, mine grandson
remembers this room. I am keeping it for him." And Jacob
beamed at the stark cubbyhole as if it were a holy place.

The refugee from Poland was a silent and almost invisible
guest. The family saw him only when one of them brought
him tea to drink at night and a plate with fish and bread.
He ate so little that Jacob, whose stomach was in love with
everything that grew in the sea or in the land, believed that
the white-bearded one would die of famine any hour.

"I don't like to see a man in mine house should starve to
death," Jacob complained. "Bring him in some *varenya.*"

This was a cherry jam that Jacob considered irresistible.
Twenty jars of it had been sent to Herman in the Carolinas.

But Sholomas left the *varenya* untouched. When the tea-
bearers opened the door of Sholomas' room, they asked politely, without entering, "Are you all right? If you want
something, just say so."

Sholomas would look up and say nothing, so it was pre-
sumed he was all right and wanted for nothing.

Sitting around the supper table, the family often discussed
their distant relative in the back room. The older ones remembered him from the time before they came to America.
He had been a man of learning, and people used to travel
miles to the town where he lived to consult him on great
problems of piety and behavior.

"You have no idea how famous this man Sholomas was,"

said Jacob. "He was a great man. A fine, handsome man. Not just a rabbi, but a poet. The finest poems that was written in our language, he wrote. We were proud in them days to have a cousin named Aaron Sholomas. Hershel, tell 'em."

Jacob nudged his rheumy-eyed brother, who spoke up at once in woebegone tones, "I am thinking of something else. Please don't interrupt me."

"Go on, tell them!" Jacob boomed, and Hershel, sighing deeply, moaned, "You are speaking from Aaron Sholomas?"

"You heard me!" Jacob cried.

"He was a dolling man," Hershel went on moaning. "He raised geese and tended beanstalks."

"Not beanstalks!" Jacob roared. "What's a matter with you? Bees! Bees, he tended."

"Beanstalks," Hershel repeated stubbornly and rubbed tears from his eyes by way of ending the argument.

"It was anyway his wife who raised geese and tended bees," Jacob said. "Because he, himself, was a student all his life. He was not only a rabbi and a poet but a wise man. In the old country, a wise man is different from here," he boomed educationally at his granddaughters. "Nobody laughs at him, but he sits around like a king, helping the people and explaining them how to live. I remember when I was leaving for America, I went to him because I wanted to make him a donation of a few dollars he could give to the poor people who was always his best friends. Because rich people don't need a wise man, either in the old country any more than over here. And he said to me, 'My boy, you keep your dollars. A man starting out on a journey must not give away presents. Because a single dollar—even a few pennies—might prevent him from arriving where he is going, you understand. After he has arrived and his journey is over, then he can give away presents.' "

Jacob chuckled at this remembered wisdom.

"I can remember exactly the words he said to me," he

went on. "I was a young boy, too. He said, 'A man must not try to buy God's good will in advance. He must only give God presents out of gratefulness. The other thing is like bribing.' "

"That saying is written in the Talmud," Hershel sighed. "Yes, yes, it is everything written down—everything." And summoning a look of hauteur into his woeful face, the dodderer quoted a proverb in Hebrew.

"I remember this Sholomas very well," Jacob interrupted the quotation. "I remember he had eyebrows so big they hung almost over his eyes. And he had such kind eyes you fell in love with him the minute you saw him."

"A dolling man," said Hershel, "and a fine swimmer. He could swim farder and longer than anybody in this room." And Hershel looked at his robust, pink-faced brother with a sneer, for Jacob had been famed in his youth as a mighty swimmer—a fame which, with the aid of Hershel's grudging corroboration, he had managed to keep alive for forty years. . . .

Several weeks after Sholomas' arrival in the Rabinowitz home, Jacob's daughter stated one evening that the old man should be coaxed into eating with them.

"It's no good for him to sit alone," she said. "He sits there like a dead man. I don't see why we keep him if he's going to sit in a hole like a dead man, day and night. He'd be just the same off in some old people's home."

"He is mine cousin," Jacob boomed, "and he shall stay in mine house. How would it look if I threw him out after the agency went to all the trouble locating some relative of his?"

"I don't care," said the daughter. "He don't enjoy himself. He makes the whole house like a tomb. I'm afraid sometimes to open his door."

"What are you afraid of?" Jacob asked. "He don't harm nobody."

"He sits there," said Jacob's daughter and shuddered.

One evening a week later, the hearty Jacob sat at the table in silence and nibbled glumly at his food.

"What's the matter with you?" his wife demanded, her head angrily to one side. "Are you sick or something? Go on, eat! What am I standing all day in the kitchen cooking for?"

Jacob frowned at his plate and drank a second glass of brandy. The family talked loudly over his silence, but their eyes looked nervously at his unemptied plate. In the middle of the meal, Jacob pressed his brother to join him in a third glass of brandy.

"You will excuse me, please," Hershel moaned. "I am not feeling so good tonight."

The statement angered Jacob. "You've been healthy as a horse for seventy-five years," he growled, "ever since I known you."

Hershel rubbed tears from his eyes, tucked the corners of his mouth down and trembled his nose.

"What have you got to cry about?" Jacob demanded. "You sit crying, day and night. For what?"

"He ain't crying," Jacob's wife called out. "That's how he looks naturally. He can't help it."

"Thank you, Sonia." The dodderer looked tenderly at her. "You was always mine favorite dolling."

Jacob pushed his plate of uneaten chicken from him. "I talked to a man from the agency today," he said. "I met him by an accident in Siegel's restaurant. He says to me, 'Are you Jacob Rabinowitz?' I told him, 'Yes, that's my name. What can I do for you, sir?' So we sat down, and he told me from Aaron Sholomas, mine cousin. The whole story. It's something you can't believe. You can't imagine such a thing."

The family nodded and became silent. Jacob scowled at the many platters of food around him.

"Go on, we're waiting," said Sonia.

Her husband looked at his two grandchildren.

"Not in front of them," he said. "Why should they hear such things?"

"We know, anyway," said the older of the girls. "He was in the massacre where all the people in the town were killed. All the Jews were killed."

"Quiet!" said her mother, seizing the child's hand and kissing it. "Let your grandfather talk."

"It is something unbelievable," said Jacob hoarsely. "It was written out in a report about what happened in the town where he lived."

"The name of the town was Scuzin," old Hershel spoke up firmly. "We used to go there in the summertime to swim in the river."

"Thot's right," said Jacob with a deep sigh; "but nobody is swimming on thot river no more. It's for dead people, thot river."

He half closed his eyes, and his voice hoarsened as he went on, "The Germans locked up four thousand Jews in the ghetto behind the walls. They wouldn't let them come out, and nobody is allowed to give them any food, and if they are sick, they can die and nobody is allowed to bring them medizin."

"Ai," said Jacob's wife and lowered her head slowly.

"They was starving and going crazy, them people," said Jacob hoarsely, "and finally they got so hungry they couldn't stand it any more and they start climbing over the walls of the ghetto and breaking down the doors, so they can get out. And they come out into the street looking like animals that are starving to death."

"Ai," said Jacob's wife and bowed her head over her plate.

"The Germans let them run in the street for a while, begging for food," said Jacob. "Then they start chasing them and shooting down everybody like it was a hunt for animals. The old men, the women, the children, they are shot down by the Germans while they run in the streets begging for food."

Jacob's work-twisted hands clutched at the table edge.

"They shoot down two thousand in the street," he resumed, "and the rest keep on running. They don't even know they are dying, they are so hungry. They run to the river and jump in and start swimming. Where are they swimming to? No place. Where can they swim? They are just crazy from hunger and swimming around and around. The report says two thousand of them was in the river swimming. Them Germans stood by the side and shot every one of them until the river was full of dead people."

Jacob paused as if he were out of breath, and old Hershel spoke up:

"Simon Meyerberg used to have a mill by the river." His voice quavered. "We used to go there in the summertime and ketch pike. He was a fine man, yes, sir." The dodderer looked far away. "He died when I was a little boy," he added.

"Mine cousin, Aaron Sholomas, was in the river when Germans are shooting," Jacob went on. "He swimmed with the dead people all day and by night he crawled out on the ground and he sat by the side and pulled the bodics out of the river. He was looking for his wife and grandchildren. He couldn't find them because it was dark, and finally he fell down unconscious by the dead people. In the morning a Polish man sawn him and took him up in a wagon and saved him."

Jacob poured himself another glass of brandy. "I can't stand it," he boomed hoarsely. "That man's wife, his grandchildren and everybody he known in the whole world, butchered in front of his eyes."

Jacob's wife began to weep, and the older of the girls whispered to her, "Grandma, don't cry. Please don't cry."

"Simon, the miller, used to have a horse," old Hershel spoke up. "It was called Spilka. Three people could ride on him. I can remember to this day."

"What happened to Sholomas?" Jacob's daughter asked. Jacob was looking at the photographs of his grandson over the bowl of fresh flowers. The humorous face above the Army overcoat seemed to straighten him in his chair, and he answered in a loud, rasping voice:

"Mine cousin lived for a month hided away by the Polish farmer. Then there was a law passed that anybody who hided Jews had to be killed the same as the Jews themselves. So mine cousin, when he heard this law, left the home of the Polish farmer and walked by night every night for weeks to Lublin. On his hands and knees, this old man crawled in the nighttime to Lublin. And what was there in Lublin for him? Only more Germans. I asked the man from the agency, 'What was he living for? What did he want to go on living for?' And the man explained to me that mine cousin was crazy now and was looking for his wife and grandchildren. He didn't remember they was all drowned in the river."

Jacob stopped, and though he looked long at the photographs of his grandson, he was unable to go on, and the group at the table sat in silence and waited.

"I don't like to think what happened in Lublin," he resumed. "In Lublin, the Germans put twelve thousand Jews behind the walls of the ghetto. Then they killed them. All of them. They took 'em in the field in wagons. Five hundred at a time in wagons on top of one another. They blown them up."

Jacob groaned, and his large hands lifted the brandy glass. The liquor spilled over his chin.

"There was a few of them who wasn't dead," he went on. "When the Germans was shooting the ones that was lying on the ground still alive, they don't shoot Aaron Sholomas. They left him lying with the dead bodies, and in the nighttime he crawled away again. And like before, he hided himself in the daytime and walked every night. Then somebody recognized him while he was crawling in the night that he was Aaron Sholomas, the wise man from Scuzin, and they saved him."

Jacob stopped, his eyes on the doorway. The bearded

figure of Sholomas in its long black coat and alien hat stood there.

"Come in," said Jacob softly. "Come in and join us. Move up a chair for him, somebody, please."

His daughter placed another chair at the table. The refugee's eyes were without greeting. They were open and staring and only the doddering Hershel was able to look into them.

"You remember me, Aaron Sholomas," said Hershel. "I am Hershel Rabinowitz, a son of Samuel from Scuzin. Simon Meyerberg who owned the mill there in Scuzin was a first cousin from mine father."

Sholomas moved a few steps into the room and then seemed to become lost. The gaunt white face under the black alien hat remained silent, and its silence struck those in the room as something terrible. There were no words that could speak to it.

Jacob Rabinowitz raised his eyes, and his pink face became chalk. Not Aaron Sholomas but all the dead Jews of Europe stood in their grave clothes beside his dining table. There were millions of them, and Jacob could hear their voices calling in the night as they died. He saw the river of Scuzin with the May flies darting over it and the frogs leaping from the mud banks, and under its willow trees he saw the water filled with dead; old men like himself floating with their arms limp and their faces hidden, old women like his wife drowned and bobbing through the hail of bullets, and many like his grandchildren clawing at the dark river as the German guns picked them off from the shore.

This river he knew and he could remember how the moon looked in it. He could see the road that led to its banks and the winding streets of Scuzin and he could remember a guitar that played and a horse that trumpeted in its stall. He knew the smell of this summer night and he knew all the dead, all the crazed figures stumbling through the little streets of Scuzin, the women with their hair streaming and their pale children locked in their arms; the old men muttering to God as they toppled over.

He knew them all, for they were people among whom he had laughed and lived and he could feel the bullets striking them down. He saw them in the river among the leaping of frogs and the hum of startled insects, spinning with the current around the trunks of the willow trees, and they called out in his heart for mercy.

Their voices that nobody heard, their helpless look at the sky as if they were dogs being slaughtered and not people—these overwhelmed Jacob, and the dining room in which he had eaten so heartily for so many years grew dark before his eyes. It became a grave in which he sat with the dead Jews of Scuzin and of all the slaughter places whose names were too many to remember. Jacob covered his face with his hands and his body shook with weeping.

His brother nudged him as he wept. "Jacob," said the dodderer, "you should not cover your face like thot. We have a guest." And in a voice full of sudden dignity, old Hershel added, "Aaron Sholomas, we are proud to have you at our table. Kindly sit down."

Jacob uncovered his face. He saw that Sholomas had seated himself next to his granddaughter. The bony hands of the refugee were resting limply on the table, his face was lowered, and his lips were moving silently.

"Shh," old Hershel looked reprovingly at his weeping niece, "he is making the prayer over bread."

Late on a September afternoon, Sholomas sat in the neighborhood park enveloped in his long black coat. The light was leaving the sky. As the glare of the sun lifted from the streets, the park in which he sat became full of sharp color and bold outline. The sudden presence of so many vivid things around him confused Sholomas. He stood up and, with his eyes to the ground, walked out of the park.

At nine o'clock Jacob Rabinowitz was worried. He had finished his third glass of tea, and his wife and daughter had cleared the table of everything but a jar of *varenya* and a plate of cookies.

"It's no use talking," said Jacob. "Something has happened to him. Where else can he be at this hour of the night?"

"You are speaking of Aaron Sholomas?" Old Hershel raised his eyes from the newspaper.

Jacob grunted. His brother was taking on daily more and more the ways of an idiot.

"Who else!" he boomed. "Nine o'clock and he ain't home yet."

"He is not a little boy," said Hershel calmly and picked the pinochle cards out of the cut-glass bowl on the sideboard.

He sat down at the dining table and started shuffling the deck. A sly look came into his rheumy eyes. Despite his trembling hands and doddering ways, he was able invariably to win a few pennies from his domineering brother.

"Don't botherin' me with the cards," said Jacob. "I'm worried about mine cousin." His large pink face scowled at the clock. "What can a man like thot be doing at this hour?"

"Maybe he dropped in some place for a glass tea," Hershel offered.

"Honest!" Jacob glared at the dodderer. "I hate to say this from my own brother. But you have got less sense than a ordinary child."

A melting look came into Hershel's woebegone face. "Don't get excited," he said softly. "There is some people got all the sense but don't know what to do with it."

Jacob shook off the insult. "I'm going to look around for him," he said.

"What is this?" Jacob's daughter peered out of the kitchen. "What is the racket for?"

"He is going to look for Aaron Sholomas," said Hershel, scowling at the cards in his hands. "You should stop him, dolling."

"You can't go running through the streets," the daughter said. "You're tired from the shop. You'll get sick. Sit down. Sholomas will come home all right by himself."

Jacob was on his feet, his head thrown back, his eyes half shut, which was his way of signaling that he was not to be contradicted further.

"Where is mine grandchildren?" he boomed. "Come on girls. We are going to look for our cousin."

The night was warm and the streets were full of idle figures. They sat on steps, stood at the curb or tilted back in chairs placed before the dimmed store fronts. Down these tranquil streets, a thought moved furtively and painfully, as if all the idlers resting after their day's work had but one head. It was a thought of death. The idlers in these tenement streets were watching the slaughter of the Jews.

On each warm night, with their tasks done, they sat sprawled in the summer dark and looked on the great killing of the Jews and listened in their hearts to the unheeded Jewish prayers rising from the German massacre grounds. They talked to one another of many things, gossiped and complained, but their souls were fastened on a faraway stage where the strange and awful murder of the Jews was then going on.

Their sons, brothers and grandsons were in the war, and their thoughts were full of Mediterranean names where battles were happening. But these battles seemed like happy events to them. Germans were being killed in these battles. The thought of their kin, armed and fighting fiercely, brought a sigh of relief into the summer streets where the many Jews sat watching the distant slaughter of their kind.

The radios squawking in the night proclaimed the hourly deeds of the distant armies; but deeper and louder in their hearts than all the other voices in the world was the unheeded call of the millions who, without any weapons in their hands, were facing the German massacre squads.

Such was the neighborhood through which Jacob Rabinowitz, holding a granddaughter by each hand, walked in search of his cousin. The tall heavy-waisted Jacob walked proudly with an old habit of arrogance in his ungrayed head. He paused now and then before idlers on the steps and in-

quired in a peremptory voice if they had seen Aaron Sholomas, the refugee from Poland, who was his cousin. None
had seen him, and Jacob marched on, clinging to the hands
of his granddaughters.

In the synagogue where he knew Sholomas spent his days,
he was told that the old man had left his prayers at seven and
walked away toward the neighborhood park. Jacob led his
granddaughters there. The two pretty girls were full of love
for their tall grandfather as they walked beside him and,
knowing that he was unhappy, they began telling him of the
fun they had had in school that day and of the fine things
their teachers had said to them. Whatever his troubles,
Jacob always chuckled proudly when he heard tales of his
grandchildren's schooling.

Many people sat on the shadowed benches of the park,
and the three searchers walked for a time, looking into their
silent faces.

"You sit down, Grandpa," the older of the girls finally
said, "and we'll go and look all over the park."

Jacob sat down with a lordly grunt. "Ask the people," he
instructed them, "if they have seen him and what way he
went. You understand?"

"We will," the girls said eagerly. "You just sit still."

They walked away and Jacob sat on the bench. His large
body was straight and his eyes peered into the dark. He felt
tired and in his weariness he kept remembering a river in
which he had once swum, and a great pain filled his heart.
For no Jew would ever laugh or swim in that river again.

"It's no good thinking about such things," he told himself
angrily. "It don't do you any good to suffer when you can't
help something. Here is a fine park, and the people are enjoying themselves. That's enough to think about."

But the memory of the river continued to hurt his heart.
He looked into the silent, shadowed faces near him, and a
miserable kinship with all the park sitters came over him.
They, too, were sitting with memories and staring at faraway
rivers and villages filled with dead Jews.

His granddaughters returned, out of breath.

"We asked everybody," they told him, "and nobody has seen him at all."

"Maybe he has come home already." Jacob frowned and stood up. He felt the night breeze on his face and sighed.

"It's a fine night," he said, smiling at his granddaughters. "Gorgeous! Look how nice it is here for the poor people."

He took the girls by the hand, and the three of them moved through the streets again.

The family had gone to bed. Jacob sat down heavily at the dining table.

"Go on, go to sleep," he said to his grandchildren. "You got to be in school early tomorrow."

The girls kissed him on each side of his forehead and cried, "Good night, Grandpa."

Jacob remained alone at the dining table, staring fearfully at the empty chairs.

When he walked out of the neighborhood park, disturbed by the sharpened colors of the dying day, Aaron Sholomas awoke from the half sleep of a year. Since the night he had crawled away from the river of dead in Scuzin, the world had been veiled for Sholomas. His soul, like a ghost, had lived only among the prayers in his head.

He looked about him now as he walked and saw the strangeness of streets and buildings, and his head nodded as at an event. He knew that reason had returned to him and he said a prayer of thanksgiving.

I have been away, he thought softly, and his eyes looked timidly on the sights of an unclouded world.

"It is a strange land," Sholomas said softly to himself.

He tried to remember his journey to it, but, when he looked into the past, a pain seized his throat and his mind grew clouded again.

There are things not to be remembered, he thought, and remained like one half asleep and half awake.

He felt the heaviness of his legs and remembered then

how old he was and was startled by the number of years.
Like many who devote their lives to thought, yesterday—
even the yesterday of his boyhood—had seemed always an
hour away from Sholomas.

Time had not touched his mind or altered its preoccupa-
tions during the whole of his life. Because of this, the great
changes it had worked on his body had often confused him.
He was confused now to find himself so old a man, and he
thought that he would never be young again because his
memories were gone. The road to youth was finally closed
in his heart and he would never run down it again to other
days.

As he moved through the new streets, he recalled the
letters that had once come to him from this strange country
describing its wonders and its oddities. Again the pain
seized his throat and his heart felt suddenly made of dust.
For the letters reminded him of the house in which he had
lived and of his wife and grandchildren to whom he had
read them aloud. He remembered his wife smiling at them
and saying, "How can people be happy away from their
homeland, Aaron? It must be they fool themselves."

The pain almost closed his mind again but he continued
defiantly to think and he saw in his soul the many burning
streets and the dead ones sprawled over one another in the
roads and fields. That had been their homeland.

Poor little nests, Sholomas thought, that never belonged
to us no matter how lovingly we warmed them.

With a strong effort he kept his thought from running to
the grave where all his kin and all his memories lay—the
wild grave of Poland.

There are things not to be remembered, he repeated, and
busied himself thinking of a history that he knew as well as
his own.

This was the history of the Jews. He looked into it now,
as he had done since his boyhood, and saw the Jews of many
countries and many centuries wrestling with the hate of the
world. A fair world, it was—full of learning and gallant

deeds. But always it darkened around the Jew and always
its wisdom and its kindness vanished in his presence. Sholomas pondered the reasons for this as he walked.

It had grown dark, but the refugee from Poland continued
his meditations unaware of the nightfall. He was eager to use
his mind but he knew it had become like a wanderer, ready
to vanish in a mist if he offended it.

A few people noticed Sholomas as he walked through
their city. They saw an old Jew in a long black coat and a
ceremonial hat moving slowly in the street. There was nothing in the gravity of the long thin face or the steadiness of
the step to tell them that this old man was wrestling with a
madness that had imprisoned him for a year.

Sholomas came to a more lighted district. He had been
walking for hours and his legs had grown too heavy to move.
He stood and mused. These were streets in which Jews were
not hated and these were people, according to what he had
heard, who were not eager to revile and slaughter them.
Sholomas wondered if this were really the truth, for it had
never been true in the history he had studied. There had
never been such streets or such people in the world. The
history he knew revealed that the Jew in moving to a new
land carried among his little belongings always the gibbet
on which he must hang.

It is not wise to rejoice, he thought softly, over the kindness of a new host.

He had walked far and didn't know where he was, nor
could he remember the name of the man in whose house he
lived.

He sighed and knew that the silence and emptiness in
which he had been living were returning to him again. He
thought faintly: I am in another country far from the Germans. But maybe I am only dreaming this is so. Out of much
pain, the soul sometimes creates dreams for itself in which
to hide.

Sholomas' head grew heavy and he murmured sadly to
himself, "God takes away life because I am too weak to look

into it. It is not certain that I know where I am. I am old and lost."

He stood with his eyes shut, and the mist covered his mind as it had done on the night in Lublin when the dead moaned in their graves. He began moving his lips soundlessly in a prayer.

After a time, he opened his eyes and what he saw overwhelmed him. He stood for moments trembling and a fear melted his heart. Not far away, a great fire was burning. He could see the flames and the reddened sky and the smoke winding out of windows. Then Sholomas saw there was a crowd moving toward him and he shut his eyes again.

He was bewildered no longer and he no longer doubted where he was. This was no longer a strange country but a familiar one. This was death, the homeland of the Jews. For he knew that where there was a crowd moving, there was death. Where fire burned, there Jews died. Where voices filled the night, there massacre moved with its wild laugh.

It was clear to Sholomas that his hour had come and that, around him, slaughter was raging again. He lifted his head and found new strength to stand erect and think of God.

"Though the Jews are slain as the lowest of beasts," he said softly to heaven, "it is as the children of God they must die, with His name on their lips. For if their goodness is not wanted by the world, they must keep it strong and bring it to God who will accept it."

The sounds of the night overcame him and he stood for a time without thought and waited. Figures rushed by him, jostling him and sending him against a wall. Here he remained with his eyes on the glare of the fire. There came back into his head the voices of the dying in the streets of Scuzin and the voices from the river under the willows and the voices from the fields outside Lublin and from the roads where death had obliterated his people.

He waited for the glare of the fire to sweep over him and for the shouts to bring him death, and he thought as he stood before his last hour: They continue to kill us. I must go talk to those who are dying. I must tell them that it is not we who are doomed. It is those who slaughter us who are doomed. For it is not we they are killing, but a thing in themselves they are destroying. And they must live without goodness or the light of God in their souls until they die. For it is not we who die as beasts but they who live on as beasts. It is written that the man of evil shall be powerless, though he vanquish cities. It is written that he can never vanquish goodness or righteousness except in his own soul.

Thus Aaron Sholomas spoke in his mind as he waited for the massacre to carry him to the wild grave of the Jews.

The policeman who had been keeping part of the Third Avenue crowd from breaking through the fire lines noticed a white-bearded old Jew against the wall.

"Hey!" he called. "Keep moving along there!"

The old man remained motionless, his face raised to the night. The policeman pushed through a group of enthralled fire-engine watchers and came to the old man's side.

"What's the matter, pop?" The policeman took his arm. "The fire scare you?"

A middle-aged woman, standing near them, spoke with sudden nervousness. "He's sick, officer," she said. "I think he's fainted."

"He's standing up by himself, ain't he?" said the policeman, frowning.

Other faces turned toward the stiffened old man at the wall.

"You better get him to a hospital," a second policeman pushed through and decided. "I'll put in a call."

"Poor old guy!" said a voice. "He looks all in."

"We ought to do something," another voice spoke. "We can't just leave him standing up like that."

The night around Sholomas became filled with the kindly voices of an American crowd in the presence of a sidewalk mishap. Someone brought a chair out of the building and

put it under the old man. Fingers unbuttoned his odd-look-
ing coat and removed his curious hat from his head. A hand
appeared and thrust a small glass of whisky toward Sholomas' mouth.

"Try and drink this," said a voice. "It'll do you good."

Sholomas remained motionless and with his eyes shut.

The faces watching the bearded old man in the chair
became silent. The fire in the building had been put out and
there was more interest now in this lean, patriarchal figure
who sat as if he were dead and yet not dead.

"He looks like a Jew," said the second policeman, returning. "Does anybody know how to speak Jewish so's
we can ask him where he lives?"

No answer came, and the silence of a crowd that held no
Jews seemed to awaken Sholomas.

"He's coming to," a voice said, and the crowd watched
the old man's eyes opening.

The aged face, white with years, raised itself and the eyes
looked frozenly out. There returned to Sholomas a flicker
of thought, and he wondered feebly where he was and in
what land he sat. Then he remembered the burning street
and the shouting and he looked at the ring of faces with
disbelief. There was no massacre around him. Voices were
talking, and two men in uniform were beside him. One was
kneeling and holding a glass to his mouth.

Sholomas sipped the liquor and his eyes continued to look
from face to face with disbelief, for he saw kindness and
compassion. They were the faces of a strange land, faces
that grew tender when they saw an old Jew sitting helpless
in the street. The liquor warmed Sholomas, and his mind
grew suddenly bright.

The wisdom of Aaron Sholomas looked on this strange
street in which he was to die and saw its goodness. Here was
the street he had never found in the history of the Jews, the
shining street in which faces smiled on the tribe of Abraham.

Many unbelievable things had happened to Sholomas, so
unbelievable that his wisdom had fled from life. But none

was as unbelievable as this street in which he sat with pounding heart, this promised street full of friends.

In these last moments of his life, the torn soul of Sholomas filled with love, and he thought eagerly as if he were young again and had never tasted agony: After many years and after a long journey, I have found goodness that does not vanish where the Jew stands. I have found a home. God is good!

Sholomas closed his eyes, and his lips moved in silence for another moment. Then his body slid from the chair.

The two policemen laid him carefully on the pavement and one of them placed the ceremonial hat under his head. For several minutes, the crowd stood in silence looking down at the dead man lying where people walked. Some of them removed their hats, and others shivered to see, staring up from this busy street, the end of life.

As he had closed his eyes, Sholomas had dreamed of this miracle—that a Jew would be lying dead among strangers and that the night would be filled with compassion.

During the 1930s, MAXWELL BODENHEIM (1892–1954), formerly an anti-Communist, became a fellow traveler. By 1940, when he was fired from a Federal Writers' Project job because of his political association, he had severed connections with the party. His last novels, *Run, Sheep, Run* (1932), *New York Madness* (1933), and *Slow Vision* (1934) showed his new political consciousness, though he was a pessimist and non-Marxist. In his late poetry, especially in *Lights in the Valley* (1942) and in "Poem to Gentlies" he stated his horror of war and intense dislike of religious persecution, especially that of the atrocities of the Holocaust.

Poem to Gentiles
from
SEVEN POETS IN SEARCH OF AN ANSWER

The butchering must be wholesale and the smell
Of dead Jews must be strong enough to drift,
Like vastly stifled echoes of a yell,
Before the easy, widespread protests lift.
How many of them are sincere?—the tears,
The blades of conscience do not wait, mild, slow,
Until the slaughter-house revolves for years
And business lags because supplies are low.
The little, harried men, depleted, glued
By warm and cumbersome monotonies,
They know quick sympathy, misguided feud,
But they at least hold sharp sincerities.
They are not politicians, mountebanks,
Smooth men who plot the time to cheer or kneel:
And when these Gentiles of the slapped, blurred ranks
Shake hands with Jews, the hard-won touch is real.
They can be poisoned, they have been the prey
Of ranting liars, rumors, kindled lure
For centuries, and yet their creeping day
Of vengeance nears, bruised, wondering, but sure.
The lists of soldier casualties arrive.
The Gentile, Jewish parents finger death.
Some fraction of this nearness must survive
Beyond the sentimental, blundering breath.
The soldiers know hard tolerance roughly snared
From times where bullets strike or barely miss,
For pain and sweat and fear defeated, shared,
Are overwhelming foes of prejudice.
In peace, the slow blend will be selfless deeds,
Hearts naked, problems flattened on the streets.
It will not spring from suave men and their greeds,
Speech-makings, brass-bands, sweet discursive seats.

EDWARD LEWIS WALLANT (1926–1962), born in New Haven, studied art and eventually became art director of a large advertising agency in New York. His four novels, *The Human Season* (1960), *The Pawnbroker* (1961), and the posthumously published *The Tenants of Moonbloom* (1963), and *The Children of the Gate* (1964), are concerned with people whose contact with suffering forced them to reestablish contact with life, belief, and love. *The Pawnbroker*, his best-known novel, tells of the horrors of the concentration camps as Sol Nazerman, the pawnbroker, in Harlem, relives his past through flashbacks. The excerpts printed here, separated by ellipses, do not appear consecutively in the novel.

The Holocaust
from
THE PAWNBROKER

His face was pressed against the wood. His eyes were in the open part between the slats of the cattle car. The plains of Poland moved by monotonously, almost repetitively, as though the train were still and the same landscape were being displayed over and over again. His son David squealed with a rodent sound of helplessness somewhere down near Sol's leg. "I'm slipping in it, Daddy, in the dirty stuff. I can't stay up." But what could he do about it? He was pressed into that one position by two hundred other bodies. So he studied the tidal landscape. Yes, it was the same view over and over. There, that house, low and black, with a broken stone chimney, he had seen that at least a dozen times. They were just standing still and, by some odd circumstance, the earth was being unrolled for their view. "Do something for him," his wife, Ruth, cried harshly beside him. She had little Naomi up against her chest, held there without her arms, for the crush of bodies held them all as in ice. "Sol, don't let him fall down in that! All our filth is down there. It would be terrible for him to lie in it!" Just moving his nose down an

inch toward the carpeting of feces nauseated Sol. The child
would turn his insides out. He tried to move a little more
than his fingers, felt the soft, damp hair of David's head as it
slid slowly downward. "I can't," he complained peevishly.
"What do you expect of me? I cannot move a muscle." In
the dim, slatted light he saw his wife's grim face. She seemed
to hate him for all this. "But I can't, I can't. I can do nothing." His voice sounded flat and unconcerned and he tried to
put more passion into it. "I am helpless, do you hear?" She
continued looking at him with burning eyes and motionless
features, like one of those startlingly lifelike wax figures. "I
can do nothing." His voice still came out in the same dis-
passionate, soulless way. There came the sound of the boy
at his feet making savage, empty retches, vomiting and
slipping around in the bottomless filth. The roar of the train,
the endless wailing of all the crushed people, and his wife's
burning glass eyes in a waxen face. "Nothing, nothing, nothing," Sol shrieked in the awful din. . . .

They could see the whole thing from where they stood in the
camp square. Sol stood with the others in a long, endless
line, halted by their guard, as were the several other work
groups. Outside the barbed-wire fence, the dogs snarled in
a closing ring around Rubin. The black-uniformed men
smoked and joked idly in the noon sunshine; even the dogs
seemed in no great hurry as they backed the small crouched
figure toward the fence.

A week before, they had taken Rubin's cross-eyed son to
the "showers." Last night, Rubin had managed to slip out
of the camp, God knew how. But the dogs had found him,
and the commandant's edifying "example" was imminent.
All night they had given Rubin his head, yet all the while
they were slyly working him back toward the camp. Now,
at high noon, he was right outside the high fence for everyone to learn from; the morbid joke was revealed to Rubin
at last.

If you kept your eyes off the small hunched figure, you

might think a harmless animal hunt was in progress, some sport of so little intrinsic excitement that the guards tried to make it interesting by jokes and side bets.

The dogs bayed in the hot light. The air was emptied of birds and insects by the loud voices of the dogs, and the prisoners stood like shades, arrested on their shuffling journey to Hell. Sol felt dust flowing from him instead of sweat, a dry, powdery secretion which smelled stale and fiery.

One of the guards of Sol's column called over to the men with the dogs, "I hope the electricity is off now, otherwise you'll ruin it."

A black-clad man answered that it was. He touched the twisty knot of wire and made a face of mock agony, as though he were being electrocuted. They all laughed at his clowning. That was the extent of the sounds; a few men's laughter and the yapping, the trumpeting of the hounds.

Rubin was only a few feet from the fence when the dogs jumped him. For a minute his figure was obscured by their tumbling, hairy bodies. Their snarls were wetly muffled by what they were doing. Sol looked away, a strange dead feeling spreading through his chest, a feeling like boredom. All the men in the column were bony-gray profiles, death masks coated by the faint dustiness of the air. A pigeon appeared on one of the sludge-colored barracks roofs; not quite sure of its roost, it fluttered its wings as it stood, then rose again and disappeared over the monotonous horizon of the camp.

The vile chorus from the beasts' throats rose to an insane pitch. Sol looked back to see Rubin rise up far bigger than he had ever been. For a few seconds the dogs fell back, surprised at the deceptive quarry which had seemed so small. Rubin was screaming, one shining red figure of blood, only his mouth definable in all the torn body, and that so vivid because it framed the scream. Everything else was dust-white, the dark figures of the guards and the dogs overladen with a cloudy, powdered light. Only Rubin had immense color, was a great crimson font that demeaned the whole day.

Suddenly Rubin turned and flung himself up on the thorny wire fence, where he clung just out of reach of the snapping dogs. One of the guards waved toward the guard tower. There came the rattly crack of electricity. The bloody figure went rigid, pulled away from the horrid life of the wires, and then seized it and pulled it tight in a lover's embrace. Then the body went limp. And the ragged bundle of blood and charred flesh, caught like some wind-tossed rubbish on the wires, was no longer Rubin or anything else.

Sol retched dryly as they ripped the ruined form from the wires. All around him he heard others doing the same, standing straight, with expressionless faces, as though the retching were something animated by their captors, too. And, like all the others, Sol brought forth only dust. . . .

He was flat on his back, staring at the glaring surgical lamp. Around him was the starched rustle of the surgeons' and nurses' white smocks. But he could see nothing except the purpling violence of the light. Some of them were laughing and making jokes as they worked just out of the periphery of his vision. He felt no pain. But he heard the sawing of bone, and he knew that it was his bone. There was such a cheery exchange between the doctors, though, as between men enjoying a mutuality of interest. It was hard to realize . . . he felt no pain. Then there came the clunking sound of parts dropping into a bucket, the sounds of leakings and drippings.

"WHAT ARE YOU TAKING OUT OF ME?" he screamed, seeing himself "boned" like some beast being prepared for someone's meal. "STOP, STOP," he shrilled, visualizing so clearly how he would be as a soft, collapsed carcass of flesh.

"Shut up, Jew," a blue-eyed nurse snarled into his face. "Shut up or we'll take your prick, too."

So he lay still after that. However small a destruction they aimed at, it was far larger than they knew. But at least he felt no pain now and he could pretend he was dead.

"All done," a doctor said. "It will be interesting to see how he functions now." A murmurous medley of voices

sounded a cold glee. "If he functions, if he functions at all, if you know what I mean."

Someone laughed in gentle admonition.

"Ah, Berger, Berger, you are a terror, you are," another voice said.

Sol howled in a fall of dizzying terror. . . .

The guard wouldn't let him turn his head from the window, knocked with menacing playfulness on the side of his jaw every time he tried. So he looked into the vast room which was broken into many cubicles. There were women in each one, some standing at the open ends with weary expressions, some seated listlessly on their beds gazing at the floor. Wild laughter echoed from various parts of the great subdivided room and, like the perverted echo of the laughter, the low crushed sound of moaning.

But for all the rest of the calibrations of the compass, the needle of his attention had only a disinterested hovering movement. His eyes swung back and forth in ever-lessening arcs until they settled with trembling force on the one cubicle. His wife, Ruth, sat on her bed with a sheet up over her nakedness and she didn't see him looking in, for her own attention was riveted on the entrance of her cubicle with terrified anticipation.

"Let me go from here," he begged the guard.

"You bothered and bothered. 'What's happened to my wife? What exactly is she doing?' you asked. 'Why did they take her from the Woman's Section?' You wouldn't be satisfied with half-truths, would you? 'I must know exactly,' you said. All right, I got fed up with you. So here we are. I'm being generous, I'm taking you to see for yourself," the guard said, giving another of those little nudges to the side of Sol's jaw. "So look, keep looking, that's what you're here for. After this you won't ask me any more, you'll know."

"I know now, I understand. It is enough. Please, I couldn't stand to see any more," he whimpered, dry spasms shaking his body like chastising hands.

"*You'll stay and you'll look, once and for all,*" the guard said, pressing his short truncheon into Sol's neck.

So he turned back for what he deserved.

A black-uniformed man entered Ruth's cubicle. He took off his clothes and for a few minutes just displayed his exposed body to the terrified woman on the bed. Finally he pulled the sheet from her nakedness. He seemed to be speaking to her, but only silence reached Sol outside the glass. Ruth began shuddering. Her face turned the color of calcimine, the texture of some powdery substance that could crumble at a touch.

For a minute or two the SS man handled her breasts and her loins vengefully. Her mouth stretched in soundless agony. As though he had been waiting for that, the SS man pulled her to her knees and forced her head down against his body.

Sol began to moan. But just before tears could bring mercy to his eyes, he saw her recognize him. And from that hideously obscene position, pierced so vilely, she endured the zenith of her agony and was able to pass through it. Until finally she was able to award him the tears of forgiveness. But he was not worthy of her award and took the infinitely meaner triumph of blindness, and though he was reamed by cancerous, fiery torments, he was no longer subject to the horrid view, no longer had to share the obscene experience with her. For a while, he could see nothing, could only feel the air moving around him, hear the familiar sounds of the camp, which now had a homely, familiar note and which made the blood beats of pain in his joints almost bearable. And then he went a step further toward the empty blackness of animal relief; he fainted and felt nothing for a long time. . . .

He was standing with his hands up to his cheeks, staring at the child's dead body twisted on a monstrous hook which pierced it from behind and came out the breast. He began

*screaming, the screams of such unbearable size that the
sensation was that of vomiting or giving birth. His grief
forced all his blood out of his pores. He could not contain
it; soon his body would fly into pieces.*

"Naomi, Naomi kinder, my baby, my baby . . ."

*And then, suddenly, there on the same childish body ap-
peared another face. It was a grotesque face for that delicate, childish body, a young man's thin, sallow face—
Morton! And then there appeared the lined, pathetically de-
praved face of George Smith. And then the face was that of
Jesus Ortiz. Each face appeared on the frail baby body with
the cruel hook pointing up toward the head. They were like
slides projected there. Yet in spite of the unreality, the suc-
cession of faces brought him no relief, indeed, made his pain
grow worse, become cumulative, and each moment he
thought to be the ultimate agony was exposed by the next
moment's increased intensity. And the faces kept changing
over the body of his child impaled on the hook, on and on,
a descent into Hell that had no ending. Mabel Wheatly took
her place on the hook, Tessie, Cecil Mapp, Mendel, Buck
White, Mrs. Harmon, Goberman, one after the other without end. . . .*

WILLIAM PILLIN (b. 1910), born in Russia, was educated
at Northwestern University and has been a hand craftsman
as well as poet for many years. Winner of the Davis *Poetry*
award in 1937, he has published in many magazines, his
poems have been collected in *Poems* (1939), *Dance Without Shoes* (1956), *Passage After Midnight* (1958), and
Pavanne for a Fading Memory (1963). In his own words,
he identifies with "the great mass of ordinary people . . . in
terms of needs, aspirations, attitudes."

Miserére
from
PAVANNE FOR A FADING MEMORY

I will not endow you with a false glow
ghetto
or say that only poets and seers
died in your ashes.
Many mourn the scholars and dreamers,
the beautiful innocent talented victims.
I will spare my tears for the
loudmouthed unhappy conniving
Jews
the usurous lenders,
tuberculous hunchbacked
scum of the ghettos (the sweeping of Europe).
For them I will weep,
                         for the whores
pale in the doorways, for the spiderous tradesmen
with their false measures
                         and for all the grey sparrows
hopping about the winters of Poland
                         the grief of whose eyes
went up in thin smoke like a final prayer.

For them I will weep, I want them returned,
the dwellers of dives, brothels and taverns.
I want them
back as they were, piteous, ignoble,
instead of those grey ashes
that like a winding sheet settles on shivering Europe.

4. The American Jews, The Jewish Americans

LESLIE FIEDLER has written that the essence of Jewishness is, quite simply, not to belong, to be an exile, to be alienated. While this may have been a valid generalization for many of his generation, it is not as acceptable today for many young Americans who are Jewish. For the writers today who have to speak to the Jews—the American Jews, and the Jewish Americans—there is only the world as it is. Still, that they have been searching for a life of significant pattern, in Bellow's words, is important. Thus Jo Sinclair and Laura Z. Hobson have tired to show the nature of inconclusive identity and anti-Semitism, and Malamud and Wallant have tried to point out the horrors and meaningfulness of suffering; Roth has contrasted the old and the new, the working class and the nouveau riche, the ordinary Jew in an extraordinary situation; and Kunitz has shown the agonies of interfamilial situations, while Shapiro and Schwartz and Gold have pictured their attempts to find themselves and their way back through a maze of America's homogenizing, standardizing thickets.

"We must get it out of our minds that this is a doomed time," wrote Bellow a few years ago. In spite of Korea, Vietnam, and the growth of centralized power, what he had in mind was what the Prophets had in mind, to confront man with the alternatives of decision, as Buber put it. Just so has this whole generation of writers been concerned with the particulars of life, the difficulties of moral involvement, the question of human experience, the question of faith— even if that meant dealing with myth, corruption, apocalypse, and skepticism. In this context, in answer to the question, What is the human being? it seems proper to answer, as Bellow has, in a Talmudic manner:

> "The fact is that modern writers sin when they suppose that they *know*, as they conceive that physics *knows* or history *knows*. The subject of the novelist is not knowable in any such way. The mystery increases, it does not grow less as types of literature wear out."

For Jews have always been distressed by not knowing. Their tradition is one of constant search for knowledge, constant interpretation. No less vigorous is the present generation's search for the unknowable.

The era of mainstream literature, mainly WASP in its characteristics, has expanded into an era of cultural pluralism. Those formerly looked at as ethnics or exotics no longer have to blend into the woodwork to get a hearing. That this may be ephemeral is possible, particularly if the writers descend to special pleading, polemics, or self-parody. At the very least, this generation of American Jewish writers has been a demonstration of the socio-historical continuum; in the best sense, they have shown themselves a literary movement, rich in its nature, that has reflected the artistic and esthetic and imaginative possibilities of the Jews in America. For this group includes many excellent, first-rate writers as well as many talented writers. With a firm foundation in traditional Judaism, some, like Bellow, experienced the ambiguities of being American and Jewish, whether they grew up in the Twenties or Thirties or Forties or Fifties. For those who grew up as secular or atheistic Jews, there has been an attempt to feel their way into Jewishness and ambiguity. For as Americans they were also Jews, and what made them different was their awareness of the ages-long past of their people, the religion and the culture that were inseparable, the energy generated by the meeting of the immigrant experience and the American present, and the vitality of the tradition, values, languages, and temperament of the people. Being Jewish was the spur, the hair shirt that drove them. This drama was the food for literature.

In selecting writers for this section, I had to bear in mind the knowledge that we are living through a period of rapid change. The young are now more impatient, better educated, and more aware than their parents of the gap between what individuals and countries say they believe in and what they in fact do. It is frustrating for them to be told that solutions cannot be neatly packaged, as they are on television. Reared in security, the young have regretted that the necessity as well as the power to make decisions is not theirs. Brought up in a religion dominated by the past, they have often drifted off. But there are signs of a turnaround. Having noted how bland and homogenized is their environment they have sought roots, innovated new institutions and new patterns in society and religion, and a new literature. And no wonder. More syntheses are on the way. Judaism has always been an evolving and living religio-cultural civilization.

Jo SINCLAIR (Ruth Seid: b. 1913), was born in Brooklyn but raised in Cleveland. The youngest in her family, raised in a melting-pot neighborhood, her experiences and her era went into her first novel, *Wasteland* (1946), which won the $10,000 Harper Prize. Seen through the eyes of a young man and his psychiatrist, this is a touching novel about a second generation American Jew's problem of identity.

The Two Seders
from
WASTELAND

For him, memory in all its sharp and delighted detail began at the table, when all were at last sitting down, and Pa, at the head of that table, sitting on a pillow (remember the matzoth hidden, for its secret, ritual reason, at the edge of that pillow!), had filled each glass with the red wine. The big, shabby book was open before Pa, the electric light gleaming on the Hebrew print. And, before Jake's place, the *Haggadah* Pa had given him was open at the first page (then he would turn the pages backward, because in Jewish books you started to read at the end, then you went toward the beginning of the book). Pa wore his little, round, black prayer cap, and Sig and he wore their hats. Men had to cover their heads when they were praying, see; but those were not really the things to remember.

For him, after twenty years, memory lay in the warm, marvelous odors which pervaded the house on that night, and in the brightness of everything, the knowledge that the dishes were special—unused since last Passover—the walls and floors washed, the candles lit in the joined, heavy candlesticks (Ma had brought them from Europe) standing on the bureau. Sitting there, you smelled the chicken stewing in the pot, the soup (with the matzoth balls floating in it), the *gefüllte* fish cooling on the sink. You smelled the rich, sweet wine in the glasses and saw the gleam of the glass through the deep, red color of the wine (Pa had made that wine himself, special for the Seder). You sat next to Pa, and you saw Debby and Roz play the matzoth game. That was one thing to remember, the matzoth game. One person shut her eyes, see, and the other person broke a piece of matzoth (in twenty years you could not forget that tiny, sharp, cracking sound as the matzoth broke!), then she held the two pieces tightly together, trying to disguise the crack, and said: "O.K., open your eyes." Then the other person would stare at the piece of matzoth and try to guess where the crack was. Boy, what fun when you had guessed right—or even wrong! Sig would be sitting there, eating little pieces of his matzoth, and Ma would be running to the stove to see if the chicken was O.K., the soup hot enough. Debby always sat opposite him, next to Pa on the other side of the table, and she sure was cute; her hair was cut Buster Brown then, and she looked like a little Dutch kid, her round face and her blue eyes so serious.

Pa would be getting ready. "Have you got the eggs and salt water?" he'd say to Ma. "Where's the horseradish? Where's the *charoseth*?" All the little dishes of things that one dipped into during the Seder service. Everything was ready, Ma said breathlessly. Here is the new box of matzoths. Have you got enough glasses for the wine? Sig, you must be starved, it's so late!

Everything was beautiful, just beautiful. Jake felt excited and solemn at once, one ear cocked for when Pa would start to pray. He was wearing his new suit, gray, with knickers that came down past the knees and slipped neatly into knee-length socks. It was a wonderful suit! He began to read the column in English on the first page of the *Haggadah*, remembering the familiar words from last Passover, when he had read them to himself before everything started: *Almost everyone is familiar with the Biblical story of Passover— the festival of the emancipation of the Jewish people from Egypt, the festival of unleavened bread (matzoths), the festival of spring.*

In a dim, scarcely understood way, he felt part of something universal, something strong and ageless. The emancipation of the Jewish people from Egypt. How long ago, before Ma and Pa were born, and before their parents were born;

and yet here they all were, sitting around a table the same
way as those Jewish people, and all over the world Jewish
people were ready to sip the wine and to take a bite of
matzoth. All over the world, families were together, waiting
for a father to start praying. All over the world, the youngest
son present (just like him!) was getting ready to ask the
questions.

Then, finally, Pa started. He followed his father's Hebrew
in the English column, which was to the left of the Hebrew
column in the *Haggadah,* followed his father's chanting voice
that always seemed to cry when it prayed.

Oh, it was so beautiful, it was so strong and so much
the-whole-world-is-doing-this. He pretended he could understand the Hebrew as he read the English. *Blessed art thou,
O Eternal, our God, King of the Universe, Creator of the
fruit of the vine.*

He didn't understand it, no, but it was so beautiful. And
Pa went on praying. No, his voice wasn't like crying, it was
like singing, but singing like a man would sing, way down
low and kind of sad, but strong. Listening, you felt like you
were dreaming about all those things that had happened such
a long time ago, all the terrible things, but how the people
had got away anyway, and how they were safe and they
were going to start all over again in a new land.

Pa took a sip of wine, and everybody else followed him
and took a sip, even Debby, whose face got all screwed up
when she tasted it. That was something you remembered
after twenty years, that first wonderful sip of wine at the
Seder table.

All the details. Pa leaving the table to wash his hands.
Then he comes back. He dips pieces of parsley into salt
water, one piece for everybody, and passes the pieces around.
A little prayer, then he eats his parsley. And, on the echo
of that mournful, chanting prayer, everyone eats his piece.
Even Debby, the baby, her eyes all shining and solemn as
they watch how everybody is doing it—and she, too.

Then Pa breaks the special matzoth and hides some of it

under the edge of the pillow, and he picks up the dish with
the bone and egg on it and everybody touches it while Pa
says the words in Hebrew (you read it in the English column): *This is the bread of affliction which our ancestors
ate in the land of Egypt; let all those who are hungry, enter
and eat thereof. . . .*

But you don't read all of that section; you wait tremu-
lously for Pa to go through the prayer. Your moment is
coming, the biggest moment of the Seder, the moment for
which you have waited so shiveringly. The moment when
the youngest son present asks the questions. This is your
own momentous role in the service. You feel it vaguely,
scarcely understanding it, but not vague is that feeling in
your chest when the moment comes. Not vague, but fierce,
strong, a solemnity and holiness you know must be terribly
important. This is the part you yourself, as the youngest son
at the services, must play. And you know that for thousands
of years Jewish boys, the youngest present on those ancient,
ageless, never-dying evenings, have been playing this same
part. No, you do not quite understand, but you are happy
in this moment because you feel what a meaningful moment
it is, you feel that you are a definite, named (in the Bible,
named) part of this holy thing. Behind you, in the shadow
of history, in the thousands of years of Jews, stand other
boys like you; ahead of you, in the future, in the tomorrow
of the world, stand still other boys not even born yet, not
alive yet, but you know they will all sit at tables like this
some day, they will all ask the meaningful, historical
questions.

Ma fills the wineglasses to brimming now. Pa is still holding up the dish with the bone and egg on it. You sit there,
clutching the *Haggadah.* Your throat is so tight it almost
hurts, your chest feels deep and arched, as if you are getting
ready to start running a race, or start shooting a ball into
the basket at gym, or as if you are ready to take a test, the
pencil poised over the exam paper, only waiting for Teacher
to say: "Go!"

How can you explain it, feeling it so dimly, not even understanding it? How can you explain that you felt like a cog in a monumental, ageless, beautiful wheel which had been turning slow, with terrific meaning, for centuries, and would continue to turn forever, for as long as there were Jews alive? You were in that wheel, and your family, and the Jewish families on earth. How can you explain how you felt?

"Well, ask the questions," Pa said in Yiddish.

There was a little silence, and then Jake, his heart pounding, spoke in an odd, hoarse voice.

"Wherefore is this night distinguished from all other nights?" he read in English from the *Haggadah*. His heart knocked at each beautiful word, at each wonderful phrase. "Any other night we may eat either leavened or unleavened bread, but on this night only unleavened bread; all other nights we may eat any species of herbs, but this night only bitter herbs; all other nights we do not dip even once, but on this night twice; all other nights we eat and drink either sitting or reclined, but on this night we all of us recline."

And it was over for him, his individual, momentous part in the evening. Trembling, he saw the dish replaced on the table. He heard his father's chant start again and rise in mourning Hebrew, and, looking across the table, he saw the solemnity and dream of the moment mirrored in Debby's shining, half-dazed eyes.

His eyes went back to the *Haggadah*. He read the English while his father's voice in Hebrew sang mournfully into the room. *Because we were slaves unto Pharaoh in Egypt, and the eternal, our God, brought us thence with a mighty hand and an outstretched arm.*

His active part in the services was over, and now he sipped wine when his father did, trying to mimic all his gestures. He played the matzoth game with Roz once, and with Debby once, while the chanting went on. He felt all happy now, his nervousness at waiting for the questions gone. He, too, like Sig, ate small pieces of matzoth from time to time, the taste adding to his delicious feeling of hunger.

Languidly, he heard his father's voice falling like sonorous, mournful, rich rain on all their heads. In that soft, dreamy way, he followed the services, sipping when his father did, in the *Haggadah* coming upon the part about the ten plagues, the part about the bitter herbs, and reading to himself as his father showed the herb to everybody and then said it in Hebrew: *It is eaten because the Egyptians embittered the lives of our ancestors in Egypt. . . .*

It was wonderful and joyous to be sitting there, listening to his father pray, reading a little of the book or looking up to see his brother's face, his mother nodding, an abstracted, musing look in her eyes, and Debby's chubby hands folded on the table edge, as if it were a desk and she listening to Teacher.

Pa passed around the bitter herbs with a piece of matzoth for each one, and Jake ate his, the familiar tears springing to his eyes at the sharp taste, familiar and well-loved tears he remembered from last year's Seder. And his tearful eyes read in the *Haggadah,* as his father prayed: *With unleavened bread and bitter herbs shall they eat it.*

Then it was all over for a little bit, because it was time to eat supper. Ma and Roz started to run around, getting the food from the stove and some from the icebox in the hall, and even Debby helped, and Sig said, "Ah, food." And Pa kept saying little pieces of prayer.

What could he remember of that last happy Seder? That all of them seemed to laugh a great deal, and the house was full of words and that laughter and the scents of holiday food.

First they ate hard-boiled egg sliced into salt water. Then came the *gefüllte* fish, cooled but with an undercurrent of warmth in it, and Ma had remembered to put lots of slices of carrot on his plate. Then they had chicken, and he helped himself to the mixture of horseradish and beet. The taste of that made his eyes smart, but he smeared the wonderful red stuff on his chicken anyway and ate it, like Sig and Pa were eating it. And then, last, there was the steaming yellow chicken soup with the two matzoth balls floating in each bowl, the soft, delicious, yellow matzoth balls of Passover.

"How are the matzoth balls?" his mother cried gaily. "Soft, or hard?"

"Soft, soft," Jake cried back. "They're so soft, they're so wonderful!"

And when she smiled with pride, he felt happy, intensely happy.

After the stewed prunes, Pa gave each of them that last small piece of matzoth to chew, the last mouthful of the evening, and Ma and Roz started to clear the table. Pa filled all the wineglasses again, the third time, and started to pray again.

"Well," Sig said, "I've got a date. See you later." He went into his bedroom, and Ma and Roz started to wash dishes.

Sig was somebody you didn't understand, but he was pretty wonderful, all right. He had a job and he brought money home, and he always went out on dates in the evening. He drove a car. Sometimes he gave Jake money to spend. He was going out on a date now, but Jake and Debby would sit at the table under the rain of Pa's praying voice, and finish out the Seder because it was so wonderful. If Sig had had enough and had eaten supper, he could go away if he wanted to; that was his business.

Chant and chant the prayers of this night, and I will remember them forever. I will watch my stern-faced father drink the third cup of wine, and, imitating him and the Jews of all the world, I shall sip from the third cup, too.

Now my mother and Roz are sitting again, talking in low voices of neighbors and relatives, but Debby and I are following the chant.

My father says, "Open the door," and I go to the kitchen door and open it wide.

Chant and chant the prayers of this night. Now the door is open, the Messiah will come into our house and drink from the full cup of wine which has been waiting for him all evening. Feel the mystery, obscurely feel the footsteps of long ago and far away in this room, and Pa praying them in, Pa praying them here.

At the signal, shut the door softly. The Messiah has been here, we have eaten and prayed, the last cup of wine has been drunk, and I have asked the questions; I too, have played my tiny, meaningful part in the Passover. The wine has lulled me. I feel lullaby soft, and I sit next to my father as he prays the last of the evening song.

Sleepily, I watch Ma take Debby's hand and whisper: "Come on to sleep now; it's late, it's after the Seder."

Chant and chant the prayers, listen and feel them inside you like song, and in the Passover dream you are sitting next to your father, you and he the only ones left at the table now as he finishes the services. Chant and chant, Pa, and I will hear and understand inside of me how it was, how the Jews were delivered from bondage and how we are here now, and Debby is going to sleep, and Sig has gone out to people, and Roz has gone outside to talk to other people in the street, and how only I am sitting with you here. I, having asked the questions, having read the *Haggadah,* having had my say as the youngest son, will sit here with my father as he comes to the end of the Seder. Tomorrow will be the second Seder, never so wonderful as the first but very nice in its way. And we will pray again, and we will all of us be here again, a family, all of us close and warm and together.

As his father and he sat alone at the table, the sorrowful deep chant became softer and softer. Jake's eyes closed and he heard his father's prayers, gentle and lullaby safe, go on and on even as he slept. . . .

"It happened at the next Passover," Jake said. "The one I just told you about was the last good Seder I remember. I was fourteen that year."

He felt deathly tired, as if he had been confronted by people long dead, and had walked with them and talked with them in rooms and streets long crumbled and covered with the dust of the years.

"Exactly what happened?" The doctor sat at the desk looking at him, his eyes compassionate. "You say *it* happened. What do you mean when you say it?"

Jake wanted to cry. He was afraid to take himself into that following year, afraid to trace its unknown mazes up until that one known hour at the Seder table.

"Exactly, exactly," he muttered, his voice hoarse. "How can I tell you what it was, exactly? There I was, sitting at the table, asking the questions, and all of a sudden it was as if entirely different people were sitting at the table with me. No, that's not right!"

He rubbed his forehead, scowling in an attempt to remember. He was starting to feel excited again, the tiredness beginning to go somehow as the faces began again to come clear out of the shadows of the years. He smelled the pungent, sweet wine for an instant.

"No," he said excitedly, "they weren't different. No, that wasn't it! It was as if I'd been looking at them through a— well, a screen, all the years up until then. And then, after I'd read the questions, when I looked up from the *Haggadah* —that was the second when the screen disappeared! That was the second when I saw them. The way they really were. Yes, that's the way it happened, Doctor. Right at that second after I'd finished reading the questions."

He started at the doctor in a panic. "Why did it happen at that second?" he cried. "I don't understand it! Why did it have to hit me then, at that second that had always been so wonderful for me? It isn't fair!"

"That was undoubtedly the only time it could have broken on you," the doctor said quickly, like a hand stretched out to him across the desk. "Any intense kind of consciousness or undertaking would have hit you at that time, John. That moment of asking your father the solemn questions of the Passover was the most meaningful moment of the evening for you. I can even say, I think, that it was

the most meaningful moment of the year. As you explained
it, that was the moment when you, an individual, the youngest son at the gathering, spoke up and took your solemn
place in the Passover story of the Jews. To you, it was the
most important time of the year. As far as religion was concerned, and culture, and your position in the family."

"But I wasn't religious! I didn't go to Hebrew school or
to *shule*. I never paid any attention to why we celebrated
the Passover every year. I mean, I didn't know a hell of a
lot about Jewish history, or praying, or anything like that."

"But you loved that holiday. When it came, each year,
you were happy. The whole family was assembled. You
loved sitting there, following the prayers in your book. And
when it came time for you to ask the questions you felt glad
that it was your place in the services. Would you willingly
have given over the asking of those questions to anyone
else?"

"Jesus Christ no!" Jake cried. "They belonged to me. I
was the youngest son there!"

The doctor continued his steady, cool pointing out of
things Jake knew, and yet did not know.

"You may not be religious in the sense that your father
is, but that Passover ritual and promise, that holding out of
spring and hope, are religion to you, John. Just as surely as
if you pray in Hebrew. They're your sense of God, your
clasped hands in prayer. Other men get it from music. Or
from poetry."

Jake stared at him. He felt as though he were swinging in
a dream, shuttling back and forth from this dream to the
one of the past.

"What do you mean, I *am* religious?" he asked painfully. "I was talking about more than twenty years ago, and
why those things happened to me. Why do you say I am,
instead of I was?"

"It strikes me you are a religious man," the doctor told
him quietly. "Just as you were a religious boy. That's not
the important point right now. We're trying to isolate that

moment twenty years ago, when you looked up and saw your family. Has it occurred to you that you had been seeing your family all along, say for the past year, but that you were not conscious of seeing them? Not until all your senses were keyed up for that minute of asking the questions. That was the minute when you were emotionally ripe to see what you had known all the past year but had not told yourself in so many words."

Jake shook his head violently. "No! I don't get that. It's too tough for me to see that."

The quiet, calm voice continued. "People grow into their hour of maturity in a variety of ways. Sometimes they don't know the approximate hour. Let's say the consciousness of your hour came to you when you were fifteen, when you were at the holiday table, when you took your individual part in that evening's pageant of religious history. Will you please try to tell me what happened that evening?"

"All right," Jake said. He felt raw down the full length of him. Some of what the doctor had said made sense, but at the same time how could all those things be true? That he was religious! He, who hated Jews and everything Jewish.

"That's when I started to hate it that I was a Jew," he blurted out.

"Yes, I know," the doctor said. "But let's find out what it was you really started to hate that evening."

Lighting a cigarette, Jake tried to digest the exciting import of that. What it was you really started to hate. There was a lot to think about in words like that. Because, look at him, sure he hated the idea that anybody would think he was Jewish—like the old man, like Sarah and Max, like his family, sure. But look at how he always wondered, kept wondering, if he'd ever meet a Jewish girl, the kind he could marry.

"John," the doctor said at that moment, "talk all those things you're thinking so hard. Put them into words, so that we can examine them."

"I'm thinking how I felt that year," Jake said hesitantly.

"I felt lots older. Sort of serious, you know what I mean? And I kept waiting for Passover. I don't know, that winter was so cold, and it seemed to go on for so long. I kept thinking it would be Passover soon, and my birthday, and then the warm weather would come. The grass, and then pretty soon it would be baseball weather, no school. I don't know, it seemed as if winter would never end. . . ."

. . . and the t had ended. Then it was Passover time, the night of the first Seder. He felt the familiar surge of excitement as he took his bath that evening and got into his suit. It was not a new suit this year, and as he buttoned the gray jacket and looked into the bathroom mirror he had a sudden, rather startling vision of his mother's face. It was tearful, the eyes pleading and the mouth trembling.

She wanted me to have a new suit, he thought, troubled. But the moment slipped away from him as he heard, beyond the bathroom door, his mother cry excitedly: "Roz, turn off the fire under the eggs! Put them in cold water. Pa'll be home soon. Debby, you found all the wineglasses?"

And then it was suddenly time. Pa was home, they were all sitting around the table and the house was crammed with the scents of holiday, the bright electric lights were reflected in the wineglasses, shone back from the dream in Debby's eyes across the table. His *Haggadah* lay open on the table in front of him, and he pushed his hat up a half inch on his forehead.

Blessed art thou, O Eternal, our God, King of the Universe, Creator of the fruit of the vine. His father's voice filled the room, and he blinked under the anticipated power and sonority of the Hebrew half chant, half song.

It was more than excitement this year, for some reason. He felt terribly solemn, almost tearful, as he followed his father's voice in the *Haggadah* English. When he lifted his glass, following his father's gesture, and sipped the wine it seemed to him that the taste was different this year; a powerful, mixed aroma of strength and solemnity seemed to come from the wine as he drank slowly, half afraid to swallow this strangely potent liquid.

He watched the familiar ritual steps, the washing of the hands, dreamily accepted the parsley dipped in salt water and ate it after his father had eaten, watched the elevation of the dish containing the bone and the egg.

He read the English, intensely curious this year about the import of each word and why it was uttered at that approximate moment. He read with a kind of avidness, not realizing with what fierceness he was searching phraseology. It was almost time for him now.

The tearful feeling mounted in him as he read the English which shaped itself on the page under the sound of the Hebrew over his head. *This year we are servants here, but next year we hope to be freemen in the land of Israel.*

"Fill the glasses," his father murmured, and his mother lifted the wine bottle and tipped it over each glass, and the red, rich color mounted to the edge of each glass.

It was time for him. It was time for his voice to go into the room, to join the prayers his father had uttered first, to prepare the way for the prayers with which his father would continue to tell the story.

"Ask the questions," his father murmured tonelessly.

Oh beautiful, Jake thought fleetingly, filled with a painful yearning. Oh mysterious, of God and of life, that is handed down through the thousands of years, oh beautiful that is so strong and meaningful that it will happen again and again, each year, forever, for as long as families sit down to tell and retell this story. And my voice has to come now, the way it's written that the youngest son has to talk at this second. Me, Jake. I have a place in this story.

"Wherefore is this night distinguished from all other nights?" he read, his voice trembling with the wonder and secrecy of life. "Any other night we may eat either leavened or unleavened bread, but on this night only unleavened bread; all other nights we may eat any species of herbs, but this night only bitter herbs; all other nights we do not dip

even once, but on this night twice; all other nights we eat
and drink either sitting or reclined, but on this night we all
of us recline."

His eyes lifted from the page, the dish was set down on
the table, and his father's voice began again.

That was the moment it happened to him. When his eyes
lifted from the words and he himself was so full and deep
with the tearfulness and the awe; at that moment, he looked
around the table to see the eyes of his family because this
had been his wonderful moment in the story and he wanted
to see his feeling reflected in those eyes.

It struck him, with an appalling clarity, that they had not
been listening. As he looked from face to face, clinging hard
at that moment to the sound of his father's voice up there,
above his head, it seemed to him that familiar and known
masks had slipped from these faces and that now the bones
and lines he had never seen before protruded in a terrible
kind of sharpness.

Sig was tapping on the table with the fingers of his left
hand and whistling soundlessly; he kept looking at his watch,
his lips shaped in that silent whistle.

He suddenly saw Roz as she sat restlessly cracking bits of
matzoth. Her face was rouged and powdered, and he was
aware, his heart sinking, of the petulant curve of her lips
under the bright lipstick. What boy's name was she saying to
herself!

His mother? His eyes flew to her face and studied it, but
he knew nothing, the eyes seemed intent on the table, the
face closed to him and to the entire Passover story.

His father's voice pulled his eyes up to the face. Stern, the
head nodding, the upper body swaying slightly, the eyes
focused on the big, worn-looking book from which he was
reading; and now Jake sensed, with a kind of half-nauseated
terror, that the prayers were being uttered mechanically, a
singsong reading of one word after another, one automatic
phrase after another.

Then Jake's eyes jumped to Debby. She was the same!

Of all there, she was the only one with meaning left to her—
the baby! The round, plump face under the Buster Brown
hair (so neatly combed, so milk-white in the electric light)
was turned toward their father. Her eyes were solemn, big
with the dream of the chanted words. He saw her little,
plump hands folded on the table, and he turned away impatiently, raging inwardly. That baby! she still believes
everything, she thinks everything is still wonderful. Look at
her, she believes every sound, every damn lie!

That was when he had first said the word. Lie. It's all a
lie. Everything he's praying, every dish Ma cooked, every
one of us sitting here—we're sitting in a lie.

That was when the terrible doubt hit him across the
heart with a sledge hammer. It all stemmed from the focal
point of that father, sitting so hypocritically at the head of
a table. A father, the teller of the story about the Jews, the
head of a family! Yes, but all the time Jake knew (my
God, how long had he really known!) that he was stingy,
without love for anyone, a smiler at tears, cold as ice and
snow.

All the details of the past year (yes, and years!) sprang
to life, sprang upon the Passover table and danced there like
little horrid, grimacing idols. The eyes of his memory recognized them, approved their taunting steps. Seeing them now,
he remembered that he must have seen them thousands of
times without recognizing them. They were all the times his
mother had asked for more money and his father had smiled
that cold, jeering smile. Dancing there on the table were his
mother's tears, her twisted lips as she cried and the half-
whispered little cries of hopelessness. There, between the
wineglasses, were the gloomy, dust-silent rooms of the house
and the coldness of never a loving word, never a kiss. There,
near the bitter herbs and the shabby book of prayers,
danced his puzzlement at a brother's silence, at the never-
closeness of a sister.

He never once put out his hand to me, Jake thought as

he watched the stranger's face of his father. The Hebrew suddenly was an alien language, and in the room it sounded mechanical, flaccid rote. He never gave me a nickel, or asked me how I felt!

And she? he thought dismally as he watched his mother's face, seeing the tired droop of mouth, the grayness of skin. Did she ever kiss me? I don't remember. But she's warm, she I know, she's my mother! Just as I know he must have done it to her, he must have made her so that she doesn't put her arms around any of us, she doesn't make us all eat together every night, like Irving's mother does. It's as if something's wrong between them, between a mother and father, and something's wrong with all of us because of that and with our house, too. Everything is a lie, because it's a lie that they're a mother and father.

He felt desperately alone. A frightened, shivering sensation accosted him as he felt how all the warm, prayerful ritual was false, and how his own part in this ritual was not true either. His identity as the youngest son asking questions of the head of the house— Why, it was not true! There was no head of the house, no identity for himself, no meaning to those questions he had thought were so beautiful. All the proud story of Jews and faith and strength, Moses smiting the Egyptians, David anointed by the prophet Samuel, all the pictures in the *Haggadah* through the years, were they all as false as this Seder table? Was it all pretense, just as his father pretended to be the head of a family, the leader of prayers, even though he had no right to be sitting there?

No right to be his father, no right to say holy words, no right to drink holy wine, no right to be asked those questions by the youngest son. A dirty, stingy, silent man who didn't flush the toilet after he'd used it, who squeezed his wife until she cried for enough money to buy a suit for a kid of theirs.

Sure, Jake said to himself grimly, why should she keep the house clean when he makes it dirty as soon as he steps into it? Why should she give a damn about everybody eating together, like a family, when he sits there and never says a word, just stuffs his face?

The wine seemed to smell sickeningly sweet, the color unreal for a moment in the glasses, and the mixed odors of the wine and the herbs and the food made him dizzy for an instant, his stomach rocking.

His father, a Jew. Was that the way it was to be a Jew? To be like his father in everyday life, then to sit at the Seder table like a patriarch of old—dignified, praying? It was a lie. His father, a Jew, lived a lie when he pretended to sit like this and tell a beautiful story. It was all a lie. If his father was a Jew, then he didn't want to be a Jew! And yet. Yes, yet how beautiful this Passover story had seemed. How could he bear not to believe it? And yet, there sat his father, a false man, a lie for a father, a Jew. How could he believe in both things?

His mother, who could cry, who could look so helpless, who could not be a strong mother full of love; how could he believe her? Sig and Roz, they did not live like a brother and a sister toward him, they lived like a lie, too. And Debby? She still believed all the lies. When he looked at her he could see how all the prayers were still shining in her eyes. She was the child he had been and was no longer. She was cut off from him because she still believed. She belonged to that father who was not a father; he no longer did. She belonged to the mother who was not really a mother; she had not seen those tears, the helpless eyes, the mother mouth twisted with crying.

He was alone. Like he didn't have a country, or a home, or a family—or even a name. He didn't want that man's name anyway! He'd make his own name. He'd get out, he didn't want any of them anyway. None of them, not even Debby with the dreamy eyes and the clean, white hair. He'd get a job, live his own life away from the lie of their lives.

But there was no comfort in these threats. As Jake sat there, the chant of his father's praying seemed to mount in a blurred, thick crescendo. He felt stifled by the heaviness of the sound and of the wine and food odors.

Listening intently, he heard Sig's amused, bored murmur in Yiddish to their mother: "Every year it seems to take him longer until we can finally eat." He heard their mother's half-apologetic whisper in answer, and tried to bury himself in the *Haggadah*, tried to match the English to the Hebrew words his father was chanting.

At that moment, a terrifying thing happened to him. It's because we're Jews, he thought, and then he was absolutely terrified because it seemed to him that he was trapped with that word, Jew. After all, he was a Jew, and it was something inside, in the blood and in the way one was born of Jews (King David and his harp, Moses smiting the Egyptians!), in the bone and in the flesh, something one could not cut out of himself, or run away from.

He did not dare lift his eyes from the blur of words on the page. How terrifying, but how strange, too, for never before had he called himself that—Jew—as if it were an extraordinary thing. Never before had he been conscious of being one or not being one. It had been simply Jake Brown, just as Passover had been, or eating chicken every Friday and every holiday, or staying home from school on holidays, like all the Jewish kids did. It had been part of life, something not to call by name or even think by name.

And now it was strange, now it was of terror and of trap, of the knowledge that his father was a dirty stranger and his mother a frightened, sad, incapable woman, that his older brother was a stranger with bored, cold eyes, that his sister was overly rouged and her flesh restless for he knew what—yes, he knew what in his own body, and that was more of the terror and lostness. And the other sister was a soft, dreaming baby with solemn eyes, a baby who might cry out in her own fear some day because she did not have mother or father strong enough or clean enough or loving enough.

All of it, the sudden, not-to-be-understood knowledge, the

abrupt premonition, the shaking of earth's foundations, all of this suddenly was tied up with the fact that they were Jews, with this Jewish evening (how beautiful it had been up until a split, jagged moment ago! how full of secrecy and meaning!).

Here they sat, these people and their lie of being Jews, of being solemn and prayerful, of being part of a story about deliverance from bondage. Here they sat, lying with every sip of wine. The old man pretending to be the head of a family on this one night, and all year round he made dirt, he made tears, he gave no love or pennies, or father words or husband looks.

Were all Jews like that? Liars. Come sit at the holy table and pray, sip wine, eat the bitter herbs, pretend to be beautiful, for this one night. Then, all the rest of the year, make your wife cry (my mother, my mother!). Sit, like a silent stranger, at the kitchen table drinking your tea and reading your Goddam Jewish paper, and belching. Not a word for your children. Not a smile for your wife. Not a reason in all the shattered world for all of us to live in this house, pretending to be a family. *Wherefore is this night distinguished from other nights?* It isn't, it isn't! That's a lie, too!

Then, finally, like the next step in a pageant, the terror left Jake. It seeped slowly out of him, and into its place stalked the next ghost, the lostness, the feeling that he was cut off from all of them (there they sat, not knowing, not feeling any of his emotions), from their blood, their kind, their name.

It was a caving in of walls, a lostness in which his identity was drowning (youngest son, wherefore is this night distinguished, but you aren't his son, or his name, so how can you ask the questions, how can you say father to him, so who are you anyway?). Motherless and fatherless, brotherless and sisterless. Nameless. Whatever name he had was a lie. And if his father was Jew, then by God all Jews were like his father and he would not be a Jew! He would not, he would not, though David played on his harp and though there was a miracle at the Red Sea and though the ten plagues were brought down upon the enemy.

As his father chanted with a dry, automatic sound above his head, Jake searched the page of the *Haggadah* for some accusing phrase, some pointed and talismanic word. But now even the English words were alien, meaningless. *And we cried unto the Eternal, the God of our fathers, and the Eternal heard our voice, saw our affliction, our sorrow, and our oppression.*

It was all a lie. These words and his father and the Passover. Jews were a lie.

As he lifted his eyes from the book, he heard Roz cracking bits of matzoth and, without looking, he knew the sullen, hard shape of her mouth, the restless ache in her eyes.

Ma was at the stove, looking into the pots, and Pa's voice went on and on until he could feel how the mumbo-jumbo was parching his own throat. He would not look across the table, into Debby's rapt eyes. He would not look at Sig, because he knew now that the brother look had never been there.

Jake reached for his wineglass and took a sip. His throat was as dry as if he had been praying for hours.

A stern promise shaped itself in his mind as he felt this bitter and nameless moment of leaving all of them. I'll never again sit down with my family at one table. We lied enough. I'll never eat with all of them again and lie that we're a family. I'll never ask him the questions again, that dirty Jew.

And he swallowed the wine solemnly, as if it could seal the promise....

"I remember how ashamed I was," Jake finished slowly. "Ashamed that he was my father, that I was a Jew. Because he was one. And all of us, the whole family, we were Jews. I blamed everything on that, I guess—on the fact that we were Jews. All the dirt and the stinginess and the way we didn't love each other. I guess I thought all Jews were like that, didn't I? I didn't want to be one, I know that. I blamed everything on that."

"You had to blame it on something," the doctor said. "You couldn't bear to face the fact that it was one man, your father, who must have been the source of all that misery."

He caught Jake's eyes, added slowly, "You couldn't face the idea that your mother had chosen this man for her husband, for your father. Did you think it would have been a betrayal on your part to face that choice of hers? To blame her? You had to blame it on the race, didn't you? You were unable to blame her. Did you think then that the Passover ritual, that beautiful thing in your life, had been betrayed, too?"

Jake thought hard about that. "Maybe I did," he said grudgingly. Then, he could not help it, he demanded: "Why should I have blamed her? It wasn't her fault that he was a dirty Jew!"

"But how could she deliberately have picked this dirty Jew for her husband?" the doctor said gently. "Did you ever ask yourself that? Did you picture them in the same bedroom? Did you want to accuse her of marrying a man like that, to ask her how and why she had dared?"

Jake shivered. "No," he said flatly. "I never thought of such things. I tell you I didn't!"

"What did you think of?"

"I remember when I'd bring my report card home," Jake said, tired. "Fathers signed report cards. Well, he'd finally sign mine. He never looked at it, or said anything about the marks I'd got. You should see him write! He sits all hunched over, and it takes him a long time, and then his name is all twisted on the card. You can hardly read it."

He sighed. "I remember how ashamed I was when I took the card back to school. I used to wait for my teachers to laugh at the way he'd written his name, all twisted up, the way it didn't look like English at all. I used to feel so ashamed."

"Did you ever think of your mother at those times?"

"She can't write at all, in any language," Jake said slowly. "She learned how to write her name in Yiddish, and that's all."

"And did you hate that?"

Jake talked more slowly, thinking it out as he talked. "No. She always seemed——. You see, I was always sorry for her. Nothing seemed to be her fault. She always seemed weak; I had to protect her. I knew if she couldn't write, it wasn't her fault."

"I see. What else did you feel about her?"

"I used to wonder," Jake admitted, "if she was ashamed of him, too. I used to wonder how she felt, especially at night, when she was——." He stopped, glared at the doctor.

"Yes?"

"All right! When she was in the same room with him! I used to feel glad, so terribly glad that they had twin beds, that they didn't have to sleep in the same bed. That she didn't have to be too close to him all the time at night."

He took a cigarette from the box the doctor pushed toward him, lit it, noticed with scarcely any feeling that his hands were shaking. Sitting back in the chair, he felt exhausted but intensely relieved, as if he had completed a job of hard labor.

"That's when you began to feel guilty about your mother?" the doctor questioned him softly.

Jake nodded. "I think so, I'm not sure."

"When you realized, however vaguely and without words, that her relationship with your father must be degrading?"

"Yeah!" His jaws seemed set. "Degrading! When I thought about them——together——I could smell how his underwear must smell. That long, thick underwear he'd wear for weeks at a time. I could smell the way it must have smelled in bed!"

"But think it out," the doctor's cool, quiet voice went on. "You can't make up to her for such a repulsive relationship. You can't make up for that dirty old man, for all the ig-

norant, foul personal habits to which he has subjected her."
The voice became firmer. "You can't, John. That would
be incest. You don't want that."

Jake looked dazed. "Listen," he said haltingly, "I was
scared. Ashamed. When I looked at her I felt how she was
asking me for something. I knew that, whatever it was, it
was his fault. Just as it was his fault that I couldn't ask the
questions any more. But I couldn't get it, I couldn't get the
point. I knew he'd spoiled Passover for me. I knew he was
dirty and rotten, that he was Jewish, that he had no business
praying, no business making a Seder for his family."

"So you blamed it on the Jews," the doctor said.

Jake's mouth dropped slackly as he looked back.

"In Germany, a lot of people blame their fear and hunger
on the Jews."

"Yeah, I know," Jake cried, his forehead gashed with
sudden lines. "And they're not Jews themselves, like I am.
That was peculiar, wasn't it? I mean that Passover business,
how I loved it so much, and all of a sudden it seemed like
a dirty lie."

"It seemed like a betrayal," the doctor said. "Beauty and
meaning betrayed by the man who was leading prayers. The
entire essence of Jewishness seemed to crumble for you."

"Yeah, I guess so," Jake mumbled. "Though I didn't
know anything about such words, essence of Jewishness."

"Except inside of you," the doctor pointed out. "You
knew all the words there. Shame for your father, who was
dirty, a Jew, a man who did not give his wife a good life.
If this man was a Jew, then one should be ashamed of being
a Jew."

"Yeah!"

"But is it the Jewishness of your father you dislike? Or
is it the personality, the mind and actions, of the man?"

Jake stared at him.

"Is it the Jews who are dirty and rotten, stingy, illiterate
as far as their adopted land is concerned? Or are all those

traits embodied in this one man, whom your mother chose to marry—who happens to be a Jew?"

The silence in the office washed over Jake warmly, softly, like slow-running, gentle water. He felt the thick, rigid bar of shame quiver for the first time, the bar he had thought so immovably fixed across his heart.

LAURA Z. HOBSON, daughter of Yiddish socialist editor Mikhail Zametkin, was one of the first American Jewish writers to move from self-consciousness to self-awareness. Using a Gentile journalist's experiences, posing as a Jew, to expose anti-Semitism, she suggested the nature of the disease through the device of mistaken identity. Arthur Miller's *Focus* (1945) had a similar theme. She has also written *First Papers* (1964) and *The Tenth Month* (1971).

Phil and Kathy
from
GENTLEMAN'S AGREEMENT

Gluey and inescapable, the extraordinary melancholy clung to him. For more than a week he was never fully free of it. The fast-thickening pile of manuscript in his desk at home, usually the rising barometer of his spirits, offered no permanent release. His mother was definitely improving, the spastic pull at her lips easing; Tom was himself again; Kathy had greeted his account of Flume Inn with disgust for Calkins and praise for him; their new plans were already in order. They were going to Nassau for the first week of February. "I came right out with it at the travel agent's, Phil —there'll be no nonsense in *this* place."

But still there persisted in him the odd sense of omen, heavy-heavy-hanging over. Almost constantly he was strung on an unhappy tension, a man racing for a train and uncertain of the watch that said he still had a minute to go. Impatiently, Phil tried to locate the source of this new infection of moodiness—the inn, his mother's stroke, the hostility of Miss Wales, the continued fruitlessness of Dave's search for a place to live, the postponement of the wedding —but not any one of them, nor the sum of them all, convinced him that he had isolated the cause of the sticky sadness in him.

He had accepted the fact that in a few weeks he'd undergone a swift and deep transfusion into his own blood of a million corpuscles of experience and emotion. He pointed that out one night to Dave, during one of their "sessions" at one in the morning, and Dave had given him a knowing and compassionate smile.

"You're not insulted yet, Phil. It's new every time, so the impact must be quite a business."

"You mean you get indifferent to it in time?"

"No—unless you're a pachyderm. But you aren't as quick and raw. *You're* concentrating a lifetime thing into a few weeks; you're *making* the thing happen every day, writing letters, asking questions, going to meet it. The facts are no different, but it does telescope it."

"Christ, it must be worse on the organism, though, to have it drag out year after year."

"It's not too good." Dave shrugged. "Know something, Phil? Remember I said the other night I've never felt that 'proud to be a Jew' stuff? Any more than you're proud or not proud to be a Christian?" Phil nodded. "Well, there's one thing about Jews that does make me feel sort of set up." He seemed to be thinking it out, and Phil said nothing. "You go talk to a psychiatrist, Phil; tell him about some guy that got his first feel of insult and contempt as a little boy, went on right through life being taunted or held apart, knew that people like him were being beaten and butchered and killed. The psychiatrist would expect a screaming psychopath as a result, wouldn't he?"

"I never thought of it that way," Phil said. "And the wonder is, you're going to say, not that some Jews are aggressive or thirsty for money or power, but that most of them are so ordinary and patient and able to lead regular lives."

Dave smiled. "Kind of remarkable, isn't it? Even happy lives, with love and work and kids and plans. Takes guts, especially the last ten years or so."

They fell silent. Phil wondered if he'd have the guts himself. A dozen times since he'd started this, he'd been called "sensitive," as if it were a failing. But who wouldn't be sensitive or oversensitive, with this sort of daily raw-rubbing technique? Only the gross, the truly vulgar, could remain untouched and unchanged, in an idiot slumber of indifference. Since when was it a flaw of character to be sensitive, anyway?

"Minify said something the other day, Dave. One of those office arguments about how you fight off Communism of Fascism in this country.'"

"The old malarky?" Dave winked. "Let me guess. True democracy!"

"Not from John. Jobs and economic security, sure—even the Fascists and Communists promise that. No, he said it had got down to a matter of equal self-respect, pride, ego, whatever. Take Communism. It's got one good thing, anyway—equality among white and black, all minorities—only the price there is so big, too. If we did it, without the price of free speech, free opposition, free everything—then we'd really be fighting the Communists where it counts."

"Smart cookie."

"So he feels beating antisemitism and antinegroism is a political must now, not just sweet decency."

"What the hell chance have we of getting decent with thirteen million Negroes if we can't lick the much easier business of antisemitism?"

"What indeed?" Phil said. "That's why *Smith's* is going

after it so hard. My stuff will be just the first—he's planning an endless amount to come."

For a long time they sat on, talking, and when he went to bed Phil felt more cheerful. *Smith's* wasn't alone; plans were afoot in many places, more than forty cities were trying their own Springfield Plans, legislatures everywhere were considering and passing anti-bias and civic-rights laws, town meetings were discussing subjects that didn't seem hot a decade ago. As the bigots got more active they inadvertently mobilized the anti-bigots. There were millions of honestly democratic people in the country; they were the great majority, and when they really knew what was in the balance, they'd throw the full weight of their convictions into the scale.

The next morning at the office, he began the fourth article of the series and knew they were holding up, perhaps even building up beyond the level of the first one. Minify had just read the first three in rough draft and asked him in and suggested arranging for a book publication later. Might be; might be. He'd never had a book published, and the suggestion excited him. He considered phoning Kathy at the school just to tell her about John's notion, but decided against it. He was calling for her and taking her home with him at four-thirty; she'd been insistent on getting the dinner there every night, with him and Tom to help and Dave doing the dirty work afterward.

But when he saw her he said nothing about the book.

"Dave's going tomorrow," he greeted her. "He just phoned me."

"Going? Where?"

"California."

"No! And give up that Quirich——"

"He can't abandon his wife and kids forever. Or find a house or apartment. The housing shortage isn't going to end overnight. You *know* he'd never let Anne give him her place for months at a time."

A knobbed something was inside his ribs. For longer than

he wanted to admit he'd waited for Kathy to say one thing. All along, stubbornly, he'd kept on believing in the flat Dave would find, the small house, the shack, the cottage. And all the time, along one fine thread of his mind, he'd listened for the thing she would finally say.

The taxi stopped, and he paid the driver. Upstairs Dave greeted them cheerily, "Hi, you two. I'm off on a date. Should I wind up here with Anne? Your mother's fine, Phil."

His bag was already packed, lying open to receive tomorrow morning's last-minute things. After he'd gone, they spent half an hour with Mrs. Green and then went into the living room. Phil told himself he was just tired. The depression was upon him once again, mucilaginous and cold.

And then Kathy said, "I suppose you're thinking of the cottage, Phil."

"I had thought of it."

"So have I. I thought of it when Anne offered to move."

She fell silent. She had brought it up herself; she'd only been waiting to see if there was not some other solution for Dave. She'd confided that she meant to work on the cottage during the spring months, changing curtains and slip covers, altering its "personality" so there'd be no associative thing with past summers when she and Bill were there. But now Dave was going back to California, driven to reject a job with twice the future of the one he'd go back to. Now a matter of redecorating would no longer hold back the words that could alone keep Dave here. She was looking at him.

"It just would be so uncomfortable for Dave, *knowing* he'd moved into one of those damn neighborhoods that won't take Jews."

"Kathy."

"I loathe it, but that's the way it is up there. New Canaan's worse—nobody can sell or rent to a Jew there. But even Darien is—well, it's a sort of gentleman's agreement when

you buy, especially in the section where Jane's place and
mine are."

"Gentleman—oh, my God, you don't *really*—you *can't*
actually——"

He was standing. He did not remember getting up. I
mustn't fight with her; she's my girl, my wife, almost; I
mustn't yell. I've been bunched up in a tangle these last
days; I've got to hang on.

"You won't buck it, Kathy? Just going to give in, play
along, let their idiotic rules stand?"

"I don't play along—but what could one person do?"

"Tell them to go to hell. What could *they* do?"

"Ostracize him. Even some of the markets. Not deliver
food. Not wait on them promptly. And I couldn't give him
guest cards to the clubs and——" She saw his eyes, and
added, "But, *Phil,* you'll be all done with the series before
we get there."

He made a gesture so sharp that she stopped as if she'd
been struck. His face was new. Rigid in self-control, half
sick. She was frightened.

"Do you expect *us* to live in the cottage," he said, "once
I know all this?"

"Oh, Phil, don't! We can't make the whole world over."

"Or go happily to the clubs?"

"You know I'm on Dave's side."

"I'm not on Dave's side or any side except against *their*
side. My God, Kathy, do you or don't you believe in this?
And if you do, then how——"

The door opened. It was Tom. Phil wanted to order
him at once to his room; interruption now was intolerable.
Tom said "Hi" in a lifeless voice and looked at neither of
them. Had he heard their angry voices on his way upstairs?

Tom had closed the door. He was standing still, just inside it. He made no move to get out of his overcoat or
throw off his cap. Phil glanced at him.

"Anything wrong?"

Tom didn't answer. Kathy took a step toward him.

"Tom," Phil said. "What's up? You look funny."

Tom shook his head. He opened his lips; they worked at something, but no sound came. He stood there, taut with effort, staring, only his jaws moving. Suddenly Phil knew he was trying not to cry.

"Fight, hey?" His voice was hearty, parental. "An argument with one of the guys?"

"Dad." The word was tight. He was ignoring Kathy, looking only at Phil.

I've never seen him like this, Phil thought, state of shock —— and he went to him, everything else forgotten. "Tell me what happened, Tom."

Bewilderment showed in Tom's eyes, and then, suddenly, he put the back of one hand up to his mouth and was sobbing.

"They called me," he said at last, " 'dirty Jew' and 'stinky kike' and——" The next was too broken to make out. "—— and they ran off and I——" His bitter crying claimed the rest of it.

Explosion in the mind—they have hurt my child. Roar of hatred different from any fury when it's only yourself they hurt. Murder for what they've done to my kid——

He put a hand on Tom's head. Kathy was down on her knees, her arms around him.

"But it's just a mistake; it's not *true*, Tom," she cried out to him. "You're not any more Jewish than I am."

Savagery toward her now, blinding, for these words rushing . . . offering the Benison, the Great Assurance that he was all right, as all right as she, with white Protestant all-rightness, unquestioned, unassailable.

Phil couldn't speak. Kathy looked up. There was no sound in the room except Tom's clutching sobs.

Slowly, she stood up, and Tom turned toward his father. "Let's get your coat off, Tom," Phil said quietly. "We'll talk about it in a minute."

Without a word to her, he led Tom from the room. In the bathroom, he took off Tom's cap and washed the streaked face as if this were years ago and Tom still a baby. Calm him first with ordinary things.

"Suppose you start over," he said then. "Was it at school? Was Jimmy in it?"

Tom shook his head to both questions. He was no longer crying, but the indrawn breathing was effort. Phil dried his face, using his own bath towel in some impulse for closeness out of the ordinary. Then he sat on the edge of the bathtub and asked, "Anybody sock anybody?"

"No. They just yelled it. It was at our corner—I sort of walked over to Lexington before I came up. You said I could."

"Sure."

"And then this bunch."

Phil saw the small face go red and contorted again and the dazed look of shock come back. He wanted to take him into his arms, hold him, but boys of eight have the right to give some signal before they are babied. Tom gave none.

"One was a kid from school, about eleven. I don't know the other two and they were playing hop and I asked———"

Phil waited. "You said could you play, too?"

"And the school one said no dirty little Jew could ever get in their games and they all yelled those other things. *Why*, Dad? Why *did* they?" He didn't wait for an answer. "And I started for the school one and he said my father had a long curly beard and they all ran away."

"Here's a glass of water, Tom. Drink some." He got the glass, filled it, offered it. Only while he was drinking did Phil notice he was still in his overcoat. "Give me your coat; it's hot in here." Tom started automatically at the buttons, and Phil said, "You didn't want to tell them you weren't really Jewish?"

Tom gave him a glance that was not only startled but critical. His hands backed each other, fingers laced, reminding Phil of the G2 pledge.

"Good boy. I like that." Phil nodded judiciously. "Lots of kids just like you are Jewish, and if you said it, it'd be sort of admitting there *was* something bad in being Jewish and something swell in not."

Tom nodded, too. Then his eyes hardened; his lower jaw pushed out. For the first time anger replaced hurt. "They wouldn't fight. They just ran."

"Damn cowards," Phil said. "There are grownups like that too, Tom. They do it with wisecracks instead of yelling." They looked at each other. Tom was getting calm again. A moment later, Phil said, "O.K. now?" Tom picked up his cap and overcoat from the wicker hamper. "Then will you go read or something? Gram's sleeping, and I have to talk to Kathy for awhile."

He put his hand on Tom's shoulder and squeezed down on it. "Let's keep it to ourselves till Gram's well." Tom hunched against the pressure and smiled uncertainly at him. Then he left.

For a moment Phil stayed on, his thoughts rocketing back to Kathy. "When something hits into your kid." Just names? Just exclusion? Or really the sly corruption, the comforting poison of superiority? "Any place can be a hotbed, Phil; each house decides it." His house would decide it for Tom—by a phrase, a nuance, an attitude. Each day it would go on being decided, through the rest of his childhood, through adolescence. A passion tore through Phil, to protect this one boy from that slow sure poison.

He went in to Kathy and could think of nothing to say at all. She sat in the chair she'd been in that night he'd first kissed her, when he'd felt the vast hope, like a drug to heal the long misery. Now she looked withdrawn, unwilling; she offered him only silence.

Idiotically, he thought of Miss Wales these last days, the punctilious politeness, the unspeaking docility with which she sat there, taking down every letter he dictated, never looking up inquiringly as he paused, never mentioning the talk they'd had, and never forgiving it. Punishing him was so much easier than questioning herself.

Kathy's silence was as unforgiving. "It was an aberration, Phil——" She would not say it now, candid, eager. He could not, simply could not, say words now to minimize and condone. The inflection in her cry to Tom betrayed her more than any action. The doctor comforting the patient, "You're as healthy as I am"; the psychiatrist saying heartily, "You're no more insane than me." He wanted to explain what he felt, but knew they would quarrel again. "Those are the toughest fights, Phil, the ones about ideas. Families split apart——" Suddenly he saw himself facing Kathy over and over with some such fight between them, next month, next summer, next year. Again and again there would be the distance, the coldness. In this one moment were all the unborn moments.

This was recognition at last. This was the underlying heaviness, the tenacious melancholy, stemming from the unwilling knowledge that they stood miles apart—once the top words were said, the easy words, the usual words. A dozen times he had overlooked, explained, blamed his own solemnity. A dozen times some new evidence had come. Each time, his yearning for her, his love and passion, had conspired to help him skirt the truth that lay, bulky and impassable, in the road before them.

"I'm pretty tired of feeling in the wrong," Kathy said slowly. "Everything I do or say is wrong, about anything Jewish."

He said nothing. He had never heard this ring in her voice.

"All I did just now was to face the facts about Dave in Darien. And then tell Tom just what you told him when he asked that day if he was one."

"Not 'just what.' "

"You really do think I'm an antisemite! And Jane and Harry and everybody who simply recognizes things."

"No, Kathy. I've just come to see more clearly that——"

"You *do* think it. You've thought it secretly a long time."

"It's just that I've come to see that lots of nice people who aren't *are* their unknowing helpers and connivers.

People who'd never beat up a Jew or yell kike at a child. They think antisemitism is something way off there, in a dark crackpot place with low-class morons. That's the biggest thing I've discovered about the whole business."

He put his hand up to span his eyes. His stretched fingers and thumb rotated the flesh at the corners of his closed eyes as if his temples throbbed there. . . . That *is* what I've come to see. She isn't consciously antisemitic, nor is Jane or all the pleasant, intelligent people at the party or the inns and clubs. They despise it; it's an "awful thing." But all of them, and the Craigies and Wales and Jordans and McAnnys, who also deplore it and protest their own innocence—they help it along and then wonder why it grows. Millions like them back up the lunatic vanguard in its war for this country—forming the rear echelons, the home front in the factories, manufacturing the silence and acquiescence. . . .

"You mean we're *not* going to Darien for the summer or to the club, even though you're through by then?"

He dropped his hand. "Let's save that for another time."

She stood up abruptly. And suddenly she was saying, "Oh, damn everything about this horrible thing. They always make trouble for everybody, even their friends. They force everybody to take sides with them——"

"Quit it." He was on his feet, facing her. "Quit that." He heard the rasping voice and was powerless to control it. " 'They' didn't suggest the series—'they' didn't give me my idea—'they' haven't one single goddam thing to do with what's happened between you and me."

"I won't have you shout at me. I know what you're thinking about marrying me—I saw it in your face when I said that to Tom."

"My God, you charge me with thinking you're an anti-semite—I answer that and you switch to Darien and the club! You blame everything on the Jews, and I lose my temper, and you switch to my face and our marriage!"

"Or swear at me or treat me to sarcasm and implication, either. I'm *not* going to marry into hothead shouting and nerves, and you might as well know it now. Let's just call it off for good."

She walked to the table where her purse and hat and gloves lay. She took up her coat and put it on.

"Kathy." The word was only half spoken. "I'm sorry I shouted. I hate it when I do it."

"It isn't the shouting. It's just everything. You've changed so since the first night at Uncle John's. I just know there's no use."

She went to the door. Phil watched her. Then she was gone.

ARTHUR MILLER (b. 1915), son of a New York textile manufacturer, worked at many jobs after his father's business failed in the Great Depression. After attending the University of Michigan, where he won two playwriting contests, he wrote *Focus* (1945), a novel on anti-Semitism, and the prize-winning plays *All My Sons* (1947), *Death of a Salesman* (1949), and *The Crucible* (1953). In his plays and in his short stories, collected in *I Don't Need You Anymore* (1967) his concerns for moral equivocation and justification are evident; above all, Miller has shown the problems inherent in the conflict between society's standards, on the one hand, and one's own moral standards (usually in a family situation) on the other.

Monte Sant' Angelo
from
I DON'T NEED YOU ANYMORE

The driver, who had been sitting up ahead in perfect silence for nearly an hour as they crossed the monotonous green plain of Foggia, now said something. Appello quickly leaned forward in the back seat and asked him what he had said.

"That is Monte Sant' Angelo before you."

Appello lowered his head to see through the windshield of the rattling little Fiat. Then he nudged Bernstein, who awoke resentfully, as though his friend had intruded. "That's the town up there," Appello said. Bernstein's annoyance vanished, and he bent forward. They both sat that way for several minutes, watching the approach of what seemed to them a comically situated town, even more comic than any they had seen in the four weeks they had spent moving from place to place in the country. It was like a tiny old lady living on a high roof for fear of thieves.

The plain remained as flat as a table for a quarter of a mile ahead. Then out of it, like a pillar, rose the butte; squarely and rigidly skyward it towered, only narrowing as it reached its very top. And there, barely visible now, the town crouched, momentarily obscured by white clouds, then appearing again tiny and safe, like a mountain port looming at the end of the sea. From their distance they could make out no road, no approach at all up the side of the pillar.

"Whoever built that was awfully frightened of something," Bernstein said, pulling his coat closer around him. "How do they get up there? Or do they?"

Appello, in Italian, asked the driver about the town. The driver, who had been there only once before in his life and knew no other who had made the trip—despite his being a resident of Lucera, which was not far away—told Appello with some amusement that they would soon see how rarely anyone goes up or comes down Monte Sant' Angelo. "The donkeys will kick and run away as we ascend, and when we come into the town everyone will come out to see. They are very far from everything. They all look like brothers up there. They don't know very much either." He laughed.

"What does the Princeton chap say?" Bernstein asked.

The driver had a crew haircut, a turned-up nose, and a red round face with blue eyes. He owned the car, and although he spoke like any Italian when his feet were on the ground, behind his wheel with two Americans riding behind him he had only the most amused and superior attitude toward everything outside the windshield. Appello, having translated for Bernstein, asked him how long it would take to ascend. "Perhaps three quarters of an hour—as long as the mountain is," he amended.

Bernstein and Appello settled back and watched the butte's approach. Now they could see that its sides were crumbled white stone. At this closer vantage it seemed as though it had been struck a terrible blow by some monstrous hammer that had split its structure into millions of seams. They were beginning to climb now, on a road of sharp broken rocks.

"The road is Roman," the driver remarked. He knew how much Americans made of anything Roman. Then he added, "The car, however, is from Milan." He and Appello laughed.

And now the white chalk began drifting into the car. At their elbows the altitude began to seem threatening. There was no railing on the road, and it turned back on itself every two hundred yards in order to climb again. The Fiat's doors were wavering in their frames; the seat on which they sat kept inching forward onto the floor. A fine film of white talc settled onto their clothing and covered their eyebrows. Both together began to cough. When they were finished Bernstein said, "Just so I understand it clearly and without prejudice, will you explain again in words of one syllable why the hell we are climbing this lump of dust, old man?"

Appello laughed and mocked a punch at him.

"No kidding," Bernstein said, trying to smile.

"I want to see this aunt of mine, that's all." Appello began taking it seriously.

"You're crazy, you know that? You've got some kind of ancestor complex. All we've done in this country is look for your relatives."

"Well, Jesus, I'm finally in the country. I want to see all

the places I came from. You realize that two of my relatives are buried in a crypt in the church up there? In eleven
hundred something."

"Oh, is this where the monks come from?"

"Sure, the two Appello brothers. They helped build that
church. It's very famous, that church. Supposed to be Saint
Michael appeared in a vision or something."

"I never thought I'd know anybody with monks in his
family. But I still think you're cracked on the whole subject."

"Well, don't you have any feeling about your ancestors?
Wouldn't you like to go back to Austria or wherever you
come from and see where the old folks lived? Maybe find
a family that belongs to your line, or something like that?"

Bernstein did not answer for a moment. He did not know
quite what he felt and wondered dimly whether he kept rag-
ging his friend a little because of envy. When they had been
in the country courthouse where Appello's grandfather's portrait and his great-grandfather's hung—both renowned pro-
vincial magistrates; when they had spent the night in Lucera
where the name Appello meant something distinctly honorable, and where his friend Vinny was taken in hand and
greeted in that intimate way because he was an Appello—
in all those moments Bernstein had felt left out and somehow deficient. At first he had taken the attitude that all the
fuss was childish, and yet as incident after incident, landmark after old landmark, turned up echoing the name
Appello, he gradually began to feel his friend combining
with this history, and it seemed to him that it made Vinny
stronger, somehow less dead when the time would come for
him to die.

"I have no relatives that I know of in Europe," he said
to Vinny. "And if I had they'd have all been wiped out by
now."

"Is that why you don't like my visiting this way?"

"I don't say I don't like it," Bernstein said and smiled by
will. He wished he could open himself as Vinny could; it

would give him ease and strength, he felt. They stared down at the plain below and spoke little.

The chalk dust had lightened Appello's black eyebrows. For a fleeting moment it occurred to Appello that they resembled each other. Both were over six feet tall, both broad-shouldered and dark men. Bernstein was thinner, quite gaunt and long-armed. Appello was stronger in his arms and stooped a little, as though he had not wanted to be tall. But their eyes were not the same. Appello seemed a little Chinese about the eyes, and they glistened black, direct, and for women, passionately. Bernstein gazed rather than looked; for him the eyes were dangerous when they could be fathomed, and so he turned them away often, or downward, and there seemed to be something defensively cruel, and yet gentle there.

They liked each other not for reasons so much as for possibilities; it was as though they both had sensed they were opposites. And they were lured to each other's failings. With Bernstein around him Appello felt diverted from his irresponsible sensuality, and on this trip Bernstein often had the pleasure and pain of resolving to deny himself no more.

The car turned a hairpin curve with a cloud below on the right, when suddenly the main street of the town arched up before them. There was no one about. It had been true, what the driver had predicted—in the few handkerchiefs of grass that they had passed on the way up the donkeys had bolted, and they had seen shepherds with hard mustaches and black shakos and long black cloaks who had regarded them with the silent inspection of those who live far away. But here in the town there was no one. The car climbed onto the main street, which flattened now, and all at once they were being surrounded by people who were coming out of their doors, putting on their jackets and caps. They did look strangely related, and more Irish than Italian.

The two got out of the Fiat and inspected the baggage strapped to the car's roof, while the driver kept edging protectively around and around the car. Appello talked laughingly with the people, who kept asking why he had come so far, what he had to sell, what he wanted to buy, until he at last made it clear that he was looking only for his aunt. When he said the name the men (the women remained at home, watching from the window) looked blank, until an old man wearing rope sandals and a knitted skating cap came forward and said that he remembered such a woman. He then turned, and Appello and Bernstein followed up the main street with what was now perhaps a hundred men behind them.

"How come nobody knows her?" Bernstein asked.

"She's a widow. I guess she stays home most of the time. The men in the line died out here twenty years ago. Her husband was the last Appello up here. They don't go much by women; I bet this old guy remembered the name because he knew her husband by it, not her."

The wind, steady and hard, blew through the town, washing it, laving its stones white. The sun was cool as a lemon, the sky purely blue, and the clouds so close their keels seemed to be sailing through the next street. The two Americans began to walk with the joy of it in their long strides. They came to a two-story stone house and went up a dark corridor and knocked. The guide remained respectfully on the sidewalk.

There was no sound within for a few moments. Then there was—short scrapes, like a mouse that started, stopped, looked about, started again. Appello knocked once more. The doorknob turned, and the door opened a foot. A pale little woman, not very old at all, held the door wide enough for her face to be seen. She seemed very worried.

"Ha?" she asked.

"I am Vincent Georgio."

"Ha?" she repeated.

"Vincenzo Giorgio Appello."

Her hand slid off the knob, and she stepped back. Appello, smiling in his friendly way, entered, with Bernstein behind him closing the door. A window let the sun flood the room, which was nevertheless stone cold. The woman's mouth was open, her hands were pressed together as in prayer, and the tips of her fingers were pointing at Vinny. She seemed crouched, as though about to kneel, and she could not speak.

· Vinny went over to her and touched her bony shoulder and pressed her into a chair. He and Bernstein sat down too. He told her of their relationship, saying names of men and women, some of whom were dead, others whom she had only heard of and never met in this sky place. She spoke at last, and Appello could not understand what she said. She ran out of the room suddenly.

"I think she thinks I'm a ghost or something. My uncle said she hadn't seen any of the family in twenty or twenty-five years. I bet she doesn't think there are any left."

She returned with a bottle that had an inch of wine at the bottom of it. She ignored Bernstein and gave Appello the bottle. He drank. It was vinegar. Then she started to whimper and kept wiping the tears out of her eyes in order to see Appello. She never finished a sentence, and Appello kept asking her what she meant. She kept running from one corner of the room to another. The rhythm of her departures and returns to the chair was getting so wild that Appello raised his voice and commanded her to sit.

"I'm not a ghost, Aunty. I came here from America—" He stopped. It was clear from the look in her bewildered, frightened eyes that she had not thought him a ghost at all, but what was just as bad—if nobody had ever come to see her from Lucera, how could anybody have so much as thought of her in America, a place that did exist, she knew, just as heaven existed and in exactly the same way. There was no way to hold a conversation with her.

They finally made their exit, and she had not said a coherent word except a blessing, which was her way of expressing her relief that Appello was leaving, for despite the unutterable joy at having seen with her own eyes an-

other of her husband's blood, the sight was itself too terrible
in its associations, and in the responsibility it laid upon her
to welcome him and make him comfortable.

They walked toward the church now. Bernstein had not
been able to say anything. The woman's emotion, so pure
and violent and wild, had scared him. And yet, glancing at
Appello, he was amazed to see that his friend had drawn
nothing but a calm sort of satisfaction from it, as though
his aunt had only behaved correctly. Dimly he remembered
himself as a boy visiting an aunt of his in the Bronx, a
woman who had not been in touch with the family and had
never seen him. He remembered how forcefully she had fed
him, pinched his cheeks, and smiled and smiled every time
he looked up at her, but he knew that there was nothing
of this blood in that encounter; nor could there be for him
now if on the next street corner he should meet a woman
who said she was of his family. If anything, he would want
to get away from her, even though he had always gotten
along well with his people and hadn't even the usual snobbery about them.

As they entered the church he said to himself that some
part of him was not plugged-in, but why he should be disturbed about it mystified him and even made him irritated
with Appello, who was asking the priest where the tombs
of the Appellos were.

They descended into the vault of the church, where the
stone floor was partly covered with water. Along the walls,
and down twisting corridors running out of a central arched
hall, were tombs so old no candle could illuminate most of
the worn inscriptions. The priest vaguely remembered an
Appello vault, but had no idea where it was. Vinny moved
from one crypt to another with the candle he had bought
from the priest. Bernstein waited at the opening of the corridor, his neck bent to avoid touching the roof with his hat.
Appello, stooped even more than usual, looked like a monk
himself, an antiquary, a gradually disappearing figure squinting down the long darkness of the ages for his name on a

stone. He could not find it. Their feet were getting soaked. After half an hour they left the church and outside fought off shivering small boys selling grimy religious postcards, which the wind kept taking from their fists.

"I'm sure it's there," Appello said with fascinated excitement. "But you wouldn't want to stick out a search, would you?" he asked hopefully.

"This is no place for me to get pneumonia," Bernstein said.

They had come to the end of a side street. They had passed shops in front of which pink lambs hung head down with their legs stiffly jutting out over the sidewalk. Bernstein shook hands with one and imagined for Vinny a scene for Chaplin in which a monsignor would meet him here, reach out to shake his hand, and find the cold lamb's foot in his grip, and Chaplin would be mortified. At the street's end they scanned the endless sky and looked over the precipice upon Italy.

"They might even have ridden horseback down there, in armor—Appellos." Vinny spoke raptly.

"Yeah, they probably did," Bernstein said. The vision of Appello in armor wiped away any desire to kid his friend. He felt alone, desolate as the dried-out chalk sides of this broken pillar he stood upon. Certainly there had been no knights in his family.

He remembered his father's telling of his town in Europe, a common barrel of water, a town idiot, a baron nearby. That was all he had of it, and no pride, no pride in it at all. Then I am an American, he said to himself. And yet in that there was not the power of Appello's narrow passion. He looked at Appello's profile and felt the warmth of that gaze upon Italy and wondered if any American had ever felt like this in the States. He had never in his life sensed so strongly that the past could be peopled, so vivid with generations, as it had been with Vinny's aunt an hour ago. A common water barrel, a town idiot, a baron who lived nearby. . . . It had nothing to do with *him*. And standing there he sensed a broken part of himself and wondered with a slight amusement if this was what a child felt on discovering that the parents who brought him up were not his own, and that he entered his house not from warmth but from the street, from a public and disordered place. . . .

They sought and found a restaurant for lunch. It was at the other edge of the town and overhung the precipice. Inside, it was one immense room with fifteen or twenty tables; the front wall was lined with windows overlooking the plain below. They sat at a table and waited for someone to appear. The restaurant was cold. They could hear the wind surging against the window-panes, and yet the clouds at eye level moved serenely and slow. A young girl, the daughter of the family, came out of the kitchen, and Appello was questioning her about food when the door to the street opened and a man came in.

For Bernstein there was an abrupt impression of familiarity with the man, although he could not fathom the reason for his feeling. The man's face looked Sicilian, round, dark as earth, high cheekbones, broad jaw. He almost laughed aloud as it instantly occurred to him that he could converse with this man in Italian. When the waitress had gone, he told this to Vinny, who now joined in watching the man.

Sensing their stares, the man looked at them with a merry flicker of his cheeks and said, *"Buon giorno."*

"Buon giorno," Bernstein replied across the four tables between them, and then to Vinny, "Why do I feel that about him?"

"I'll be damned if I know," Vinny said, glad now that he could join his friend in a mutually interesting occupation.

They watched the man, who obviously ate here often. He had already set a large package down on another table and now put his hat on a chair, his jacket on another chair, and his vest on a third. It was as though he were making companions of his clothing. He was in the prime of middle age and very rugged. And to the Americans there was something mixed up about his clothing. His jacket might have been worn by a local man; it was tight and black and wrinkled and chalkdust-covered. His trousers were dark brown and very thick, like a peasant's, and his shoes were snubbed up at the ends and of heavy leather. But he wore a black hat, which was unusual up here where all had caps, and he had a tie. He wiped his hands before loosening the knot; it was a striped tie, yellow and blue, of silk, and no tie to be bought in this part of the world, or worn by these people. And there was a look in his eyes that was not a peasant's inward stare; nor did it have the innocence of the other men who had looked at them on the streets here.

The waitress came with two dishes of lamb for the Americans. The man was interested and looked across his table at the meat and at the strangers. Bernstein glanced at the barely cooked flesh and said, "There's hair on it."

Vinny called the girl back just as she was going to the newcomer and pointed at the hair.

"But it's lamb's hair," she explained simply.

They said, "Oh," and pretended to begin to cut into the faintly pink flesh.

"You ought to know better, signor, than to order meat today."

The man looked amused, and yet it was unclear whether he might not be a trifle offended.

"Why not?" Vinny asked.

"It's Friday, signor," and he smiled sympathetically.

"That's right!" Vinny said although he had known all along.

"Give me fish," the man said to the girl and asked with intimacy about her mother, who was ill these days.

Bernstein had not been able to turn his eyes from the man. He could not eat the meat and sat chewing bread and feeling a rising urge to go over to the man, to speak to him. It struck him as being insane. The whole place—the town, the clouds in the streets, the thin air—was turning into a hallucination. He knew this man. He was sure he knew him. Quite clearly that was impossible. Still, there was a thing beyond the impossibility of which he was drunkenly sure, and it was that if he dared he could start speaking Italian fluently with this man. This was the first moment since leaving America that he had not felt the ill-ease of traveling and of being a traveler. He felt as comfortable as Vinny now, it seemed to him. In his mind's eye he could envisage the inside of the kitchen; he had a startlingly clear image of what the cook's face must be like, and he knew where a certain kind of soiled apron was hung.

"What's the matter with you?" Appello asked.

"Why?"

"The way you're looking at him."

"I want to talk to him."

"Well, talk to him," Vinny smiled.

"I can't speak Italian, you know that."

"Well, I'll ask him. What do you want to say?"

"Vinny—" Bernstein started to speak and stopped.

"What?" Appello asked, leaning his head closer and looking down at the tablecloth.

"Get him to talk. Anything. Go ahead."

Vinny, enjoying his friend's strange emotionalism, looked across at the man, who was now eating with careful but immense satisfaction. "*Scusi, signor.*"

The man looked up.

"I am a son of Italy from America. I would like to talk to you. We're strange here."

The man, chewing deliciously, nodded with his amiable and amused smile and adjusted the hang of his jacket on the nearby chair.

"Do you come from around here?"

"Not very far."

"How is everything here?"

"Poor. It is always poor."

"What do you work at, if I may ask?"

The man had now finished his food. He took a last long drag of his wine and got up and proceeded to dress and pull his tie up tightly. When he walked it was with a slow, wide sway, as though each step had to be conserved.

"I sell cloth here to the people and the stores, such as they are," he said. And he walked over to the bundle and set it carefully on a table and began untying it.

Bernstein's cheeks began to redden. From where he sat he could see the man's broad back, ever so slightly bent over the bundle. He could see the man's hands working at the knot and just a corner of the man's left eye. Now the man was laying the paper away from the two bolts of cloth, carefully pressing the wrinkles flat against the table. It was as though the brown paper were valuable leather that must not be cracked or rudely bent. The waitress came out of the kitchen with a tremendous round loaf of bread at least two feet in diameter. She gave it to him, and he placed it flat on top of the cloth, and the faintest feather of a smile curled up on Bernstein's lips. Now the man folded the paper back and brought the string around the bundle and tied the knot, and Bernstein uttered a little laugh, a laugh of relief.

Vinny looked at him, already smiling, ready to join the laughter, but mystified. "What's the matter?" he asked.

Bernstein took a breath. There was something a little triumphant, a new air of confidence and superiority in his face and voice. "He's Jewish, Vinny," he said.

Vinny turned to look at the man. "Why?"

"The way he works that bundle. It's exactly the way my father used to tie a bundle—and my grandfather. The whole history is packing bundles and getting away. Nobody else can be as tender and delicate with bundles. That's a Jewish man tying a bundle. Ask him his name."

Vinny was delighted. "Signor," he called with that warmth reserved in his nature for members of families.

The man, tucking the end of the string into the edge of the paper, turned to them with his kind smile.

"May I ask your name, signor?"

"My name? Mauro di Benedetto."

"Mauro di Benedetto. Sure!" Vinny laughed, looking at Bernstein. "That's Morris of the Blessed. Moses."

"Tell him I'm Jewish," Bernstein said, a driving eagerness charging his eyes.

"My friend is Jewish," Vinny said to the man, who now was hoisting the bundle onto his shoulder.

"Heh?" the man asked, confused by their sudden vivacity. As though wondering if there were some sophisticated American point he should have understood, he stood there smiling blankly, politely, ready to join in this mood.

"*Judeo,* my friend."

"*Judeo?*" he asked, the willingness to get the joke still holding the smile on his face.

Vinny hesitated before this steady gaze of incomprehension. "*Judeo.* The people of the Bible," he said.

"Oh, yes, yes!" The man nodded now, relieved that he was not to be caught in ignorance. "*Ebreo,*" he corrected. And he nodded affably to Bernstein and seemed a little at a loss for what they expected him to do next.

"Does he know what you mean?" Bernstein asked.

"Yeah, he said 'Hebrew,' but it doesn't seem to connect. Signor," he addressed the man, "why don't you have a glass of wine with us? Come, sit down."

"Thank you, signor," he replied appreciatively, "but I must be home by sundown and I'm already a little late."

Vinny translated, and Bernstein told him to ask why he had to be home by sundown.

The man apparently had never considered the question before. He shrugged and laughed and said, "I don't know. All my life I get home for dinner on Friday night, and I like to come into the house before sundown. I suppose it's a habit; my father—you see, I have a route I walk, which is this route. I first did it with my father, and he did it with his father. We are known here for many generations past. And my father always got home on Friday night before sundown. It's a manner of the family, I guess."

"*Shabbas* begins at sundown on Friday night," Bernstein said when Vinny had translated. "He's even taking home the fresh bread for the Sabbath. The man is a Jew, I tell you. Ask him, will you?"

"*Scusi*, signor," Vinny smiled. "My friend is curious to know whether you are Jewish."

The man raised his thick eyebrows not only in surprise but as though he felt somewhat honored by being identified with something exotic. "Me?" he asked.

"I don't mean American," Vinny said, believing he had caught the meaning of the man's glance at Bernstein. "*Ebreo*," he repeated.

The man shook his head, seeming a little sorry he could not oblige Vinny. "No," he said. He was ready to go but wanted to pursue what obviously was his most interesting conversation in weeks. "Are they Catholics? The Hebrews?"

"He's asking me if Jews are Catholics," Vinny said.

Bernstein sat back in his chair, a knotted look of wonder in his eyes. Vinny replied to the man, who looked once again at Bernstein as though wanting to investigate this strangeness further, but his mission drew him up and he wished them good fortune and said good-by. He walked to the kitchen door and called thanks to the girl inside, saying the loaf would warm his back all the way down the mountain, and he opened the door and went out into the wind of the street and the sunshine, waving to them as he walked away.

They kept repeating their amazement on the way back to the car, and Bernstein told again how his father wrapped bundles. "Maybe he doesn't know he's a Jew, but how could he not know what Jews are?" he said.

"Well, remember my aunt in Lucera?" Vinny asked. "She's a schoolteacher, and she asked me if you believed in Christ. She didn't know the first thing about it. I think the ones in these small towns who ever heard of Jews think they're a Christian sect of some kind. I knew an old Italian once who thought all Negroes were Jews and white Jews were only converts."

"But his name . . ."

"Benedetto is an Italian name too. I never heard of 'Mauro' though. 'Mauro' is strictly from the old sod."

"But if he had a name like that, wouldn't it lead him to wonder if. . . ?"

"I don't think so. In New York the name 'Salvatore' is turned into 'Sam.' Italians are great for nicknames; the first name never means much. 'Vincenzo' is 'Enzo,' or 'Vinny' or even 'Chico.' Nobody would think twice about 'Mauro' or damn near any other first name. He's obviously a Jew, but I'm sure he doesn't know it. You could tell, couldn't you? He was baffled."

"But, my God, bringing home a bread for *Shabbas!*" Bernstein laughed, wide-eyed.

They reached the car, and Bernstein had his hand on the door but stopped before opening it and turned to Vinny. He looked heated; his eyelids seemed puffed. "It's early. If you still want to I'll go back to the church with you. You can look for the boys."

Vinny began to smile, and then they both laughed together, and Vinny slapped him on the back and gripped his shoulder as though to hug him. "Goddam, now you're starting to enjoy this trip!"

As they walked briskly toward the church the conversation returned always to the same point, when Bernstein would say, "I don't know why, but it gets me. He's not only acting like a Jew, but an Orthodox Jew. And doesn't even know—I mean it's strange as hell to me."

"You look different, you know that?" Vinny said.

"Why?"

"You do."

"You know a funny thing?" Bernstein said quietly as they entered the church and descended into the vault beneath it. "I feel like—at home in this place. I can't describe it."

Beneath the church, they picked their way through the shallower puddles on the stone floor, looking into vestibules, opening doors, searching for the priest. He appeared at last—they could not imagine from where—and Appello bought another candle from him and was gone in the shadows of the corridors where the vaults were.

Bernstein stood—everything was wet, dripping. Behind him, flat and wide, rose the stairway of stones bent with the tread of millions. Vapor steamed from his nostrils. There was nothing to look at but shadow. It was dank and black and low, an entrance to hell. Now and then in the very far distance he could hear a step echoing, another, then silence. He did not move, seeking the root of an ecstasy he had not dreamed was part of his nature; he saw the amiable man trudging down the mountains, across the plains, on routes marked out for him by generations of men, a nameless traveler carrying home a warm bread on Friday night—and kneeling in church on Sunday. There was an irony in it he could not name. And yet pride was running through him. Of what he should be proud he had no clear idea; perhaps it was only that beneath the brainless crush of history a Jew had secretly survived, shorn of his consciousness but forever caught by that final impudence of a Saturday Sabbath in a Catholic country; so that his very unawareness was proof, a proof as mute as stones, that a past lived. A past for me, Bernstein thought, astounded by its importance for him, when in fact he had never had a religion or even, he realized now, a history.

He could see Vinny's form approaching in the narrow corridor of crypts, the candle flame flattening in the cold draft. He felt he would look differently into Vinny's eyes; his condescension had gone and with it a certain embarrassment. He felt loose, somehow the equal of his friend—and how odd that was when, if anything, he had thought of himself as superior. Suddenly, with Vinny a yard away, he saw that his life had been covered with an unrecognized shame.

"I found it! It's back there!" Vinny was laughing like a young boy, pointing back toward the dark corridor.

"That's great, Vinny," Bernstein said. "I'm glad."

They were both stooping slightly under the low, wet ceiling, their voices fleeing from their mouths in echoed whispers. Vinny held still for an instant, catching Bernstein's respectful happiness, and saw there that his search was not worthless sentiment. He raised the candle to see Bernstein's face better, and then he laughed and gripped Bernstein's wrist and led the way toward the flight of steps that rose to the surface. Bernstein had never liked anyone grasping him, but from this touch of a hand in the darkness, strangely, there was no implication of a hateful weakness.

They walked side by side down the steep street away from the church. The town was empty again. The air smelled of burning charcoal and olive oil. A few pale stars had come out. The shops were all shut. Bernstein thought of Mauro di Benedetto going down the winding, rocky road, hurrying against the setting of the sun.

DELMORE SCHWARTZ (b. 1913), born in Brooklyn, went to several universities before taking his BA at New York University in 1935. One of America's major poets, his poems have been described as both controlled and cerebral. His favorite theme is what he calls "the wound of consciousness," a compound of the ego, a sense of Jewish-oriented guilt and alienation, and an awareness of history and time. Among his principal works are *Shenandoah, A Verse Play* (1941), *Genesis Book I* (1943), *The World is a Wedding* (1948), *Vaudeville for a Princess* (1950), and *Summer Knowledge* (1958).

Abraham
from
SUMMER KNOWLEDGE

I was a mere boy in a stone-cutter's shop
When, early one evening, my raised hand
Was halted and the soundless voice said:
"Depart from your father and your country
And the things to which you are accustomed,
Go now into a country unknown and strange,
I will make of your children a great nation,
Your generations will haunt every generation of
   all the nations,
They will be like the stars at midnight, like the sand
   of the sea."
Then I looked up at the infinite sky,
Star-pointing and silent, and it was then, on that evening,
   that I
Became a man: that evening was my manhood's birthday.

I went then to Egypt, the greatest of nations.
There I encountered the Pharaoh who built the tombs,
Great public buildings, many theaters, and seashore villas:
And my wife's beauty was such that, fearing his power and
   lust,
I called her my sister, a girl neither for him nor for me.
And soon was fugitive, homeless and almost helpless again.
Living alone with my sister, becoming very rich
In all but children, in herds, in possessions, the herds
   continually and newly
Increased my possessions through subline prodigies of
   progeny.

From time to time, in the afternoon's revery
In the late sunlight or the cool of the evening

I called to mind the protracted vanity of the promise
Which had called me forth from my father's house
   unwillingly
Into the last strangeness of Egypt and the childless desert.
Then Sarah gave me her handmaid, a young girl
That I might at least at last have children by another.
And later, when a great deal else had occurred,
I put away Hagar, with almost unbearable remorse
Because the child was the cause of so much rivalry and
   jealousy.
At last when all this had passed or when
The promise seemed the puzzle parts of an old dream,
When we were worn out and patient in all things
The stranger came, sauve and elegant,
A messenger who renewed the promise, making Sarah
Burst out laughing hysterically!

But the boy was born and grew and I saw
What I had known, I knew what I had seen, for he
Possessed his mother's beauty and his father's humility,
And was not marked and marred by her sour irony and
   my endless anxiety.

Then the angel returned, asking that I surrender
My son as a lamb to show that humility
Still lived in me, and was not altered by old age
   and prosperity.

I said nothing, shocked and passive. Then I said, but to
   myself alone:
"This was to be expected. These promises
Are never unequivocal or unambiguous, in this
As in all things which are desired the most:
I have had great riches and great beauty.

I cannot expect the perfection of every wish
And if I deny the command, who knows what will happen?"

But his life was forgiven and given back to me:
His children and their children are an endless nation:
Dispersed on every coast. And I am not gratified
Nor astonished. It has never been otherwise:
Exiled, wandering, dumbfounded by riches,
Estranged among strangers, dismayed by the infinite sky,
An alien to myself until at last the caste of the last
  alienation,
The angel of death comes to make the alienated and
  indestructible one a part of his famous and democratic
  society.

KARL SHAPIRO (b. 1913), whose grandparents came from
Eastern Europe, was born and brought up in Baltimore,
Chicago, and Norfolk. His first volume of poetry, *Person,
Place and Thing* (1942), and *V-Letter* (1944) were edited
by his wife. *Poems 1940–1953* (1953), *Poems of a Jew*
(1958), *The Bourgeois Poet* (1964), and *Selected Poems*
(1968) are his more recent works. Stephen Spender wrote
that Shapiro is "a poet of rare intellectual strength."

The 151st Psalm
from
POEMS OF A JEW

Are You looking for us? We are here.
Have You been gathering flowers, Elohim?
We are Your flowers, we have always been.
When will You leave us alone?
5 We are in America.

We have been here three hundred years.
And what new altar will You deck us with?

Whom are You following, Pillar of Fire?
What barn do You seek shelter in?
10 At whose gate do You whimper
In this great Palestine?
Whose wages do You take in this New World?
But Israel shall take what it shall take,
Making us ready for Your hungry Hand!

15 Immigrant God, You follow me;
You go with me, You are a distant tree;
You are the beast that lows in my heart's gates;
You are the dog that follows at my heel;
You are the table on which I lean;
20 You are the plate from which I eat.

Shepherd of the flocks of praise,
Youth of all youth, ancient of days,
Follow us.

The Leg
from
POEMS OF A JEW

Among the iodoform, in twilight-sleep,
What have I lost? he first inquires,
Peers in the middle distance where a pain,
Ghost of a nurse, hazily moves, and day,
Her blinding presence pressing in his eyes
And now his ears. They are handling him
With rubber hands. He wants to get up.

One day beside some flowers near his nose
He will be thinking, *When will I look at it?*
And pain, still in the middle distance, will reply,

At what? and he will know it's gone,
O where! and begin to tremble and cry.
He will begin to cry as a child cries
Whose puppy is mangled under a screaming wheel.

Later, as if deliberately, his fingers
Begin to explore the stump. He learns a shape
That is comfortable and tucked in like a sock.
This has a sense of humor, this can despise
The finest surgical limb, the dignity of limping,
The nonsense of wheel chairs. Now he smiles to the wall:
The amputation becomes an acquisition.

For the leg is wondering where he is (all is not lost)
And surely he has a duty to the leg;
He is its injury, the leg is his orphan,
He must cultivate the mind of the leg,
Pray for the part that is missing, pray for peace
In the image of man, pray, pray for its safety,
And after a little it will die quietly.

The body, what is it, Father, but a sign
To love the force that grows us, to give back
What in Thy palm is senselessness and mud?
Knead, knead the substance of our understanding
Which must be beautiful in flesh to walk,
That if Thou take me angrily in hand
And hurl me to the shark, I shall not die!

Jew
from
POEMS OF A JEW

The name is immortal but only the name, for the rest
Is a nose that can change in the weathers of time or persist
Or die out in confusion or model itself on the best.

But the name is a language itself that is whispered and
  hissed
Through the houses of ages, and ever a language the same,
And ever and ever a blow on our heart like a fist.

And this last of our dream in the desert, O curse of our
  name,
Is immortal as Abraham's voice in our fragment of prayer
Adonai, Adonai, for our bondage of murder and shame!

And the word for the murder of God will cry out on the air
Though the race is no more and the temples are closed of
  our will
And the peace is made fast on the earth and the earth is
  made fair;

Our name is impaled in the heart of the world on a hill
Where we suffer to die by the hands of ourselves, and to
  kill.

BERNARD MALAMUD (b. 1914), a product of Brooklyn,
was educated at CCNY and Columbia University. A writer
noted for his compassion, he has been concerned with the
commonplace and the grotesques in a Jewish setting. "The
Jews are the very stuff of drama," wrote Malamud, for it
is uncertainty that produces drama. *The Natural* (1952),
a surrealistic baseball story, has been his only novel in a
non-Jewish framework. *The Assistant* (1957), about a
Jewish grocer, was followed by *The Magic Barrel* (1958),
A New Life (1961), *Idiots First* (1963), *The Fixer*
(1966), *The Tenants* (1972), and *Rembrandt's Hat*
(1973).

The Lady of the Lake
from
THE MAGIC BARREL

Henry Levin, an ambitious, handsome thirty, who walked the floors in Macy's book department wearing a white flower in his lapel, having recently come into a small inheritance, quit, and went abroad seeking romance. In Paris, for no reason he was sure of, except that he was tired of the past—tired of the limitations it had imposed upon him; although he had signed the hotel register with his right name, Levin took to calling himself Henry R. Freeman. Freeman lived for a short while in a little hotel on a narrow gas lamp-lit street near the Luxembourg Gardens. In the beginning he liked the sense of foreignness of the city—of things different, anything likely to happen. He liked, he said to himself, the possible combinations. But not much did happen; he met no one he particularly cared for (he had sometimes in the past deceived himself about women, they had come to less than he had expected); and since the heat was hot and tourists underfoot, he felt he must flee. He boarded the Milan express, and after Dijon, developed a painful, palpitating anxiety. This grew so troublesome that he had serious visions of leaping off the train, but reason prevailed and he rode on. However, he did not get to Milan. Nearing Stresa, after a quick, astonished look at Lake Maggiore, Freeman, a nature lover from early childhood, pulled his suitcase off the rack and hurriedly left the train. He at once felt better.

An hour later he was established in a pensione in a villa not far from the line of assorted hotels fronting the Stresa shore. The padrona, a talkative woman, much interested in her guests, complained that June and July had been lost in unseasonable cold and wet. Many had cancelled; there were few Americans around. This didn't exactly disturb Freeman, who had had his full share of Coney Island. He lived in an airy, French-windowed room, including soft

bed and spacious bath, and though personally the shower
type, was glad of the change. He was very fond of the
balcony at his window, where he loved to read, or study
Italian, glancing up often to gaze at the water. The long
blue lake, sometimes green, sometimes gold, went out of
sight among distant mountains. He liked the red-roofed
town of Pallanza on the opposite shore, and especially the
four beautiful islands in the water, tiny but teeming with
palazzi, tall trees, gardens, visible statuary. The sight of
these islands aroused in Freeman a deep emotion; each a
universe—how often do we come across one in a lifetime?
—filled him with expectancy. Of what, he wasn't sure.
Freeman still hoped for what he hadn't, what few got in
the world and many dared not to think of; to wit, love,
adventure, freedom. Alas, the words by now sounded
slightly comical. Yet there were times, when he was staring
at the islands, if you pushed him a little he could almost
cry. Ah, what names of beauty: Isola Bella, dei Pescatori,
Madre, and del Dongo. Travel is truly broadening, he
thought; who ever got emotional over Welfare Island?

But the islands, the two he visited, let him down. Freeman walked off the vaporetto at Isola Bella amid a crowd
of late-season tourists in all languages, especially German,
who were at once beset by many vendors of cheap trinkets.
And he discovered there were guided tours only—strictly
no unsupervised wandering—the pink palazzo full of old
junk, surrounded by artificial formal gardens, including
grottoes made of seashells, the stone statuary a tasteless
laugh. And although Isola dei Pescatori had some honest
atmosphere, old houses hugging crooked streets, thick nets
drying in piles near fishermen's dories drawn up among
trees; again there were tourists snapping all in pictures,
and the whole town catering to them. Everybody had something to sell you could buy better in Macy's basement.
Freeman returned to his pensione, disappointed. The islands, beautiful from afar, up close were so much stage
scenery. He complained thus to the padrona and she urged

him to visit Isola del Dongo. "More natural," she persuaded him. "You never saw such unusual gardens. And the palazzo is historical, full of the tombs of famous men of the region, including a cardinal who became a saint. Napoleon, the emperor slept there. The French have always loved this island. Their writers wept at its beauty."

However, Freeman showed little interest. "Gardens I've seen in my time." So, when restive, he wandered in the back streets of Stresa, watching the men playing at boccia, avoiding the laden store windows. Drifting by devious routes back to the lake, he sat at a bench in the small park, watching the lingering sunset over the dark mountains and thinking of a life of adventure. He watched alone, talked now and then to stray Italians—almost everybody spoke a good broken English—and lived too much on himself. On weekends, there was, however, a buzz of merriment in the streets. Excursionists from around Milan arrived in busloads. All day they hurried to their picnics; at night one of them pulled an accordion out of the bus and played sad Venetian or happy Neapolitan songs. Then the young Italians and their girls got up and danced in tight embrace in the public square; but not Freeman.

One evening at sunset, the calm waters so marvelously painted they drew him from inactivity, he hired a rowboat, and for want of anyplace more exciting to go, rowed toward the Isola del Dongo. He had no intention other than reaching it, then turning back, a round trip completed. Two-thirds of the way there, he began to row with growing uneasiness which soon became dread, because a stiff breeze had risen, driving the sucking waves against the side of the boat. It was a warm wind, but a wind was a wind and the water was wet. Freeman didn't row well —had learned late in his twenties, despite the nearness of Central Park—and he swam poorly, always swallowing water, never enough breath to get anywhere; clearly a landlubber from the word go. He strongly considered returning to Stresa—it was at least a half mile to the island,

then a mile and a half in return—but chided himself for
his timidity. He had, after all, hired the boat for an hour;
so he kept rowing though he feared the risk. However, the
waves were not too bad and he had discovered the trick of
letting them hit the prow head-on. Although he handled
his oars awkwardly, Freeman, to his surprise, made good
time. The wind now helped rather than hindered; and daylight—reassuring—still lingered in the sky among streaks
of red.

At last Freeman neared the island. Like Isola Bella, it
rose in terraces through hedged gardens crowded with
statuary, to a palazzo on top. But the padrona had told the
truth—this island looked more interesting than the others,
the vegetation lush, wilder, exotic birds flying around. By
now the place was bathed in mist, and despite the thickening dark, Freeman recaptured the sense of awe and beauty
he had felt upon first beholding the islands. At the same
time he recalled a sad memory of unlived life, his own,
of all that had slipped through his fingers. Amidst these
thoughts he was startled by a movement in the garden by
the water's edge. It had momentarily seemed as though a
statue had come to life, but Freeman quickly realized a
woman was standing this side of a low marble wall, watching the water. He could not, of course, make out her face,
though he sensed she was young; only the skirt of her white
dress moved in the breeze. He imagined someone waiting
for her lover, and was tempted to speak to her, but then
the wind blew up strongly and the waves rocked his rowboat. Freeman hastily turned the boat with one oar, and
pulling hard, took off. The wind drenched him with spray,
the rowboat bobbed among nasty waves, the going grew
frighteningly rough. He had visions of drowning, the rowboat swamped, poor Freeman slowly sinking to the bottom,
striving fruitlessly to reach the top. But as he rowed, his
heart like a metal disk in his mouth, and still rowed on,
gradually he overcame his fears; also the waves and wind.
Although the lake was by now black, though the sky still

dimly reflected white, turning from time to time to peer
ahead, he guided himself by the flickering lights of the
Stresa shore. It rained hard as he landed, but Freeman, as
he beached the boat, considered his adventure an accom-
plishment and ate a hearty supper at an expensive restaurant.

The curtains billowing in his sunny room the next
morning, awoke him. Freeman rose, shaved, bathed, and
after breakfast got a haircut. Wearing his bathing trunks
under slacks, he sneaked onto the Hotel Excelsior beach
for a dip, short but refreshing. In the early afternoon he
read his Italian lesson on the balcony, then snatched a
snooze. At four-thirty—he felt he really hadn't made up
his mind until then—Freeman boarded the vaporetto making its hourly tour of the islands. After touching at Isola
Madre, the boat headed for the Isola del Dongo. As they
were approaching the island, coming from the direction
opposite that which Freeman had taken last night, he
observed a lanky boy in bathing trunks sunning himself on
a raft in the lake—nobody he recognized. When the vaporetto landed at the dock on the southern side of the
island, to Freeman's surprise and deep regret, the area was
crowded with the usual stalls piled high with tourist gew-
gaws. And though he had hoped otherwise, inspection of
the island was strictly in the guide's footsteps, and *vietato*
trying to go anywhere alone. You paid a hundred lire for
a ticket, then trailed behind this unshaven, sad-looking
clown, who stabbed a jaunty cane at the sky as he announced in three languages to the tourists who followed
him: "Please not stray nor wander. The family del Dongo,
one of the most illustrious of Italy, so requests. Only thus
ees eet able to remain open thees magnificent 'eestorical
palatz and supreme jardens for the inspection by members
of all nations."

They tailed the guide at a fast clip through the palace,
through long halls hung with tapestries and elaborate
mirrors, enormous rooms filled with antique furniture, old

books, paintings, statuary—a lot of it in better taste than the stuff he had seen on the other island; and he visited where Napoleon had slept—a bed. Yet Freeman secretly touched the counterpane, though not quickly enough to escape the all-seeing eye of the Italian guide, who wrathfully raised his cane to the level of Freeman's heart and explosively shouted, "Basta!" This embarrassed Freeman and two British ladies carrying parasols. He felt bad until the group—about twenty—were led into the garden. Gazing from here, the highest point of the island, at the panorama of the golden-blue lake, Freeman gasped. And the luxuriant vegetation of the island was daring, voluptuous. They went among orange and lemon trees (he had never known that lemon was a perfume), magnolia, oleander—the guide called out the names. Everywhere were flowers in great profusion, huge camellias, rhododendron, jasmine, roses in innumerable colors and varieties, all bathed in intoxicating floral fragrance. Freeman's head swam; he felt dizzy, slightly off his rocker at this extraordinary assailment of his senses. At the same time, though it was an "underground" reaction, he experienced a painful, contracting remembrance—more like a warning—of personal poverty. This he had difficulty accounting for, because he usually held a decent opinion of himself. When the comical guide bounced forward, with his cane indicating cedars, eucalyptus, camphor and pepper trees, the former floorwalker, overcome by all he was for the first time seeing, at the same moment choked by almost breathless excitement, fell behind the group of tourists, and pretended to inspect the berries of a pepper tree. As the guide hurried forward, Freeman, although not positive he had planned it so, ducked behind the pepper tree, ran along a path beside a tall laurel shrub and down two flights of stairs; he hopped over a marble wall and went hastily through a small wood, expectant, seeking, he thought only God knew what.

He figured he was headed in the direction of the garden

by the water where he had seen the girl in the white dress last night, but after several minutes of involved wandering, Freeman came upon a little beach, a pebbly strand, leading down stone steps into the lake. About a hundred feet away a raft was anchored, nobody on it. Exhausted by the excitement, a little moody, Freeman sat down under a tree, to rest. When he glanced up, a girl in a white bathing suit was coming up the steps out of the water. Freeman stared as she sloshed up the shore, her wet skin glistening in bright sunlight. She had seen him and quickly bent for a towel she had left on a blanket, draped it over her shoulders and modestly held the ends together over her high-arched breast. Her wet black hair fell upon her shoulders. She stared at Freeman. He rose, forming words of apology in his mind. A haze that had been before his eyes, evaporated. Freeman grew pale and the girl blushed.

Freeman was, of course, a New York City boy from away back. As the girl stood there unselfconsciously regarding him—it could not have been longer than thirty seconds—he was aware of his background and certain other disadvantages; but he also knew he wasn't a bad-looking guy, even, it could be said, quite on the handsome side. Though a pinprick bald at the back of his noggin—not more than a dime could adequately cover—his head of hair was alive, expressive; Freeman's gray eyes were clear, unenvious, nose well-molded, the mouth generous. He had well-proportioned arms and legs and his stomach lay respectfully flat. He was a bit short, but on him, he knew, it barely showed. One of his former girl friends had told him she sometimes thought of him as tall. This counterbalanced the occasions when he had thought of himself as short. Yet though he knew he made a good appearance, Freeman feared this moment, partly because of all he hungered for from life, and partly because of the uncountable obstacles existing between strangers, may the word forever perish.

She, apparently, had no fear of their meeting; as a matter

of surprising fact, seemed to welcome it, immediately curious about him. She had, of course, the advantage of position—which included receiving, so to speak, the guest-intruder. And she had grace to lean on; herself also favored physically—mama, what a queenly· high-assed form— itself the cause of grace. Her dark, sharp Italian face had that quality of beauty which holds the mark of history, the beauty of a people and civilization. The large brown eyes, under straight slender brows, were filled with sweet light; her lips were purely cut as if from red flowers; her nose was perhaps the one touch of imperfection that perfected the rest—a trifle long and thin. Despite the effect, a little of sculpture, her ovoid face, tapering to a small chin, was soft, suffused with the loveliness of youth. She was about twenty-three or -four. And when Freeman had, to a small degree, calmed down, he discovered in her eyes a hidden hunger, or memory thereof; perhaps it was sadness; and he felt he was, for this reason, if not unknown others, sincerely welcomed. Had he, Oh God, at last met his fate?

"Si è perduto?" the girl asked, smiling, still tightly hold-ing her white towel. Freeman understood and answered in English. "No, I came on my own. On purpose you might say." He had in mind to ask her if she remembered having seen him before, namely in last night's rowboat, but didn't.

"Are you an American?" she inquired, her Italian ac-cent pleasantly touched with an English one.

"That's right."

The girl studied him for a full minute, and then hes-itantly asked, "Are you, perhaps, Jewish?"

Freeman suppressed a groan. Though secretly shocked by the question, it was not, in a way, unexpected. Yet he did not look Jewish, could pass as not—had. So without batting an eyelash, he said, no, he wasn't. And a moment later added, though he personally had nothing against them.

"It was just a thought. You Americans are so varied," she explained vaguely.

"I understand," he said, "but have no worry." Lifting his hat, he introduced himself: "Harry R. Freeman, traveling abroad."

"My name," she said after an absent-minded pause, "is Isabella del Dongo."

Safe on first, thought Freeman. "I'm proud to know you." He bowed. She gave him her hand with a gentle smile. He was about to surprise it with a kiss when the comical guide appeared at a wall a few terraces above. He gazed at them in astonishment, then let out a yell and ran down the stairs, waving his cane like a rapier.

"Transgressor," he shouted at Freeman.

The girl said something to calm him, but the guide was too furious to listen. He grabbed Freeman's arm, yanking him toward the stairs. And though Freeman, in the interest of good manners, barely resisted, the guide whacked him across the seat of the pants; but the ex-floorwalker did not complain.

Though his departure from the island had been, to put it mildly, an embarrassment (the girl had vanished after her unsuccessful momentary intercession), Freeman dreamed of a triumphant return. The big thing so far was that she, a knockout, had taken to him; he had been favored by her. Just why, he couldn't exactly tell, but he could tell yes, had seen in her eyes. Yet wondering if yes why yes—an old habit—Freeman, among other reasons he had already thought of, namely the thus and therefore of man-woman attraction—laid it to the fact that he was different, had dared. He had, specifically, dared to duck the guide and be waiting for her at the edge of the lake when she came out of it. And she was different too, (which of course quickened her response to him). Not only in her looks and background, but of course different as regards past. (He had been reading with fascination about the del Dongos in all the local guide books.) Her past he could see boiling in her all the way back to the knights of old, and then some; his own history was something else again, but men were malleable, and he wasn't afraid of attempting to create daring combinations: Isabella and Henry Freeman..Hoping to meet someone like her was his main reason for having come abroad. And he had also felt he would be appreciated more by a European woman; his personality, that is. Yet, since their lives were *so* different, Freeman had moments of grave doubt, wondered what trials he was in for if he went after her, as he had every intention of doing: with her unknown family—other things of that sort. And he was in afterthought worried because she had asked him if he was Jewish. Why had the question popped out of her pretty mouth before they had even met? He had never before been asked anything like this by a girl, under let's call it similar circumstances. Just when they were looking each other over. He was puzzled because he absolutely did not look Jewish. But then he figured her question might have been a "test" of some kind, she making it a point, when a man attracted her, quickly to determine his "eligibility." Maybe she had once had some sort of unhappy experience with a Jew? Unlikely, but possible, they were now everywhere. Freeman finally explained it to himself as "one of those things," perhaps a queer thought that had for no good reason impulsively entered her mind. And because it was queer, his answer, without elaboration, was sufficient. With ancient history why bother? All these things—the odds against him, whetted his adventurous appetite.

He was in the grip of an almost unbearable excitement and must see her again soon, often, become her friend—not more than a beginning but where begin? He considered calling her on the telephone, if there was one in a palazzo where Napoleon had slept. But if the maid or somebody answered the phone first, he would have a ridiculous time identifying himself; so he settled for sending her a note. Freeman wrote a few lines on good stationery he had bought for the purpose, asking if he might have the pleasure of seeing her again under circumstances favorable to leisurely conversation. He suggested a carriage ride to one of the other lakes in the neighborhood, and signed his name not Levin, of course, but Freeman. Later he told the padrona that anything addressed to that name was meant for him. She was always to refer to him as Mr. Freeman. He gave no explanation, although the padrona raised interested brows; but after he had slipped her—for reasons of friendship—a thousand lire, her expression became serene. Having mailed the letter, he felt time descend on him like an intricate trap. How would he ever endure until she answered? That evening he impatiently hired a rowboat and headed for Isola del Dongo. The water was glassy smooth but when he arrived, the palazzo was dark, almost gloomy, not a single window lit; the whole island looked dead. He saw no one, though he imagined her presence. Freeman thought of tying up at a dock and searching around a bit, but it seemed like folly. Rowing back to Stresa, he was stopped by the lake patrol and compelled to show his passport. An officer advised him not to row on the lake after dark; he might have an accident. The next morning, wearing sunglasses, a light straw, recently purchased, and a seersucker suit, he boarded the vaporetto and soon landed on the island of his dreams, together with the usual group of tourists. But the fanatic guide at once spied Freeman, and waving his cane like a schoolmaster's rod, called on him to depart peacefully. Fearing a scene that the girl would surely hear of, Freeman left at once, greatly annoyed. The padrona, that night, in a confidential mood, warned him not to have anything to do with anybody on the Isola del Dongo. The family had a perfidious history and was known for its deceit and trickery.

On Sunday, at the low point of a depression after an afternoon nap, Freeman heard a knock on his door. A long-legged boy in short pants and a torn shirt handed him an envelope, the corner embossed with somebody's coat of arms. Breathlessly, Freeman tore it open and extracted a sheet of thin bluish paper with a few lines of spidery writing on it: "You may come this afternoon at six. Ernesto will accompany you. I. del D." It was already after five. Freeman was overwhelmed, giddy with pleasure.

"Tu sei Ernesto?" he asked the boy.

The boy, perhaps eleven or twelve, who had been watching Freeman with large curious eyes, shook his head. "No, Signore. Sono Giacobbe."

"Dov'è Ernesto?"

The boy pointed vaguely at the window, which Freeman took to mean that whoever he was was waiting at the lake front.

Freeman changed in the bathroom, emerging in a jiffy with his new straw hat on and the seersucker suit. "Let's go." He ran down the stairs, the boy running after him.

At the dock, to Freeman's startled surprise, "Ernesto" turned out to be the temperamental guide with the pestiferous cane, probably a major domo in the palazzo, long with the family. Now a guide in another context, he was obviously an unwilling one, to judge from his expression! Perhaps a few wise words had subdued him and though haughty still, he settled for a show of politeness. Freeman greeted him courteously. The guide sat not in the ritzy launch Freeman had expected to see, but at the stern of an oversize, weatherbeaten rowboat, a cross between a fishing dory and a small lifeboat. Preceded by the boy, Freeman climbed in over the unoccupied part of the rear seat, then, as Giacobbe took his place at the oars, hesitantly sat down next to Ernesto. One of the boatmen on the shore gave them a shove off and the boy began to row. The big boat seemed hard to maneuver, but Giacobbe, working deftly with a pair of long, heavy oars, managed with ease. He rowed quickly from the shore and toward the island where Isabella was waiting.

Freeman, though heartened to be off, contented, loving the wide airy world, wasn't comfortable sitting so snug with Ernesto, who smelled freshly of garlic. The talkative guide was a silent traveler. A dead cheroot hung from the corner of his mouth, and from time to time he absently poked his cane in the slats at the bottom of the boat; if there was no leak, Freeman thought, he would create one. He seemed tired, as if he had been carousing all night and had found no time to rest. Once he removed his black felt hat to mop his head with a handkerchief, and Freeman realized he was bald and looked surprisingly old.

Though tempted to say something pleasant to the old man—no hard feelings on this marvelous journey, Freeman had no idea where to begin. What would he reply to a grunt? After a time of prolonged silence, now a bit on edge, Freeman remarked, "Maybe I'd better row and give the boy a rest?"

"As you weesh." Ernesto shrugged.

Freeman traded places with the boy, then wished he hadn't. The oars were impossibly heavy; he rowed badly, allowing the left oar to sink deeper into the water than the right, thus twisting the boat off course. It was like pulling a hearse, and as he awkwardly splashed the oars around, he was embarrassedly aware of the boy and Ernesto, alike in their dark eyes and greedy beaks, a pair of odd birds, openly staring at him. He wished them far far away from the beautiful island and in exasperation pulled harder. By dint of determined effort, though his palms were painfully blistered, he began to row rhythmically, and the boat went along more smoothly. Freeman gazed up in triumph but they were no longer watching him, the boy trailing a straw in the water, the guide staring dreamily into the distance.

After a while, as if having studied Freeman and decided, when all was said and done, that he wasn't exactly a villain, Ernesto spoke in a not unfriendly tone.

"Everybody says how reech ees America?" he remarked.

"Rich enough," Freeman grunted.

"Also thees ees the same with you?" The guide spoke

with a half-embarrassed smile around his drooping cheroot butt.

"I'm comfortable," Freeman replied, and in honesty added, "but I have to work for a living."

"For the young people ees a nice life, no? I mean there ees always what to eat, and for the woman een the house many remarkable machines?"

"Many," Freeman said. Nothing comes from nothing, he thought. He's been asked to ask questions. Freeman then gave the guide an earful on the American standard of living, and he meant living. This for whatever it was worth to such as the Italian aristocracy. He hoped for the best. You could never tell the needs and desires of others.

Ernesto, as if memorizing what he had just heard, watched Freeman row for a while.

"Are you in biziness?" he ultimately asked.

Freeman searched around and came up with, "Sort of in public relations."

Ernesto now threw away his butt. "Excuse me that I ask. How much does one earn in thees biziness in America?"

Calculating quickly, Freeman replied, "I personally average about a hundred dollars a week. That comes to about a quarter million lire every month."

Ernesto repeated the sum, holding onto his hat in the breeze. The boy's eyes had widened. Freeman hid a satisfied smile.

"And your father?" Here the guide paused, searching Freeman's face.

"What about him?" asked Freeman, tensing.

"What ees hees trade?"

"Was. He's dead—insurance."

Ernesto removed his respectful hat, letting the sunlight bathe his bald head. They said nothing more until they had reached the island, then Freeman, consolidating possible gain, asked him in a complimentary tone where he had learned his English.

"Everywhere," Ernesto replied, with a weary smile, and,

Freeman, alert for each shift in prevailing wind, felt that if he hadn't made a bosom friend, he had at least softened an enemy; and that, on home grounds, was going good.

They landed and watched the boy tie up the boat; Freeman asked Ernesto where the signorina was. The guide now looking bored by it all, pointed his cane at the top terraces, a sweeping gesture that seemed to take in the whole upper half of the luscious island. Freeman hoped the man would not insist on accompanying him and interfering with his meeting with the girl; but when he looked down from looking up without sighting Isabella, both Ernesto and Giacobbe had made themselves scarce. Leave it to the Italians at this sort of thing, Freeman thought.

Warning himself to be careful, tactful, he went quickly up the stairs. At each terrace he glanced around, then ran up to the next, his hat already in his hand. He found her after wandering through profusions of flowers, where he had guessed she would be, alone in the garden behind the palazzo. She was sitting on an old stone bench near a little marble fountain, whose jets from the mouths of mocking elves sparkled in mellow sunlight.

Beholding her, the lovely face, sharply incised, yet soft in its femininity, the dark eyes pensive, her hair loosely knotted at the nape of her graceful neck, Freeman ached to his oar-blistered fingers. She was wearing a linen blouse of some soft shade of red that fell gently upon her breasts, and a long, slender black skirt; her tanned legs were without stockings; and on her narrow feet she wore sandals. As Freeman approached her, walking slowly to keep from loping, she brushed back a strand of hair, a gesture so beautiful it saddened him, because it was gone in the doing; and though Freeman, on this miraculous Sunday evening was aware of his indefatigable reality, he could not help thinking as he dwelt upon her lost gesture, that she might be as elusive as it, as evanescent; and so might this island be, and so, despite all the days he had lived through, good, bad and boring, that too often sneaked into his thoughts—

so, indeed, might he today, tomorrow. He went toward her with a deep sense of the transitoriness of things, but this feeling was overwhelmed by one of pure joy when she rose to give him her hand.

"Welcome," Isabella said, blushing; she seemed happy, yet, in her manner, a little agitated to see him—perhaps one and the same thing—and he wanted then and there to embrace her but could not work up the nerve. Although he felt in her presence a fulfillment, as if they had already confessed love for one another, at the same time Freeman sensed an uneasiness in her which made him think, though he fought the idea, that they were far away from love; or at least were approaching it through opaque mystery. But that's what happened, Freeman, who had often been in love, told himself. Until you were lovers you were strangers.

In conversation he was at first formal. "I thank you for your kind note. I have been looking forward to seeing you."

She turned toward the palazzo. "My people are out. They have gone to a wedding on another island. May I show you something of the palace?"

He was at this news both pleased and disappointed. He did not at the moment feel like meeting her family. Yet if she had presented him, it would have been a good sign.

They walked for a while in the garden, then Isabella took Freeman's hand and led him through a heavy door into the large rococo palazzo.

"What would you care to see?"

Though he had superficially been through two floors of the building, wanting to be led by her, this close to him, Freeman replied, "Whatever you want me to."

She took him first to the chamber were Napoleon had slept. "It wasn't Napoleon himself, who slept here," Isabella exclaimed. "He slept on Isola Bella. His brother Joseph may have been here, or perhaps Pauline, with one of her lovers. No one is sure."

"Oh ho, a trick," said Freeman.

"We often pretend," she remarked. "This is a poor country."

They entered the main picture gallery. Isabella pointed out the Titians, Tintorettos, Bellinis, making Freeman breathless; then at the door of the room she turned with an embarrassed smile and said that most of the paintings in the gallery were copies.

"Copies?" Freeman was shocked.

"Yes, although there are some fair originals from the Lombard school."

"All the Titians are copies?"

"All."

This slightly depressed him. "What about the statuary —also copies?"

"For the most part."

His face fell.

"Is something the matter?"

"Only that I couldn't tell the fake from the real."

"Oh, but many of the copies are exceedingly beautiful," Isabella said. "It would take an expert to tell they weren't originals."

"I guess I've got a lot to learn," Freeman said.

At this she squeezed his hand and he felt better.

But the tapestries, she remarked as they traversed the long hall hung with them, which darkened as the sun set, were genuine and valuable. They meant little to Freeman: long floor-to-ceiling, bluish-green fabrics of woodland scenes: stags, unicorns and tigers disporting themselves, though in one picture, the tiger killed the unicorn. Isabella hurried past this and led Freeman into a room he had not been in before, hung with tapestries of somber scenes from the *Inferno*. One before which they stopped, was of a writhing leper, spotted from head to foot with pustulaing sores which he tore at with his nails but the itch went on forever.

"What did he do to deserve his fate?" Freeman inquired.

"He falsely said he could fly."

"For that you go to hell?"

She did not reply. The hall had become gloomily dark, so they left.

From the garden close by the bench where the raft was anchored, they watched the water turn all colors. Isabella had little to say about herself—she seemed to be quite often pensive—and Freeman, concerned with the complexities of the future, though his heart contained multitudes, found himself comparatively silent. When the night was complete, as the moon was rising, Isabella said she would be gone for a moment, and stepped behind a shrub. When she came forth, Freeman had this utterly amazing vision of her, naked, but before he could even focus his eyes on her flowerlike behind, she was already in the water, swimming for the raft. After an anguished consideration of could he swim that far or would he drown, Freeman, eager to see her from up close (she was sitting on the raft, showing her breasts to the moon) shed his clothes behind the shrub where her delicate things lay, and walked down the stone steps into the warm water. He swam awkwardly, hating the picture he must make in her eyes, Apollo Belvedere slightly maimed; and still suffered visions of drowning in twelve feet of water. Or suppose she had to jump in to rescue him? However, nothing risked, nothing gained, so he splashed on and made the raft with breath to spare, his worries always greater than their cause.

But when he had pulled himself up on the raft, to his dismay, Isabella was no longer there. He caught a glimpse of her on the shore, darting behind the shrub. Nursing gloomy thoughts, Freeman rested a while, then, when he had sneezed twice and presupposed a nasty cold, jumped into the water and splashed his way back to the island. Isabella, already clothed, was waiting with a towel. She threw it to Freeman as he came up the steps, and withdrew while he dried himself and dressed. When he came forth in his seersucker, she offered salami, prosciutto, cheese, bread, and red wine, from a large platter delivered from the kitchen. Freeman, for a while angered at the run-around on the raft, relaxed with the wine and feeling of freshness after a bath. The mosquitoes behaved long enough for him to say he loved her. Isabella kissed him tenderly, then Ernesto and Giacobbe appeared and rowed him back to Stresa.

Monday morning Freeman didn't know what to do with himself. He awoke with restless memories, enormously potent, many satisfying, some burdensome; they ate him, he ate them. He felt he should somehow have made every minute with her better, hadn't begun to say half of what he had wanted—the kind of man he was, what they could get out of life together. And he regretted that he hadn't gotten quickly to the raft, still excited by what might have happened if he had reached it before she had left. But a memory was only a memory—you could forget, not change it. On the other hand, he was pleased, surprised by what he had accomplished: the evening alone with her, the trusting, intimate sight of her beautiful body, her kiss, the unspoken promise of love. His desire for her was so splendid it hurt. He wandered through the afternoon, dreaming of her, staring often at the glittering islands in the opaque lake. By nightfall he was exhausted and went to sleep oppressed by all he had lived through.

It was strange, he thought, as he lay in bed waiting to sleep, that of all his buzzing worries he was worried most about one. If Isabella loved him, as he now felt she did or would before very long; with the strength of this love they could conquer their problems as they arose. He anticipated a good handful, stirred up, in all probability, by her family; but life in the U.S.A. was considered by many Italians, including aristocrats (else why had Ernesto been sent to sniff out conditions there?) a fine thing for their marriageable daughters. Given this additional advantage, things would somehow get worked out, especially if Isabella, an independent girl, gazed a little eagerly at the

star-spangled shore. Her family would give before flight in
her eyes. No, the worry that troubled him most was the
lie he had told her, that he wasn't a Jew. He could, of
course, confess, say she knew Levin, not Freeman, a man
of adventure, but that might ruin all, since it was quite clear
she wanted nothing to do with a Jew, or why, at first sight,
had she asked so searching a question? Or he might admit
nothing and let her, more or less, find out after she had
lived a while in the States and seen it was no crime to be
Jewish; that a man's past was, it could safely be said,
expendable. Yet this treatment, if the surprise was upset-
ting, might cause recriminations later on. Another solution
might be one he had thought of often: to change his name
(he had considered Le Vin but preferred Freeman) and
forget he had ever been born Jewish. There was no question of hurting family, or being embarassed by them, he
the only son of both parents dead. Cousins lived in Toledo,
Ohio, where they would always live and never bother. And
when he brought Isabella to America they could skip
N.Y.C. and go to live in a place like San Francisco, where
nobody knew him and nobody "would know." To arrange
such details and prepare other minor changes was why
he figured on a trip or two home before they were married;
he was prepared for that. As for the wedding itself, since
he would have to marry her here to get her out of Italy,
it would probably have to be in a church, but he would
go along with that to hasten things. It was done everyday.
Thus he decided, although it did not entirely satisfy him;
not so much the denial of being Jewish—what had it
brought him but headaches, inferiorities, unhappy memories?—as the lie to the beloved. At first sight love and a
lie; it lay on his heart like a sore. Yet, if that was the way
it had to be, it was the way.

He awoke the next morning, beset by a swarm of doubts
concerning his plans and possibilities. When would he see
Isabella again, let alone marry her? ("When?" he had

whispered before getting into the boat, and she had vaguely promised, "Soon.") Soon was brutally endless. The mail brought nothing and Freeman grew dismayed. Had he, he asked himself, been constructing a hopeless fantasy, wish seducing probability? Was he inventing a situation that didn't exist, namely, her feeling for him, the possibility of a future with her? He was desperately casting about for something to keep his mood from turning dark blue, when a knock sounded on his door. The padrona, he thought, because she often came up for one unimportant thing or another, but to his unspeakable joy it was Cupid in short pants—Giacobbe holding forth the familiar envelope. She would meet him, Isabella wrote, at two o'clock in the piazza where the electric tram took off for Mt. Mottarone, from whose summit one saw the beautiful panorama of lakes and mountains in the region. Would he share this with her?

Although he had quashed the morning's anxiety, Freeman was there at one P.M., smoking impatiently. His sun rose as she appeared, but as she came towards him he noticed she was not quite looking at him (in the distance he could see Giacobbe rowing away) her face neutral, inexpressive. He was at first concerned, but she had, after all, written the letter to him, so he wondered what hot nails she had had to walk on to get off the island. He must sometime during the day drop the word "elope" to see if she savored it. But whatever was bothering her, Isabella immediately shook off. She smiled as she greeted him; he hoped for her lips but got instead her polite fingers. These he kissed in broad daylight (let the spies tell papa) and she shyly withdrew her hand. She was wearing—it surprised him, though he gave her credit for resisting foolish pressures—exactly the same blouse and skirt she had worn on Sunday. They boarded the tram with a dozen tourists and sat alone on the open seat in front; as a reward for managing this she permitted Freeman to hold her hand. He sighed.

The tram, drawn by an old electric locomotive moved slowly through the town and more slowly up the slope of the mountain. They rode for close to two hours, watching the lake fall as the mountains rose. Isabella, apart from pointing to something now and then, was again silent, withdrawn, but Freeman, allowing her her own rate at flowering, for the moment without plans, was practically contented. A long vote for an endless journey; but the tram at last came to a stop and they walked through a field thick with wildflowers, up the slope to the summit of the mountain. Though the tourists followed in a crowd, the mountain top was broad and they stood near its edge, to all intents and purposes alone. Below them, on the green undulating plains of Piedmont and Lombardy, seven lakes were scattered, each a mirror reflecting whose fate? And high in the distance rose a ring of astonishing snow-clad Alps. Ah, he murmured, and fell silent.

"We say here," Isabella said, " 'un pezzo di paradiso caduto dal cielo.' "

"You can say it again." Freeman was deeply moved by the sublimity of the distant Alps. She named the white peaks from Mt. Rosa to the Jungfrau. Gazing at them, he felt he had grown a head taller and was inspired to accomplish a feat men would wonder at.

"Isabella—" Freeman turned to ask her to marry him; but she was standing apart from him, her face pale.

Pointing to the snowy mountains, her hand moving in a gentle arc, she asked, "Don't those peaks—those seven— look like a Menorah?"

"Like a what?" Freeman politely inquired. He had a sudden frightening remembrance of her seeing him naked as he came out of the lake and felt constrained to tell her that circumcision was de rigueur in stateside hospitals; but he didn't dare. She may not have noticed.

"Like a seven-branched candalabrum holding white candles in the sky?" Isabella asked.

"Something like that."

"Or do you see the Virgin's crown adorned with jewels?"

"Maybe the crown," he faltered. "It all depends how you look at it."

They left the mountain and went down to the water. The tram ride was faster going down. At the lake front, as they were waiting for Giacobbe to come with the rowboat, Isabella, her eyes troubled, told Freeman she had a confession to make. He, still eager to propose, hoped she would finally say she loved him. Instead, she said, "My name is not del Dongo. It is Isabella della Seta. The del Dongos have not been on the island in years. We are the caretakers of the palace, my father, brother and I. We are poor people."

"Caretakers?" Freeman was astonished.

"Yes."

"Ernesto is your father?" His voice rose.

She nodded.

"Was it his idea for you to say you were somebody else?"

"No, mine. He did what I asked him to. He has wanted me to go to America, but under the right circumstances."

"So you had to pretend," he said bitterly. He was more greatly disturbed than he could account for, as if he had been expecting just this to happen.

She blushed and turned away. "I was not sure of the circumstances. I wanted you to stay until I knew you better."

"Why didn't you say so?"

"Perhaps I wasn't serious in the beginning. I said what I thought you wanted to hear. At the same time I wished you to stay. I thought you would be clearer to me after a while."

"Clearer how?"

"I don't really know." Her eyes searched his, then she dropped her glance.

"I'm not hiding anything," he said. He wanted to say more but warned himself not to.

"That's what I was afraid of."

Giacobbe had come with the boat and steadied it for his sister. They were alike as the proverbial peas—two dark Italian faces, the Middle Ages looking out of their eyes. Isabella got into the boat and Giacobbe pushed off with one oar. She waved from afar.

Freeman went back to his pensione in a turmoil, hurt where it hurts—in his dreams, thinking he should have noticed before how worn her blouse and skirt were, should have seen more than he had. It was this that irked. He called himself a damn fool for making up fairy tales— Freeman in love with the Italian aristocracy. He thought of taking off for Venice or Florence, but his heart ached for love of her, and he could not forget that he had originally come in the simple hope of finding a girl worth marrying. If the desire had developed complications, the fault was mostly his own. After an hour in his room, burdened by an overpowering loneliness, Freeman felt he must have her. She mustn't get away from him. So what if the countess had become a caretaker? She was a natural-born queen, whether by del Dongo or any other name. So she had lied to him, but so had he to her; they were quits on that score and his conscience was calm. He felt things would be easier all around now that the air had been cleared.

Freeman ran down to the dock; the sun had set and the boatmen were home, swallowing spaghetti. He was considering untying one of the rowboats and paying tomorrow, when he caught sight of someone sitting on a bench—Ernesto, in his hot winter hat, smoking a cheroot. He was resting his wrists on the handle of his cane, his chin on them.

"You weesh a boat?" the guide asked in a not unkindly tone.

"With all my heart. Did Isabella send you?"

"No."

He came because she was unhappy, Freeman guessed—maybe crying. There's a father for you, a real magician despite his appearance. He waves his stick and up pops Freeman for his little girl.

"Get een," said Ernesto.

"I'll row," said Freeman. He had almost added "father," but had caught himself. As if guessing the jest, Ernesto smiled, a little sadly. But he sat at the stern of the boat, enjoying the ride.

In the middle of the lake, seeing the mountains surrounding it lit in the last glow of daylight, Freeman thought of the "Menorah" in the Alps. Where had she got the word, he wondered, and decided anywhere, a book or picture. But wherever she had, he must settle this subject once and for all tonight.

When the boat touched the dock, the pale moon rose. Ernesto tied up, and handed Freeman a flashlight.

"Een the jarden," he said tiredly, pointing with his cane.

"Don't wait up." Freeman hastened to the garden at the lake's edge, where the roots of trees hung like hoary beards above the water; the flashlight didn't work, but the moon and his memory were enough. Isabella, God bless her, was standing at the low wall among the moonlit statuary: stags, tigers and unicorns, poets and painters, shepherds with pipes, and playful shepherdesses, gazing at the light shimmering on the water.

She was wearing white, the figure of a future bride; perhaps it was an altered wedding dress—he would not be surprised if a hand-me-down, the way they saved clothes in this poor country. He had pleasant thoughts of buying her some nifty outfits.

She was motionless, her back toward him—though he could picture her bosom breathing. When he said good evening, lifting his light straw, she turned to him with a sweet smile. He tenderly kissed her lips; this she let him do, softly returning the same.

"Goodbye," Isabella whispered.

"To whom goodbye?" Freeman affectionately mocked. "I have come to marry you."

She gazed at him with eyes moistly bright, then came the soft, inevitable thunder: "Are you a Jew?"

"Why should I lie?" he thought; she's mine for the asking. But then he trembled with the fear of at the last moment losing her, so Freeman answered, though his scalp prickled, "How many no's make never? Why do you persist with such foolish questions?"

"Because I hoped you were." Slowly she unbuttoned her bodice, arousing Freeman, though he was thoroughly confused as to her intent. When she revealed her breasts —he could have wept at their beauty (now recalling a former invitation to gaze at them, but he had arrived too late on the raft)—to his horror he discerned tatooed on the soft and tender flesh a bluish line of distorted numbers.

"Buchenwald," Isabella said, "when I was a little girl. The Fascists sent us there. The Nazis did it."

Freeman groaned, incensed at the cruelty, stunned by the desecration.

"I can't marry you. We are Jews. My past is meaningful to me. I treasure what I suffered for."

"Jews," he muttered, "—you? Oh, God, why did you keep this from me, too?"

"I did not wish to tell you something you would not welcome. I thought at one time it was possible you were—I hoped but was wrong."

"Isabella—" he cried brokenly. "Listen, I—I am—"

He groped for her breasts, to clutch, kiss or suckle them; but she had stepped among the statues, and when he vainly sought her in the veiled mist that had risen from the lake, still calling her name, Freeman embraced only moonlit stone.

PHILIP ROTH (b. 1933), brought up in Elizabeth, New
Jersey, is noted for his ability to exploit his Jewish background for comic effect, as well as to satirize the Jewish
middle class. Concerned with identity, he is trying to discover how one can be an American and a Jew. *Goodbye
Columbus and Five Short Stories* (1959) brought Roth
fame and strong criticism. After *Letting Go* (1961) and
When She Was Good (1966), *Portnoy's Complaint* (1969)
stirred up another storm. *The Breast* (1972) exacerbated
the situation; the charges that he was a pornographer and
anti-Semite did not diminish until several political satires
and *The Great American Novel* (1973) cleared the air.
Regardless of what else he contributes, Roth has given us,
in Alfred Kazin's words, a "deepened sense of the painful
decisions on which life rests."

Neil and the Patimkins
from
GOODBYE COLUMBUS

That morning was supposed to have been my last at the
Patimkin house; however, when I began to throw my things
into my bag late in the day, Brenda told me I could unpack
—somehow she'd managed to inveigle another week out
of her parents, and I would be able to stay right through
till Labor Day, when Ron would be married; then, the following morning Brenda would be off to school and I would
go back to work. So we would be with each other until the
summer's last moment.

This should have made me overjoyed, but as Brenda
trotted back down the stairs to accompany her family to
the airport—where they were to pick up Harriet—I was
not joyful but disturbed, as I had been more and more with
the thought that when Brenda went back to Radcliffe, that
would be the end for me. I was convinced that even Miss
Winney's stool was not high enough for me to see clear up
to Boston. Nevertheless, I tossed my clothing back into

the drawer and was able, finally, to tell myself that there'd been no hints of ending our affair from Brenda, and any suspicions I had, any uneasiness, was spawned in my own uncertain heart. Then I went into Ron's room to call my aunt.

"Hello?" she said.

"Aunt Gladys," I said, "how are you?"

"You're sick."

"No, I'm having a fine time. I wanted to call you, I'm going to stay another week."

"Why?"

"I told you. I'm having a good time. Mrs. Patimkin asked me to stay until Labor Day."

"You've got clean underwear?"

"I'm washing it at night. I'm okay, Aunt Gladys."

"By hand you can't get it clean."

"It's clean enough. Look, Aunt Gladys, I'm having a wonderful time."

"*Shmutz* he lives in and I shouldn't worry."

"How's Uncle Max?" I asked.

"What should he be? Uncle Max is Uncle Max. You, I don't like the way your voice sounds."

"Why? Do I sound like I've got on dirty underwear?"

"Smart guy. Someday you'll learn."

"What?"

"What do you mean *what?* You'll find out. You'll stay there too long you'll be too good for us."

"Never, sweetheart," I said.

"I'll see it I'll believe it."

"Is it cool in Newark, Aunt Gladys?"

"It's snowing," she said.

"Hasn't it been cool all week?"

"You sit around all day it's cool. For me it's not February, believe me."

"Okay, Aunt Gladys. Say hello to everybody."

"You got a letter from your mother."

"Good. I'll read it when I get home."

"You couldn't take a ride down you'll read it?"

"I'll wait. I'll drop them a note. Be a good girl," I said.

"What about your socks?"

"I go barefoot. Goodbye, honey." And I hung up.

Down in the kitchen Carlota was getting dinner ready. I was always amazed at how Carlota's work never seemed to get in the way of her life. She made household chores seem like illustrative gestures of whatever it was she was singing, even, if as now, it was "I Get a Kick out of You." She moved from the oven to the automatic dishwasher—she pushed buttons, turned dials, peeked in the glass-doored oven, and from time to time picked a big black grape out of a bunch that lay on the sink. She chewed and chewed, humming all the time, and then, with a deliberated casualness, shot the skin and the pit directly into the garbage disposal unit. I said hello to her as I went out the back door, and though she did not return the greeting, I felt a kinship with one who, like me, had been partially wooed and won on Patimkin fruit.

Out on the lawn I shot baskets for a while; then I picked up an iron and drove a cotton golf ball limply up into the sunlight; then I kicked a soccer ball towards the oak tree; then I tried shooting foul shots again. Nothing diverted me—I felt open-stomached, as though I hadn't eaten for months, and though I went back inside and came out with my own handful of grapes, the feeling continued, and I knew it had nothing to do with my caloric intake; it was only a rumor of the hollowness that would come when Brenda was away. The fact of her departure had, of course, been on my mind for a while, but overnight it had taken on a darker hue. Curiously, the darkness seemed to have something to do with Harriet, Ron's intended, and I thought for a time that it was simply the reality of Harriet's arrival that had dramatized the passing of time: we had been talking about it and now suddenly it was here—just as Brenda's departure would be here before we knew it.

But it was more than that: the union of Harriet and Ron reminded me that separation need not be a permanent state. People could marry each other, even if they were young! And yet Brenda and I had never mentioned marriage, except perhaps for that night at the pool when she'd said, "When you love me, everything will be all right." Well, I loved her, and she me, and things didn't seem all right at all. Or was I inventing troubles again? I supposed I should really have thought my lot improved considerably; yet, there on the lawn, the August sky seemed too beautiful and temporary to bear, and I wanted Brenda to marry me. Marriage, though, was not what I proposed to her when she drove the car up the driveway, alone, some fifteen minutes later. That proposal would have taken a kind of courage that I did not think I had. I did not feel myself prepared for any answer but "Hallelujah!" Any other kind of yes wouldn't have satisfied me, and any kind of no, even one masked behind the words, "Let's wait, sweetheart," would have been my end. So I imagine that's why I proposed the surrogate, which turned out finally to be far more daring than I knew it to be at the time.

"Harriet's plane is late, so I drove home," Brenda called.

"Where's everyone else?"

"They're going to wait for her and have dinner at the airport. I have to tell Carlota," and she went inside.

In a few minutes she appeared on the porch. She wore a yellow dress that cut a wide-bottomed U across her shoulders and neck, and showed where the tanned flesh began above her breasts. On the lawn she stepped out of her heels and walked barefoot over to where I was sitting under the oak tree.

"Women who wear high heels all the time get tipped ovaries," she said.

"Who told you that?"

"I don't remember. I like to think everything's ship-shape in there."

"Brenda, I want to ask you something . . ."

She yanked the blanket with the big O on it over to us and sat down.

"What?" she said.

"I know this is out of the blue, though really it's not . . . I want you to buy a diaphragm. To go to a doctor and get one."

She smiled. "Don't worry, sweetie, we're careful. Everything is okay."

"But that's the safest."

"We're safe. It'd be a waste."

"Why take chances?"

"But we *aren't*. How many things do you need?"

"Honey, it isn't bulk I'm interested in. It's not even safety," I added.

"You just want me to own one, is that it? Like a walking stick, or a pith helmet—"

"Brenda, I want you to own one for . . . for the sake of pleasure."

"Pleasure? Whose? The doctor's?"

"Mine," I said.

She did not answer me, but rubbed her fingers along the ridge of her collarbone to wipe away the tiny globes of perspiration that had suddenly formed there.

"No, Neil, it's silly."

"Why?"

"Why? It just is."

"You know why it's silly, Brenda—because *I* asked you to do it?"

"That's sillier."

"If you asked *me* to buy a diaphragm we'd have to go straight to the Yellow Pages and find a gynecologist open on Saturday afternoon."

"I would never ask you to do that, baby."

"It's the truth," I said, though I was smiling. "It's the truth."

"It's not," she said, and got up and walked over to the

basketball court, where she walked on the white lines that Mr. Patimkin had laid the day before.

"Come back here," I said.

"Neil, it's silly and I don't want to talk about it."

"Why are you being so selfish?"

· "Selfish? You're the one who's being selfish. It's your pleasure . . ."

"That's right. My pleasure. Why not!"

"Don't raise your voice, Carlota."

"Then get the hell over here," I said.

She walked over to me, leaving white footprints on the grass. "I didn't think you were such a creature of the flesh," she said.

"Didn't you?" I said. "I'll tell you something that you ought to know. It's not even the pleasures of the flesh I'm talking about."

"Then frankly, I don't know *what* you're talking about. Why you're even bothering. Isn't what we use sufficient?"

"I'm bothering just because I want you to go to a doctor and get a diaphragm. That's all. No explanation. Just do it. Do it because I asked you to."

"You're not being reasonable—"

"Goddamit, Brenda!"

"Goddamit yourself!" she said and went up into the house.

I closed my eyes and leaned back and in fifteen minutes, or maybe less, I heard somebody stroking at the cotton golf ball. She had changed into shorts and a blouse and was still barefoot.

We didn't speak with each other, but I watched her bring the club back of her ear, and then swing through, her chin tilted up with the line of flight a regular golf ball would have taken.

"That's five hundred yards," I said.

She didn't answer but walked after the cotton ball and then readied for another swing.

"Brenda. Please come here."

She walked over, dragging the club over the grass.

"What?"

"I don't want to argue with you."

"Nor I with you," she said. "It was the first time."

"Was it such an awful thing for me to ask?"

She nodded.

"Bren, I know it was probably a surprise. It was for me. But we're not children."

"Neil, I just don't want to. It's not because you asked me to, either. I don't know where you get that from. That's not it."

"Then why is it?"

"Oh everything. I just don't feel *old* enough for all that equipment."

"What does age have to do with it?"

"I don't mean age. I just mean—well, *me*. I mean it's so conscious a thing to do."

"Of course it's conscious. That's exactly it. Don't you see? It would change us."

"It would change me."

"Us. Together."

"Neil, how do you think I'd feel lying to some doctor?"

"You can go to Margaret Sanger, in New York. They don't ask any questions."

"You've done this before?"

"No," I said. "I just know. I read Mary McCarthy."

"That's exactly right. That's just what I'd feel like, somebody out of *her*."

"Don't be dramatic," I said.

"You're the one who's being dramatic. You think there would be something affairish about it, then. Last summer I went with this whore who I sent out to buy—"

"Oh, Brenda, you're a selfish egotistical bitch! You're the one who's thinking about 'last summer,' about an end for us. In fact, that's the whole thing, isn't it—"

"That's right, I'm a bitch. I want this to end. That's why I ask you to stay another week, that's why I let you sleep with me in my own house. What's the *matter* with you! Why don't you and my mother take turns—one day she can plague me, the next you—"

"Stop it!"

"Go to hell, all of you!" Brenda said, and now she was crying and I knew when she ran off I would not see her, as I didn't, for the rest of the afternoon.

Harriet Ehrlich impressed me as a young lady singularly unconscious of a motive in others or herself. All was surfaces, and she seemed a perfect match for Ron, and too for the Patimkins. Mrs. Patimkin, in fact, did just as Brenda prophesied: Harriet appeared, and Brenda's mother lifted one wing and pulled the girl in towards the warm underpart of her body, where Brenda herself would have liked to nestle. Harriet was built like Brenda, although a little chestier, and she nodded her head insistently whenever anyone spoke. Sometimes she would even say the last few words of your sentence with you, though that was infrequent; for the most part she nodded and kept her hands folded. All evening, as the Patimkins planned where the newlyweds should live, what furniture they should buy, how soon they should have a baby—all through this I kept thinking that Harriet was wearing white gloves, but she wasn't.

Brenda and I did not exchange a word or a glance; we sat, listening, Brenda somewhat more impatient than me. Near the end Harriet began calling Mrs. Patimkin "Mother," and once, "Mother Patimkin," and that was when Brenda went to sleep. I stayed behind, mesmerized almost by the dissection, analysis, reconsideration, and finally, the embracing of the trivial. At last Mr. and Mrs. Patimkin tumbled off to bed, and Julie, who had fallen asleep on her chair, was carried into her room by Ron. That left us two non-Patimkins together.

"Ron tells me you have a very interesting job."

"I work in the library."

"I've always liked reading."

"That'll be nice, married to Ron."

"Ron likes music."

"Yes," I said. What had I *said?*

"You must get first crack at the best-sellers," she said.

"Sometimes," I said.

"Well," she said, flapping her hands on her knees, "I'm sure we'll all have a good time together. Ron and I hope you and Brenda will double with us soon."

"Not tonight." I smiled. "Soon. Will you excuse me?"

"Good night. I like Brenda very much."

"Thank you," I said as I started up the stairs.

I knocked gently on Brenda's door.

"I'm sleeping."

"Can I come in?" I asked.

Her door opened an inch and she said, "Ron will be up soon."

"We'll leave the door open. I only want to talk."

She let me in and I sat in the chair that faced the bed.

"How do you like your sister-in-law?"

"I've met her before."

"Brenda, you don't have to sound so damn terse."

She didn't answer and I just sat there yanking the string on the shade up and down.

"Are you still angry?" I asked at last.

"Yes."

"Don't be," I said. "You can forget about my suggestion. It's not worth it if this is what's going to happen."

"What did you expect to happen?"

"Nothing. I didn't think it would be so horrendous."

"That's because you can't understand my side."

"Perhaps."

"No perhaps about it."

"*Okay*," I said. "I just wish you'd realize what it is you're getting angry about. It's not my suggestion, Brenda."

"No? What is it?"

"It's me."

"Oh don't start that again, will you? I can't win, no matter what I say."

"Yes, you can," I said. "You have."

I walked out of her room, closing the door behind me for the night.

When I got downstairs the following morning there was a great deal of activity. In the living room I heard Mrs. Patimkin reading a list to Harriet while Julie ran in and out of rooms in search of a skate key. Carlota was vacuuming the carpet; every appliance in the kitchen was bubbling, twisting, and shaking. Brenda greeted me with a perfectly pleasant smile and in the dining room, where I walked to look out at the back lawn and the weather, she kissed me on the shoulder.

"Hello," she said.

"Hello."

"I have to go with Harriet this morning," Brenda told me. "So we can't run. Unless you want to go alone."

"No. I'll read or something. Where are you going?"

"We're going to New York. Shopping. She's going to buy a wedding dress. For after the wedding. To go away in."

"What are *you* going to buy?"

"A dress to be maid of honor in. If I go with Harriet then I can go to Bergdorf's without all that Ohrbach's business with my mother."

"Get me something, will you?" I said.

"Oh, Neil, are you going to bring that up again!"

"I was only *fooling*. I wasn't even thinking about that."

"Then why did you say it?"

"Oh Jesus!" I said, and went outside and drove my car down into Millburn Center where I had some eggs and coffee.

When I came back, Brenda was gone, and there were only Carlota, Mrs. Patimkin, and myself in the house. I tried to stay out of whichever rooms they were in, but finally Mrs. Patimkin and I wound up sitting opposite each other in the TV room. She was checking off names on a long sheet of paper she held; next to her, on the table, were two thin phone books which she consulted from time to time.

"No rest for the weary," she said to me.

I smiled hugely, embracing the proverb as though Mrs. Patimkin had just then coined it. "Yes. Of course," I said. "Would you like some help? Maybe I could help you check something."

"Oh, no," she said with a little head-shaking dismissal, "it's for Hadassah."

"Oh," I said.

I sat and watched her until she asked, "Is your mother in Hadassah?"

"I don't know if she is now. She was in Newark."

"Was she an active member?"

"I guess so, she was always planting trees in Israel for someone."

"Really?" Mrs. Patimkin said. "What's her name?"

"Esther Klugman. She's in Arizona now. Do they have Hadassah there?"

"Wherever there are Jewish women."

"Then I guess she is. She's with my father. They went there for their asthma. I'm staying with my aunt in Newark. She's not in Hadassah. My Aunt Sylvia is, though. Do you know her, Aaron Klugman and Sylvia? They belong to your club. They have a daughter, my cousin Doris—" I couldn't stop myself "—They live in Livingston. Maybe it isn't Hadassah my Aunt Sylvia belongs to. I think it's some TB organization. Or cancer. Muscular dystrophy, maybe. I know she's interested in *some* disease."

"That's very nice," Mrs. Patimkin said.

"Oh yes."

"They do very good work."

"I know."

Mrs. Patimkin, I thought, had begun to warm to me; she let the purple eyes stop peering and just look out at the world for a while without judging. "Are you interested in B'nai Brith?" she asked me. "Ron is joining, you know, as soon as he gets married."

"I think I'll wait till then," I said.

Petulantly, Mrs. Patimkin went back to her lists, and I realized it had been foolish of me to risk lightheartedness with her about Jewish affairs. "You're active in the Temple, aren't you?" I asked with all the interest I could muster.

"Yes," she said.

"What Temple do *you* belong to?" she asked in a moment.

"We used to belong to Hudson Street Synagogue. Since my parents left, I haven't had much contact."

I didn't know whether Mrs. Patimkin caught a false tone in my voice. Personally I thought I had managed my rueful confession pretty well, especially when I recalled the decade of paganism prior to my parents' departure. Regardless, Mrs. Patimkin asked immediately—and strategically it seemed—"We're all going to Temple Friday night. Why don't you come with us? I mean, are you orthodox or conservative?"

I considered. "Well, I haven't gone in a long time . . . I sort of switch . . ." I smiled. "I'm just Jewish," I said wellmeaningly, but that too sent Mrs. Patimkin back to her Hadassah work. Desperately I tried to think of something that would convince her I wasn't an infidel. Finally I asked: "Do you know Martin Buber's work?"

"Buber . . . Buber," she said, looking at her Hadassah list. "Is he orthodox or conservative?" she asked.

". . . He's a philosopher."

"Is he *reformed?*" she asked, piqued either at my evasiveness or at the possibility that Buber attended Friday night services without a hat, and Mrs. Buber had only one set of dishes in her kitchen.

"Orthodox," I said faintly.

"That's very nice," she said.

"Yes."

"Isn't Hudson Street Synagogue orthodox?" she asked.

"I don't know."

"I thought you belonged."

"I was bar-mitzvahed there."

"And you don't know that it's orthodox?"

"Yes. I do. It is."

"Then *you* must be."

"Oh, yes, I am," I said. "What are you?" I popped, flushing.

"Orthodox. My husband is conservative," which meant, I took it, that he didn't care. "Brenda is nothing, as you probably know."

"Oh?" I said. "No, I didn't know that."

"She was the best Hebrew student I've ever seen," Mrs. Patimkin said, "but then, of course, she got too big for her britches."

Mrs. Patimkin looked at me, and I wondered whether courtesy demanded that I agree. "Oh, I don't know," I said at last, "I'd say Brenda is conservative. Maybe a little reformed . . ."

The phone rang, rescuing me, and I spoke a silent orthodox prayer to the Lord.

"Hello," Mrs. Patimkin said. ". . . no . . . I can *not,* I have all the Hadassah calls to make . . ."

I acted as though I were listening to the birds outside, though the closed windows let no natural noises in.

"Have Ronald drive them up . . . But we can't wait, not if we want it on time . . ."

Mrs. Patimkin glanced up at me; then she put one hand over the mouthpiece. "Would you ride down to Newark for me?"

I stood. "Yes. Surely."

"Dear?" she said back into the phone, "Neil will come for it . . . No, *Neil,* Brenda's friend . . . Yes . . . Goodbye.

"Mr. Patimkin has some silver patterns I have to see. Would you drive down to his place and pick them up?"

"Of course."

"Do you know where the shop is?"

"Yes."

"Here," she said, handing a key ring to me, "take the Volkswagen."

"My car is right outside."

"Take these," she said.

Patimkin Kitchen and Bathroom Sinks was in the heart of the Negro section of Newark. Years ago, at the time of the great immigration, it had been the Jewish section, and still one could see the little fish stores, the kosher delicatessens, the Turkish baths, where my grandparents had shopped and bathed at the beginning of the century. Even the smells had lingered: whitefish, corned beef, sour tomatoes—but now, on top of these, was the grander greasier smell of auto wrecking shops, the sour stink of a brewery, the burning odor from a leather factory; and on the streets, instead of Yiddish, one heard the shouts of Negro children playing at Willie Mays with a broom handle and half a rubber ball. The neighborhood had changed: the old Jews like my grandparents had struggled and died, and their offspring had struggled and prospered, and moved further and further west, towards the edge of Newark, then out of it, and up the slope of the Orange Mountains, until they had reached the crest and started down the other side, pouring into Gentile territory as the Scotch-Irish had poured through the Cumberland Gap. Now, in fact, the Negroes were making the same migration, following the steps of the Jews, and those who remained in the Third Ward lived the most squalid of lives and dreamed in their fetid mattresses of the piny smell of Georgia nights.

I wondered, for an instant only, if I would see the colored kid from the library on the streets here. I didn't, of course, though I was sure he lived in one of the scabby, peeling buildings out of which dogs, children, and aproned women moved continually. On the top floors, windows were

open, and the very old, who could no longer creak down
the long stairs to the street, sat where they had been put,
in the screenless windows, their elbows resting on fluffless
pillows, and their heads tipping forward on their necks,
watching the push of the young and the pregnant and the
unemployed. Who would come after the Negroes? Who
was left? No one, I thought, and someday these streets,
where my grandmother drank hot tea from an old *jahrzeit*
glass, would be empty and we would all of us have moved
to the crest of the Orange Mountains, and wouldn't the
dead stop kicking at the slats in their coffins then?

I pulled the Volkswagen up in front of a huge garage
door that said across the front of it:

PATIMKIN KITCHEN AND BATHROOM SINKS
"Any Size—Any Shape"

Inside I could see a glass-enclosed office; it was in the center of an immense warehouse. Two trucks were being
loaded in the rear, and Mr. Patimkin, when I saw him, had
a cigar in his mouth and was shouting at someone. It was
Ron, who was wearing a white T-shirt that said Ohio State
Athletic Association across the front. Though he was taller
than Mr. Patimkin, and almost as stout, his hands hung
weakly at his sides like a small boy's; Mr. Patimkin's cigar
locomoted in his mouth. Six Negroes were loading one of
the trucks feverishly, tossing—my stomach dropped—sink
bowls at one another.

Ron left Mr. Patimkin's side and went back to directing
the men. He thrashed his arms about a good deal, and
though on the whole he seemed rather confused, he didn't
appear to be at all concerned about anybody dropping a
sink. Suddenly I could see myself directing the Negroes—
I would have an ulcer in an hour. I could almost hear the
enamel surfaces shattering on the floor. And I could hear
myself: "Watch it, you guys. Be careful, will you? *Whoops!*

Oh, please be—*watch* it! Watch! Oh!" Suppose Mr. Patimkin should come up to me and say, "Okay, boy, you
want to marry my daughter, let's see what you can do."
Well, he would see: in a moment that floor would be a
shattered mosaic, a crunchy path of enamel. "Klugman,
what kind of worker are you? You work like you eat!"
"That's right, that's right, I'm a sparrow, let me go."
"Don't you even know how to load and unload?" "Mr.
Patimkin, even breathing gives me trouble, sleep tires me
out, let me go, let me go . . ."

Mr. Patimkin was headed back to the fish bowl to answer a ringing phone, and I wrenched myself free of my
reverie and headed towards the office too. When I entered,
Mr. Patimkin looked up from the phone with his eyes; the
sticky cigar was in his free hand—he moved it at me, a
greeting. From outside I heard Ron call in a high voice,
"You can't all go to lunch at the same time. We haven't
got all day!"

"Sit down," Mr. Patimkin shot at me, though when he
went back to his conversation I saw there was only one
chair in the office, his. People did not sit at Patimkin
Sink—here you earned your money the hard way, standing up. I busied myself looking at the several calendars
that hung from filing cabinets; they showed illustrations
of women so dreamy, so fantastically thighed and uddered,
that one could not think of them as pornographic. The
artist who had drawn the calendar girls for "Lewis Construction Company," and "Earl's Truck and Auto Repair,"
and "Grossman and Son, Paper Box" had been painting
some third sex I had never seen.

"Sure, sure, sure," Mr. Patimkin said into the phone.
"Tomorrow, don't tell me tomorrow. Tomorrow the world
could blow up."

At the other end someone spoke. Who was it? Lewis
from the construction company? Earl from truck repair?

"I'm running a business, Grossman, not a charity."

So it was Grossman being browbeaten at the other end.

"Shit on that," Mr. Patimkin said. "You're not the only one in town, my good friend," and he winked at me.

Ah-ha, a conspiracy against Grossman. Me and Mr. Patimkin. I smiled as collusively as I knew how.

"All right then, we're here till five . . . No later."

He wrote something on a piece of paper. It was only a big X.

"My kid'll be here," he said. "Yea, he's in the business."

Whatever Grossman said on the other end, it made Mr. Patimkin laugh. Mr. Patimkin hung up without a goodbye.

He looked out the back to see how Ron was doing. "Four years in college he can't unload a truck."

I didn't know what to say but finally chose the truth. "I guess I couldn't either."

"You could learn. What am I, a genius? I learned. Hard work never killed anybody."

To that I agreed.

Mr. Patimkin looked at his cigar. "A man works hard he's got something. You don't get anywhere sitting on your behind, you know . . . The biggest men in the country worked hard, believe me. Even Rockefeller. Success don't come easy . . ." He did not say this so much as he mused it out while he surveyed his dominion. He was not a man enamored of words, and I had the feeling that what had tempted him into this barrage of universals was probably the combination of Ron's performance and my presence— me, the outsider who might one day be an insider. But did Mr. Patimkin even consider that possibility? I did not know; I only knew that these few words he did speak could hardly transmit all the satisfaction and surprise he felt about the life he had managed to build for himself and his family.

He looked out at Ron again. "Look at him, if he played basketball like that they'd throw him the hell off the court." But he was smiling when he said it.

He walked over to the door. "Ronald, let them go to lunch."

Ron shouted back, "I thought I'd let some go now, and some later."

"Why?"

"Then somebody'll always be—"

"No fancy deals here," Mr. Patimkin shouted. "We all go to lunch at once."

Ron turned back. "All right, boys, lunch!"

His father smiled at me. "Smart boy? Huh?" He tapped his head. "That took brains, huh? He ain't got the stomach for business. He's an idealist," and then I think Mr. Patimkin suddenly realized who *I* was, and eagerly corrected himself so as not to offend. "That's all right, you know, if you're a schoolteacher, or like you, you know, a student or something like that. Here you need a little of the *gonif* in you. You know what that means? *Gonif?*"

"Thief," I said.

"You know more than my own kids. They're *goyim*, my kids, that's how much they understand." He watched the Negro loading gang walk past the office and shouted out to them, "You guys know how long an hour is? All right, you'll be back in an hour!"

Ron came into the office and of course shook my hand.

"Do you have that stuff for Mrs. Patimkin?" I asked.

"Ronald, get him the silver patterns." Ron turned away and Mr. Patimkin said, "When I got married we had forks and knives from the five and ten. This kid needs gold to eat off," but there was no anger; far from it.

I drove to the mountains in my own car that afternoon, and stood for a while at the wire fence watching the deer lightly prance, coyly feed, under the protection of signs that read, DO NOT FEED THE DEER, *By Order of South Mountain Reservation*. Alongside me at the fence were dozens of kids; they giggled and screamed when the deer licked the popcorn from their hands, and then were sad when their own excitement sent the young loping away towards the far end of the field where their tawny-skinned mothers stood regally watching the traffic curl up the mountain road. Young white-skinned mothers, hardly older than I, and in many instances younger, chatted in their convertibles behind me, and looked down from time to time to see what their children were about. I had seen them before, when Brenda and I had gone out for a bite in the afternoon, or had driven up here for lunch: in clotches of three and four they sat in the rustic hamburger joints that dotted the Reservation area while their children gobbled hamburgers and malteds and were given dimes to feed the jukebox. Though none of the little ones were old enough to read the song titles, almost all of them could holler out the words, and they did, while the mothers, a few of whom I recognized as high school mates of mine, compared suntans, supermarkets, and vacations. They looked immortal sitting there. Their hair would always stay the color they desired, their clothes the right texture and shade; in their homes they would have simple Swedish modern when that was fashionable, and if huge, ugly baroque ever came back, out would go the long, midget-legged marble coffee table and in would come Louis Quatorze. These were the goddesses, and if I were Paris I could not have been able to choose among them, so microscopic were the differences. Their fates had collapsed them into one. Only Brenda shone. Money and comfort would not erase her singleness—they hadn't yet, or had they? What was I loving, I wondered, and since I am not one to stick scalpels into myself, I wiggled my hand in the fence and allowed a tiny-nosed buck to lick my thoughts away.

When I returned to the Patimkin house, Brenda was in the living room looking more beautiful than I had ever seen her. She was modeling her new dress for Harriet and her mother. Even Mrs. Patimkin seemed softened by the sight of her; it looked as though some sedative had been injected into her, and so relaxed the Brenda-hating muscles around her eyes and mouth.

Brenda, without glasses, modeled in place; when she looked at me it was a kind of groggy, half-waking look I got, and though others might have interpreted it as sleepiness it sounded in my veins as lust. Mrs. Patimkin told her finally that she'd bought a very nice dress and I told her she looked lovely and Harriet told her she was very beautiful and that *she* ought to be the bride, and then there was an uncomfortable silence while all of us wondered who ought to be the groom.

Then when Mrs. Patimkin had led Harriet out to the kitchen, Brenda came up to me and said, "I *ought* to be the bride."

"You ought, sweetheart." I kissed her, and suddenly she was crying.

"What is it, honey?" I said.

"Let's go outside."

On the lawn, Brenda was no longer crying but her voice sounded very tired.

"Neil, I called Margaret Sanger Clinic," she said. "When I was in New York."

I didn't answer.

"Neil, they *did* ask if I was married. God, the woman sounded like my mother . . ."

"What did you say?"

"I said *no*."

"What did she say?"

"I don't know. I hung up." She walked away and around the oak tree. When she appeared again she'd stepped out of her shoes and held one hand on the tree, as though it were a Maypole she were circling.

"You can call them back," I said.

She shook her head. "No, I can't. I don't even know why I called in the first place. We were shopping and I just walked away, looked up the number, and called."

"Then you can go to a doctor."

She shook again.

"Look, Bren," I said, rushing to her, "we'll go together, to a doctor. In New York—"

"I don't want to go to some dirty little office—"

"We won't. We'll go to the most posh gynecologist in New York. One who gets *Harper's Bazaar* for the reception room. How does that sound?"

She bit her lower lip.

"You'll come with me?" she asked.

"I'll come with you."

"To the office?"

"Sweetie, your husband wouldn't come to the office."

"No?"

"He'd be working."

"But you're not," she said.

"I'm on vacation," I said, but I had answered the wrong question. "Bren, I'll wait and when you're all done we'll buy a drink. We'll go out to dinner."

"Neil, I shouldn't have called Margaret Sanger—it's not right."

"It is, Brenda. It's the most right thing we can do." She walked away and I was exhausted from pleading. Somehow I felt I could have convinced her had I been a bit more crafty; and yet I did not want it to be craftiness that changed her mind. I was silent when she came back, and perhaps it was just that, my *not* saying anything, that prompted her finally to say, "I'll ask Mother Patimkin if she wants us to take Harriet too . . ."

HOWARD NEMEROV (b. 1920), brought up in New York, went to Harvard College, and then flew for the RAF in the Second World War. He has taught at Hamilton College and Bennington College and is a prolific writer of short

stories, essays, and poems. Once described by James
Dickey as "the best poet under forty that we have", after
The Salt Garden (1955), he has also written *Mirrors and
Windows* (1958), *New and Selected Poems* (1960), *The
Next Room of the Dream* (1962), and *The Blue Swallows*
(1967).

Boom

from

THE NEXT ROOM OF THE DREAM

SEES BOOM IN RELIGION, TOO

Atlantic City, June 23, 1957 (AP.)—*President Eisenhower's
pastor said tonight that Americans are living in a period of
"unprecedented religious activity" caused partially by paid
vacations, the eight-hour day and modern conveniences.*

*"These fruits of material progress," said the Rev. Edward
L. R. Elson of the National Presbyterian Church, Washington,
"have provided the leisure, the energy, and the means for a
level of human and spiritual values never before reached."*

Here at the Vespasian-Carlton, it's just one
religious activity after another; the sky
is constantly being crossed by cruciform
airplanes, in which nobody disbelieves
for a second, and the tide, the tide
of spiritual progress and prosperity
miraculously keeps rising, to a level
never before attained. The churches are full,
the beaches are full, and the filling-stations
are full, God's great ocean is full
of paid vacationers praying an eight-hour day
to the human and spiritual values, the fruits,
the leisure, the energy, and the means, Lord,
the means for the level, the unprecedented level,
and the modern conveniences, which also are full.
Never before, O Lord, have the prayers and praises
from belfry and phonebooth, from ballpark and barbecue

the sacrifices, so endlessly ascended.
It was not thus when Job in Palestine
sat in the dust and cried, cried bitterly;
when Damien kissed the lepers on their wounds
it was not thus; it was not thus
when Francis worked a fourteen-hour day
strictly for the birds; when Dante took
a week's vacation without pay and it rained
part of the time, O Lord, it was not thus.

But now the gears mesh and the tires burn
and the ice chatters in the shaker and the priest
in the pulpit, and Thy Name, O Lord,
is kept before the public, while the fruits
ripen and religion booms and the level rises
and every modern convenience runneth over,
that it may never be with us as it hath been
with Athens and Karnak and Nagasaki,
nor Thy sun for one instant refrain from shining
on the rainbow Buick by the breezeway
or the Chris Craft with the uplift life raft;
that we may continue to be the just folks we are,
plain people with ordinary superliners and
disposable diaperliners, people of the stop'n'shop
'n'pray as you go, of hotel, motel, boatel,
the humble pilgrims of no deposit no return
and please adjust thy clothing, who will give to Thee,
if Thee will keep us going, our annual
Miss Universe, for Thy Name's Sake, Amen.

One Forever Alien
from
THE NEXT ROOM OF THE DREAM

When I become the land, when they will build
Blast furnaces over me, and lay black asphalt
For hundreds of miles across my ribs, and wheels

Begin to bounce interminably on the bone;
When I enter, at last, America, when I am
Part of her progress and a true patriot,
And the schoolchildren sing of my sacrifice,
Remembering the burial day of my birth—
Then even the efficient will have to forgive me,
The investigators approve my security,
And those that harden their hearts welcome me home.

Then, in that day, my countrymen,
When I shall come among you fleeced as the lamb
And in the diaper of the grave newly arrayed,
The Adam Qadmon, the greenhorn immigrant,
Shall pass the customs at the port of entry
Where the Guardian Lady lifts her flaming sword.
Forgiven the original sin of his origin,
He comes as a bond redeemed, as newly negotiable,
        To be as a soybean before you.

NORMA ROSEN was born in New York and educated at
Mount Holyoke College and Columbia University. She has
taught at The New School for Social Research, the University of Pennsylvania, and the Radcliffe Institute, Harvard
University. She has written *Joy to Levine* (1962), *Touching Evil* (1969), and *Green* (1967), from which this story
is taken.

A Thousand Tears
from
GREEN

Twice in one day Sandra Loeb, who lives a careful life
in New York City, hears a tale of murder close by. The
day, as it happens, is one during a newspaper strike. People

feel a need to tell what they hear, some revived obligation
to pass on news of the world's woe. That, at least, is Sandra's
explanation to herself, and afterward to her husband Ben
when they get a chance to talk. On top of everything else,
this day is Sandra and Ben's tenth wedding anniversary—a
time of welled-up feelings that, in the rush of things, must
be swallowed again, making a hot friction around the heart.
One tale in the morning, one in the evening, form brackets
around Sandra's well-ordered hours and squeeze from them
drops of blood.

Ben never brings flowers. They are in the same category
as tears, and to be avoided. Sandra understands this. All the
same, to be sure there will be no gap into which hurt feelings might stumble, on her way home from work the evening before the anniversary she buys armfuls of fresh greens
—rhododendron and magnolia leaves—and fills all the vases
in the house. Then late at night she remembers that Lily,
their day maid, has asked for extra cream to make the cake.
So early in the morning, while Ben can still be home with
their two preschool children and before Sandra herself must
leave for work, she hurries out to buy some.

Now! How stupid! The moment Sandra is in the street
she sees what she has done—quite automatically put on the
new fur coat that she means to wear to work today. For a
moment she hesitates, then decides, "No, I won't go in."

Sandra has lived all her life in or close to this part of New
York's West Side, where great blocks of buildings line the
avenues from park to park. "Democratic people" were her
mother's words for those who preferred the West Side's rich
population mix to the distilled elements of the East Side. The
description holds good, Sandra feels, although she has added
to it her own: "Hopeful people." Hopeful of education.
Renewal. Good will. Above all, good will. "We're all idealists. . . ." Sandra frowns. Who was it who said that to her
quite recently?

The store she does not enter is a small *bodega* where she

often goes for dairy items and bananas. The Puerto Rican woman who keeps the store has pictures of her grandchildren taped to the counter. The woman is unquestionably better off, in money as well as English, than most of the Puerto Ricans Sandra sees on the streets. No doubt the friendliness between them would survive the interpolation of a fur coat. But it might not, Sandra thinks, survive the effort they would have to make to convince each other that the fur coat did not matter. She hurries on, annoyed with herself, to the specialty grocer's, half a block farther on.

The store is cold. Along with the new coat, Sandra has hastily pulled a scarf from the closet and tied it around her head. A black alligator shoulder bag, which Ben calls "the survivor" because it is as old as their marriage, hangs at her side like animal armor. All the same, an iciness creeps in at her shoulder blades and travels down her back. A policeman —in Sandra's youth a symbol of order as substantial as the West Side itself—is speaking.

"So the Puerto Ricans got up a little excitement around here last night." He takes a quick check of the faces in the store. Then he goes on, telling the grocer, "Some guy runs with a gun to an apartment on Eighty-first Street and he shoots two bullets into a guy, and then he finds out he shot the wrong guy so then he runs to an apartment on Eighty-fourth Street and shoots the guy he thinks he wants. Meantime the first, *wrong* guy runs down into the street and then runs up Amsterdam Avenue but in the middle of running he drops dead."

The policeman stops for another quick look around. He then says his last word: "Well, at least as long as they only kill each other . . ."

The grocer, whom Sandra knows for a simple man, looks bewildered. "Why'd he do it? For what reason?"

Sandra by now has placed the policeman—a traffic cop from a Broadway corner in the Seventies. He is a serious-faced young man. His open-air life has not yet given him the invulnerable look of ruddy-faced policemen. He shakes his head in a quick movement that is almost a shudder. "How much does it take in this town to send somebody nuts?" His words seem to hold an angry sympathy that softens his earlier, callous remark.

Is the remark callous? Sandra hears it again and again: "As long as they only kill each other . . ." It is the West Side's policy of containment. In this the West Side is like the world, holding its skirts lest they brush against intolerable dangers: the small war ("As long as it doesn't get big"), the cold war ("As long as it doesn't get hot"), atomic stockpiles ("As long as some maniac doesn't set one off"). But even "as long as they only kill each other," there is always the chance of the stray bullet, the miscalculated knife throw, the splashing drop of acid, the warring gangs made up of "each other" who may fall on a boy of no gang at all. It is infuriating to live, in the world, with the fear of the bomb that some maniac may set off. And along with one's hope one lives, on the West Side, in a state of anger as well, because of this overflow of danger that cannot be contained.

Sandra's hope now, at this early hour, is to be spared any encounters as she strides quickly home. But at the corner of Seventy-fifth Street she crosses paths with a Puerto Rican boy of four or five. One hand holds his wedge of breakfast pizza; the other is fisted against his chest as if to beat out the cold there. He gives her a brief, brown stare as he passes and she, before she knows what she is up to, turns her head after him to check. She learns nothing she didn't already know. There are no socks in his shoes, no jacket over his shirt, and from the flapping around his skinny thighs, no underwear under his dirty white shorts with a green stripe down the outer seam—a discard from the camp outfit of some boy who lives in another world.

What will become of him? Sandra finds herself paying out the question like a toll before she can pass along. *Mira! Mira!* What will become . . . Then her first thoughts repossess her and she hurries. Shooting in the street not ten blocks from us! That is what, if there is time, she must tell Ben.

But as usual, there is no time. Lily arrives, Ben goes, and soon Sandra is hurrying after, swinging her gloved hand in the street for a cab. She has a picture of herself standing in this spot morning after morning, waving the same hand, differently gloved with the seasons. Then she takes the short ride, made dear by the waits at intersections, to her desk.

At lunchtime Sandra is again in a cab. This time she is going farther downtown to meet a friend who particularly wants Sandra's advice because the friend is about to vacation in Puerto Rico.

"I know you went there on your honeymoon," Elizabeth had said on the phone the previous week when they made the date.

"Do you know what that Tuesday we're meeting will be? My tenth anniversary," Sandra said.

"Congratulations. You must remember something about the place."

"As a matter of fact, I remember quite a bit. I've even got some folders somewhere, and a journal—I kept a journal in those days."

"Oh, bring it! That's my idea of *lunch*." Then Elizabeth asked, "Was it a good honeymoon?" and when Sandra stopped for a thoughtful moment, added: "Aren't they all sort of sad?" Elizabeth is divorced, so there was nothing to say but yes.

At lunch Sandra warns Elizabeth, who lives singly and elegantly East, "You're in for some heartbreaking sights. We see them every day in our neighborhood, so things can't have changed that much in ten years."

Elizabeth raises mildly reproachful eyes. "I no longer travel as the shocked American. Haven't for some time."

"Worst of all is when you *don't* see them. Sometimes they walk right by and you don't see them."

Elizabeth nods and sips her drink.

"I'm talking about my *own* neighborhood." Sandra gropes and shrugs helplessly. "It's like—"

"Blindness," Elizabeth supplies. "I loathe that in me too. But it's indispensable. I know it is."

Sandra then tells Elizabeth about the shooting.

"How horrible for you," Elizabeth says. "I *loathe* their being here."

Sandra wonders if it is possible to hate the sympathy of women—that good trait with its own reverse image stamped to its back.

"Although I would hate to see you move . . ." Elizabeth says.

"No. No suburbs, thank you."

Because Sandra is engaged in the working woman's race to stand for Home and Mother in the nick of time, she suggests to her last cab driver of the day that he try the route through Central Park. Soon they are rounding the curves of the road at a good speed. Sandra, watching the movement of the snowy landscape, is suddenly aware that this evening looks more like dusk than the pitch-black it was a few weeks before, around Christmas. A thin purple lifts the sky above the filamented trees.

When the driver stops for the light near the Seventy-second Street exit she sees a small parade of mounted police coming along the bridle path in twos. They do not, as she expects they will, turn off at the cross-park highway. Instead they allow their horses to trot across the highway and take the bridle path on the other side. The policemen chatter and gesture within their pairs like pilgrims to Canterbury and their horses converse in steam.

"I didn't know," Sandra says to the back of her cab driver's head, "that there were all these mounted police in the park at night. I'm so glad." She feels a rising hope—because the evening sky is lifting—that this lovely, lost park is to be reclaimed.

"Sure," says the driver. "Since what happened."

Sandra notices that the ear pieces of his glasses are taped with adhesive, one white, one black.

"I guess you don't get the chance to know these things during the strike," says the cabbie. Stimulated by her silence, he half turns toward her while his hands and feet, at the light change, work out the rhythm of shifting into first. "They found some guy in pieces. Some Puerto Rican." He gestures at a snowy hill. "Right around here someplace."

While she is still blocks from home Sandra estimates the fare, adds the tip, readies her money and finds when they get to her door that she has guessed close enough so that she needn't open her purse again, and she is already swinging one leg to the curb when the driver's words catch her—one foot in, one foot out and back absurdly bent. "At least," he says, "as long as they only kill each other."

What in the world makes her wonder at this moment if they have candles? Surely they have some left over from a birthday. But if they haven't? Sandra is scrupulous about these ceremonies. She can't, as a mother who gives her day to her children might do, fob them off with some story— "Anniversary cakes don't *need* candles." They must have candles, and it's simpler to get them now than go upstairs first and check. She heads again—it's a day of repetitions— for the little grocery store.

Near the corner, in front of the doughnut shop, the nightly group is forming. Henna-haired boys, with hips fined down to a sole suggestion, converse in clattering Spanish. Sandra gives them the barest side glance as she passes. They are what they are—the oldest no more than seventeen, perhaps—as stoical and tough as a band of Elizabethan mummers. But on the walk back, having bought her candles, she sees a new boy has been added, with the face of a dark angel—beauty with no place to go but down. He stands with his hands in his pockets, watching the charade to be learned.

What will become of him—the voice inside Sandra's head begins its chant—when he's twenty? Then she stops in the

street for a moment because the obscene parody jumps with
such force into her head: "At least as long as they only
seduce each other."

Sandra's clean, beautiful children, whom Lily has dressed
in brother and sister outfits of red velvet, race each other
to her arms. Almost as soon as Sandra is in, Lily is out—she
has her own dinner to fix at home. But first, quickly, information passes from Lily to Sandra: The children ate good
lunches, they were good about their rest times, and Lily
kept them in the sunny part of the playground where it
wasn't so cold.

Sandra steps into the hall for a minute with Lily. "I
heard about—an accident in the park today," she says.

"Oh, my," Lily says. "Was it a car?"

"No." Sandra is whispering now. "Someone was
murdered."

Lily's eyebrows lift at the inner edges, making down-
curves of pity. "It's hard to raise children in the city," she
says. A ring of grayish-white rims the iris of each eye. How
old is Lily? Her black face seems ageless, no gray in her
neatly bunned hair. Good Lily, lend us your protection for
a few more years. Why should you? But do it.

"I was thinking, Lily, perhaps you could keep the children
out of the park for a while. It must be awfully cold there,
anyway. Just—go window-shopping with them?"

"Yes, I'll do that, Mrs. Loeb."

Moments after Lily goes, Ben is home.

"Oh-oh!" Ben says when he sees the faces of the children, pale with excitement above the red velvet.

They hang their arms around his neck and bow his head
with their weight. Content for now to let the children's greeting stand for their own, Sandra and Ben exchange a look
above the shouts and then Sandra slips back to the kitchen
to keep her eye on Lily's roast. Unexpectedly—the children
are busy in the hall dividing Ben's spoils of rubbers, muffler,
and gloves—Ben appears. Sandra intercepts the myriad
possibilities of his greeting with a thick whisper: "Two peo-

ple were shot right around here last night. And somebody
else was chopped up in the park. Near where the children
play!"

"All right," Ben says quietly. He takes a quick turn
around the kitchen and his loose arms bang against the
dishwasher. Sandra wishes she had spoken differently. She
had forgotten (how could she?) that Ben longs to protect
them—against bullets, maniacs, bombs. But he can't, so his
voice gets quiet and thin and his arms throw themselves use-
lessly about. "We'll leave. Let's go. Move."

"Well, we can't say it happens often." Sandra pays double
dues now to the tact she forgot. "There are *hundreds* of
police out now." After a short wait she asks, "Do you ever
think about Puerto Rico?" It sounds so coy, though she
hadn't meant the honeymoon part, that she doesn't blame
Ben for looking as if she'd rolled marbles under his feet.

"No," he says. "I've forgotten. Is that where we went?"

This is silly, Sandra says to herself. She supposes hurt
feelings show in her face. Now it is Ben's turn to weave and
spin. To show how much he remembers—every moment, in
fact—he begins to _hum_, in an appropriately dying voice.
After a quick glance at her, he goes to change. The children
follow him, asking in loud whispers to see the box with the
present. Sandra takes up Ben's tune while she looks after
Lily's dinner: *"Mil lágrimas, mil lágrimas de amor."* She
fishes in her apron pocket for a tissue. It is something, after
all, to be able to blow your nose unobserved.

She knows what the trouble is. It's the research she did
for Elizabeth. Her memories of ten years ago have been
freshened. Unless you were Proust there was little point in
having memories come back so fresh. The blessing of passing time—that it could carry off foreground and dwindle it
into background—was lost. If everything came back stark,
staring and foregrounded again, like a primitive painting—
well, there was little point to that either. All it led to was a
lot of secret nose-blowing in the kitchen. Idiotic. She and
Ben and everybody else live, as any moron could point out,

in difficult times. It's time to get used to the times. But her
memories have been freshened. . . .

Their room in the hotel had a balcony that overlooked
the sea and the mountains beyond the distant town. There
was one wall of glass through which they could, while lying
in bed, look out at the large, unbroken clouds. Below were
the coconut palms and the pool. Next to that was the dining
plaza, mosaic-floored, open on three sides to the trade winds
and the view. At lunch the tables and the waiters wore white
starched cloth, but the guests could sit like pampered children with dripping suits and bare feet. Next to this alfresco
delight was the evening dining room—as enclosed, carpeted,
and muffled as this one was open and fresh. The three
guitarists and the girl who wore purple lipstick came to the
dining room twice nightly to shed their thousand tears—
"Mil Lágrimas," the song with which they opened and
closed their program. So twice each evening (their contempt
made them tireless) Ben and Sandra clutched each other's
hands and monkeyed up anguish into their faces. They did
so well that one night the group came and sang at their
table. Afterward Sandra was ashamed. But Ben said they
deserved to be fooled.

"Mil lágrimas, for God's sake!" Ben said. "That's no way
to talk about sorrow."

"What is, then?" Sandra had asked. She thought that
Ben, who knew a great deal, would also know that.

But Ben only scowled and rummaged in his crew cut.
"It's just no way!"

After that, mil lágrimas was shown its place. When the
unfamiliar rum drinks went to Ben's head in a night club
and they had to leave before the dancers came on, Ben told
her with mock gravity that he was suffering from mil lágrimas. And when Sandra got sick on the twisty ride up the
mountain to El Yunque, the rain forest, it was the same
thing.

The Sandra who stands in the kitchen over Lily's dinner now sees, with idiotically pricking eyelids, the other Sandra and Ben. She no longer sees them tiny, through ten year's distance. But still they stumble and suffer like children. She sees the other Sandra and Ben signing up for the trip to the rain forest—their one and only venture into organized sight-seeing—with disdain, naturally. Then, half hoping they will miss it, they are late, the last ones to enter the shiny black limousine parked at the entrance to their hotel.

Their driver and guide is a tan-skinned man of athletic though portly build. His hair is well brushed; he wears a natty sports shirt and slacks. Down here, until he speaks, he might be mistaken for an American businessman with a really good tan. But of course he is not. He is only the driver and guide, with much good will toward the United States.

In the back of the car are two young men close in age, possibly brothers, the older no more than twenty. They sit tall and look clean, with long, clean fingers wearing gold college rings. Sandra sits beside the younger brother and Ben takes the well-padded jump seat ahead, turning halfway round to her. A plump, dark-haired woman, perhaps in her middle forties, sits up front and is quickly classified, by signs and looks, as one of the dreadful drawbacks of sight-seeing trips. She wears more jewelry than she ought with a cotton dress, and she rivals the guide for cheery chattiness in a situation that obviously, unless you are a guide, calls for aloof silence. Other than that it is not clear why Ben and Sandra make their uncompromising judgment of her, though they seem in perfect agreement on it.

Aproned Sandra now gives her nose another blow. Poor, talkative woman, worried all during the trip about their being so young and possibly coldhearted, and trying to rouse them. . . .

They drive through the open country that connects the

towns. Words flow from the driver as easily as miles from
the wheels.

". . . Here was once coconut plantations. Now no more.
Why? Pay very little. Coconuts not so much any more in
demand. What they get? A man who pick a thousand coconuts . . ."

Sandra and Ben crane necks upward, following the curv-
ing trunks, to the fruit high above. Then how many trees
would he have to climb to pick . . . They calculate, are
shocked by their own arithmetic. He must climb all day,
monkey-fashion, with only the aid of a band of cloth tied
ankle to ankle.

". . . An' how much you think the man who chop the
coconut get?" the guide goes on. "Chop off the husk with
the machete?"

Ben and Sandra listen, stricken again. He must chop all
day, all day, never straightening his back.

The woman in front gives her bracelets a jangle. "And
let's hope," she says, "he doesn't lose a hand in the process."

More flatness. They begin to see at intervals some cement-
block buildings. Stuck in the earth before each is a sign with
a picture of a spoked wheel, like a party symbol. One of the
brothers wants to know what that is. The plump woman in
the front looks knowingly around to the back and then up at
the guide.

"That is *Fomento*," the guide says. "That is our government's effort to establish our own industry on the island.
With the help, of course, of the United States. But is a
wonderful effort to help the people by giving them industry
here."

The older brother wants to know if it is working out. He
doesn't see much going on.

"Is going on," the guide says. "Sometimes wait for
machines from the United States, sometimes wait for the
people to show how to use machines, sometimes wait for
material, but is going on. *Fomento* is the same in English
—to rouse the people?"

The woman up front moves restlessly and then twists to the back. "It is going on, you can take it from me," she says.

The two brothers continue to gaze out their near window as if to show that no matter how baffled they may be, *her* reassurance is not wanted.

Soon the car begins the slow climb up the mountain that leads to the rain forest. They see clumps of bamboo and ferns grown into trees—long, slender trunks leaping up, absurd as giraffe necks. Now and then they see wet in the road. Spatters of rain fall all the time, but never for very long, the guide tells them, as if he has arranged everything for their comfort. Suddenly, at a bend, there is a lovely waterfall, a flat cutout for cars, with a few people standing around and several little boys with wooden crates that serve as tables for bananas and flowers. The driver pulls over to the cutout and parks.

"Only a few minutes . . ." The driver is already out the door, pursing his lips in a very Latin, very deprecating manner. "To stretch, to look at the water, eat a banana, smell a flower . . ."

The little boys chatter at the tourists. They lift up their wares—brown-skinned bananas, some so ripe their seams have burst, and the heavy-scented, white ginger flowers.

Nearby, a couple from the States are arguing. The man has heard the fruit is not safe to eat. He stands balky as a child while his wife stares at him with fury. Ben draws Sandra away. They are so newly married they feel that any quarrel between husband and wife diminishes their honor. *"Mil lágrimas,"* he whispers to her, his voice doleful with irony. *"Ay-ay-ay,"* Sandra whispers back.

The car resumes its twisting climb. The flower stalk Ben tosses onto Sandra's lap ("I just boomed the economy," he says, frowning) begins to ooze. Scent hangs in the humid air, bringing on a memory of the near-nauseating excitement of their wedding and translating itself into *mil lágrimas* in Sandra's stomach. Ben sees, then rolls down his window and leans forward so she can get the air.

At last they are at the top of the road. Of course it is disappointing. Of course there is nothing to be seen there that they have not already seen on the way up. The sole point of this forest on the mountain seems to be to draw more height from its plant stalks. Everything Sandra has seen at home, growing nicely as a plant in a pot, is here a tree.

In the silence of the descent the woman in the front seat grows restless again. She alters her position, gazes more than once at the guide, jangles her bracelets above her head and consults her watch. At last the guide clears his throat. "We are going to make an extra little sight-seeing today. At no extra cost. Something very interesting for you."

Ben, Sandra's protector against *mil lágrimas*, strengthens his shy voice to give it authority: "It's out if it means additional riding."

"No additional riding," the guide says, holding up his brown hand. "We go back to the hotel another way, that is all. Through some villages in the mountains. There we make one little stop. You will see our sad poor people and also what we do for them. Very interesting for you."

After the car twists down some more of the mountain, he parks at the side of a narrow road. They all sit in the car and stare. Sandra is not well traveled, but she is willing to accept as truth the guide's sad boast that "nobody has less than they do." The stilt village of crazily sloping walls and roofs (made of what—paper? tin cans?) is dark with the darkness of a forest and of the faces that seem to sleep with open eyes. The bodies to which the faces belong sit in the dirt, leaning against a tree trunk or, like last straws, against a hut whose side already leans halfway to the ground. Children peep from every corner, some wearing little filthy shirts, some naked. They are testimony to the fact that there is one activity that still goes on in the motionless village. The children, though they do not know it yet, are its thousand tears.

The plump woman in the front seat begins to instruct them, her voice breaking in like the voice in a documentary. "This is how they live. This is the meaning of *Fomento*.

From this village and from others like it the workers will come."

They all look at her. She flushes, shakes her bracelets, rocks her head a little in nervousness and pride.

"My husband has a factory," she says. "He gave up a thriving business in New York to start again here. It isn't easy. He has to teach everything. Machines are broken, cloth is ruined."

She puts her hands to her cheeks, mottled with excitement. "Americans should see this. To know what's being done. . . ."

Sandra feels the young man next to her take a deep breath. "I suppose," he says coldly, "it has nothing to do with the fact that it's tax-free. Nothing to do with cheap labor."

The woman looks stunned. Her eyes shine with tears of disappointment. "I resent that," she manages to say. "I resent that very much." Her voice trembles under its weight of feeling. "These people will have an industry, these children will have a future. . . ." She twists to the back, reaches out a banglejangling arm to the brothers. "I understand your feelings. You're afraid a few will do something to disappoint you." The brothers' faces redden. No one looks at the plump woman and no one answers her. "We're all of us idealistic. All Americans . . ."

To the guide's credit it must be said that he gets them home as fast as he can—without chatter, without slowdowns and with nothing but a no-no wave to a little brown boy who calls frantically to him from behind a pile of ripe bananas. But it is hardly fast enough for Sandra. As soon as they are back she flings herself on the bed.

"I think I'll sleep," she mutters to Ben. "Why don't you go down and swim?"

"Good idea." He watches from a chair, his hands wrung together. "Maybe I'll stay and just be quiet."

"No—go down, go down!"

Ben gets up slowly. It is as if she had depressed one side of a scale and he were rising with the other side, to be weighted. Just before he leaves, Sandra pats her belly and whispers, *"Mil lágrimas."* In a way it is true. The dinners *en brochette*, the icy rum drinks, the dessert-heavy luncheons by the pool, all curdle in her stomach. Beyond their honeymoon, surrounding it like plague outside the walls, has been all the while, running like fire, this terrible cycle of the people who have no luck.

She has already heard, in New York, stories about Puerto Ricans. But now—what if some of these forgotten ones she has just seen are to become the unknown ones about whom the tales in New York are told? What if, when *Fomento* rolls on, some of these people, roused from their lethargy, go north with their new trade? Or with no trade? Killed in brawls; killed when the gas heaters fail or fire breaks out, overwhelming ten children at once; killed with bullets or clubs. It is like terror in childhood. A giant hand covers the universe. "I'll get you in your bed or I'll get you on the ship or I'll get you . . ."

Next morning they take the plane home, where Sandra promptly develops flu. Watched by her mother, who had hoped to see her fatted and calmed by the mystery of consummation. Sandra hacks and sneezes and loses her tan. It is all very satisfying. When she recovers, everything is normal again. Ben is Ben and Puerto Rico is far away. The bits of it that have come to New York sink easily from her sight. . . .

The children shout, "Happy anniversary!" at her again. Her son stops to joggle on one foot as he follows his father into the kitchen.

"Why," Ben asks without warning, "were you thinking of Puerto Rico?" He pretends to grumble. "It wasn't that long ago."

Sandra isn't looking at Ben. She is peering into the oven at Lily's roast. But she is sure that Ben is smiling at the children to show them: "This is nothing serious. Your mother and I have this joke."

In the same way Sandra turns to smile at them when she answers, "I was thinking of the people we saw in the villages there. Remember how they looked?" And in the same way again she smiles at the children after the gifts are opened, because a queer feeling has taken hold of her. It seems to Sandra that as the children's eyes shift from one face to the other, doting on their parents' pleasure (Sandra's bangle, Ben's cuff links), they are foreshadowing their own far-off time as parents. Sandra's heart thuds once, as if it had run ahead of itself and collided with something. *Mira! Mira!* What will become . . .

When the children are in bed Ben pours brandy. He fits the glass into Sandra's lifted hand and kisses her. "Anyway, darling, happy anniversary. . . ."

"Happy anniversary anyway, darling," Sandra says.

Ben sits beside her on the sofa and stretches his legs. "Do you remember . . ." he begins. At the same time a hoarse wail pierces the room. It is the siren of a police van or an ambulance, racing along the freezing streets. "Do you remember . . ." Ben begins again. "We took a tour. And there was this woman . . ." The siren reaches full cry, as if at their door. Elsewhere at that moment—Sandra feels it with a resonant certainty—klaxons scream; bombers roar aloft. From the city and from the world, the clamor that goes up fills the house. Ben and Sandra sit in silence, waiting for it to recede.

SAUL BELLOW (b. 1915), born in Lachine, Quebec, was brought up in Chicago and educated at the University of Chicago. *Dangling Man* (1944), his first novel, dealt with contemporary man's confusion and indecisiveness when faced with freedom. After *The Victim* (1947), *The Adventures of Augie March* (1953), *Seize the Day* (1956), and *Henderson the Rain King* (1959), *Herzog* (1964) celebrated ideas in a young man's struggle to find himself, *Mr. Sammler's Planet* (1970), probed the past and present of an elderly European Jew in urban New York.

Saul Bellow has written about the problem of freedom and responsibility in American society at the same time that he has demonstrated his feeling for the problems of urban America. For Moses Herzog it was necessary to find his way out of the Romantic, Faustian past into a world of the Jewish present. For Artur Sammler, born and raised in Europe, with an excellent education and a concentration camp behind him, America represented a puzzle. He saw its energy, its attempts to bring justice to minorities, its passion for success and wealth. He also saw its imperfections, and the possibility that anarchic individualism might obliterate love and community. As Sammler realized, in view of these conditions, a man must fulfil his contract, he must do what ought to be done.

Mr. Sammler and Dr. Lal
from
MR. SAMMLER'S PLANET

Dr. Lal was saying that we did not get much from our brains, considering what brains were, electronically, with billions of instantaneous connections. "What goes on within a man's head," he said, "is far beyond his comprehension, of course. In very much the same way as a lizard or a rat or a bird cannot comprehend being organisms. But a human being, owing to dawning comprehension, may well feel that he is a rat who lives in a temple. In his external development, as a thing, a creature, in cerebral electronics he enjoys an adaptation, a fitness which makes him feel the unfitness of his personal human efforts. Therefore, at the lowest, a rat in a temple. At best, a clumsy thing, with dawning awareness of the finesse of internal organization employed in crudities."

"Yes," said Mr. Sammler, "that is a very nice way to put

it, though I am not sure that there are many people so fine that they can feel this light weight of being so much more than they can grasp."

"I should be extremely interested to hear your views," said Lal.

"My views?"

"Oh, yes, Papa."

"Yes, dear Uncle Sammler."

"My views."

A strange thing happened. He felt that he was about to speak his full mind. Aloud! That was the most striking part of it. Not the usual self-communing of an aged and peculiar person. He was about to say what he thought, and *viva voce*.

"Shula is fond of lectures, I am not," he said. "I am extremely skeptical of explanations, rationalistic practices. I dislike the modern religion of empty categories, and people who make the motions of knowledge."

"View it as a recital rather than a lecture," said Lal. "Consider the thing from a musical standpoint."

"A recital. It is Dr. Lal who should give it—he has a musical voice. A recital—that is more inviting," said Sammler putting his cup down. "Recitals are for trained performers. I am not ready for the stage. But there isn't much time. So, ready or not . . . I keep my own counsel much too much, and I *am* tempted to pass on some of my views. Or impressions. Of course, the old always fear they have decayed unaware. How do I know I have not? Shula, who thinks her papa is a powerful wizard, and Margotte, who likes discussion of ideas so much, they will deny it."

"Of course," said Margotte. "It simply is not so."

"Well, I have seen it happen to others, why not to me? One must live with all combinations of the facts. I remember a famous anecdote about a demented man: Someone said, 'You are a paranoiac, my dear fellow,' and he answered, 'Perhaps, but that doesn't prevent people from

plotting against me.' That is an important ray of light
from a dark source. I can't say that I have felt any weakness in the head, but it may be there. Luckily, my views
are short. I suppose, Dr. Lal, that you are right. Biologi-
cally, chemically, the subtlety of the creature is beyond
the understanding of the creature. We have an inkling of
it, and feel how, by comparison, the internal state is so
chaotic, such a hodgepodge of *odi et amo*. They say our
protoplasm is like sea water. Our blood has a Mediterranean base. But now we live in a social and human sea. In-
ventions and ideas bathe our brains, which sometimes, like
sponges, must receive whatever the currents bring and
digest the mental protozoa. I do not say there is no alterna-
tive to such passivity, which is partly comical, but there
are times, states, in which we lie under and feel the awful
volume of cumulative consciousness, we feel the weight of
the world. Not at all funny. The world is a terror, certainly,
and mankind in a revolutionary condition becoming, as we
say, modern—more and more mental, the realm of nature,
as it used to be called, turning into a park, a zoo, a botani-
cal garden, a world's fair, an Indian reservation. And then
there are always human beings who take it upon themselves to represent or interpret the old savagery, tribalism,
the primal fierceness of the fierce, lest we forget prehistory,
savagery, animal origins. It is even said, here and there,
that the real purpose of civilization is to permit us all to live
like primitive people and lead a neolithic life in an auto-
mated society. That is a droll point of view. I don't want
to lecture you, however. If one lives in his room, as I do,
though Shula and Margotte take such excellent care of me,
one has fantasies about addressing a captive audience.
Very recently, I tried to give a speech at Columbia. It did
not go well. I think I made a fool of myself."

"Oh, but please continue," said Dr. Lal. "We are most
attentive."

"A person's views are either necessary or superfluous,"
said Sammler. "The superfluous irritates me sharply. I am

an extremely impatient individual. My impatience sometimes borders on rage. It is clinical."

"No, no, Papa."

"However, it is sometimes necessary to repeat what all know. All mapmakers should place the Mississippi in the same location, and avoid originality. It may be boring, but one has to know where he is. We cannot have the Mississippi flowing toward the Rockies for a change. Now, as everyone knows, it has only been in the last two centuries that the majority of people in civilized countries have claimed the privilege of being individuals. Formerly they were slave, peasant, laborer, even artisan, but not person. It is clear that this revolution, a triumph for justice in many ways—slaves should be free, killing toil should end, the soul should have liberty—has also introduced new kinds of grief and misery, and so far, on the broadest scale, it has not been altogether a success. I will not even talk about the Communist countries, where the modern revolution has been most thwarted. To us the results are monstrous. Let us think only about our own part of the world. We have fallen into much ugliness. It is bewildering to see how much these new individuals suffer, with their new leisure and liberty. Though I feel sometimes quite disembodied, I have little rancor and quite a lot of sympathy. Often I wish to do something, but it is a dangerous illusion to think one can do much for more than a very few."

"What is one supposed to do?" said Lal.

"Perhaps the best is to have some order within oneself. Better than what many call love. Perhaps it *is* love."

"Please do say something about love," said Margotte.

"But I don't want to. What I was saying—you see I am getting old. I was saying that this liberation into individuality has not been a great success. For a historian of great interest, but for one aware of the suffering it is appalling. Hearts that get no real wage, souls that find no nourishment. Falsehoods, unlimited. Desire, unlimited. Possibility, unlimited. Impossible demands upon complex realities, un-

limited. Revival in childish and vulgar form of ancient
religious ideas, mysteries, utterly unconscious of course—
astonishing. Orphism, Mithraism, Manichaeanism, Gnos-
ticism. When my eye is strong, I sometimes read in the
Hastings *Encyclopedia of Religion and Ethics*. Many fascinating resemblances appear. But one notices most a peculiar play-acting, an elaborate and sometimes quite artistic
manner of presenting oneself as an individual and a strange
desire for originality, distinction, *interest*—yes, *interest!* A
dramatic derivation from models, together with the repudia-
tion of models. Antiquity accepted models, the Middle Ages
—I don't want to turn into a history book before your eyes
—but modern man, perhaps because of collectivization, has
a fever of originality. The idea of the uniqueness of the soul.
An excellent idea. A true idea. But in these forms? In these
poor forms? Dear God! With hair, with clothes, with drugs
and cosmetics, with genitalia, with round trips through evil,
monstrosity, and orgy, with even God approached through
obscenities? How terrified the soul must be in this vehemence, how little that is really dear to it it can see in these
Sadic exercises. And even there, the Marquis de Sade in his
crazy way was an Enlightenment philosophe. Mainly he intended blasphemy. But for those who follow (unaware) his
recommended practices, the idea no longer is blasphemy,
but rather hygiene, pleasure which is hygiene too, and a
charmed and *interesting* life. An *interesting* life is the supreme concept of dullards. . . ."

HERBERT GOLD (b. 1924), born in Ohio, was educated at
Columbia University but prefers the West Coast. Beginning
with *Birth of a Hero* (1951), several novels chronicled the
Fifties. *The Age of Happy Problems* (1962) was a book of
essays. *Salt* (1963), a novel satirizing New York's middle

class, was an early part of his continuing preoccupation with himself, first and second generation Americans, and his Jewishness. *Fathers* (1967) and *My Last Two Thousand Years* (1972) continuing his interest, also describe his return to peoplehood.

A Return
from
MY LAST TWO THOUSAND YEARS

The movements of blood and glands explain much, but they don't explain why some words are magical and others not. Even the vainest writer eventually lies victim of the fact that his heart, lungs, and circulation of blood are very like the pumps and pipes of others. I have found it difficult to write about my books and the portion of my life which has been spent in solitary spaces writing them. I suppose this is because they are still tender, personal, and secret to me, and I mustn't lay retrospective hands on them in composing this narrative. They are encapsulated formulations of my own history, the completed stage on a way, and therefore, even in their imperfections, circled in upon themselves, with their own integrity. I am thinking here about my history as a man and a member of the community of men, not about these secretions from my life which I have called novels and stories. They are the work I do and the dreams I have. My life moves among them and away from them, as the spider moves among and finally away from the web it has spun.

Along with girls, writing, adventure, and distractions. I have sought the answer to a question which is only dimly expressed in the acts of my life. *What is a Jew?* I hardly earned the right to ask it, so much absent as I was from the history of Jews. But it is a specific form of the general question which haunts all of us: Who am I? where are we headed? why have we come from we-know-not-what to die we-know-not-how? Within the silence which surrounds us at both ends of life, what is the significance of our brief and noisy sojourn on earth? I accept the peculiarity of the question. I am left with tribal connections, loyalty to family and perished kin, and must try to begin with these simple matters.

Another question seems paired with my mysterious accident in being born a Jew. What does it mean to be a writer? The writer fits into the Jew who fits into the writer, who fits into the Jew. The interpenetration is continuous. Words, hope of meaning, quest for community, essential choices still to be made; incomplete as a Jew, I am incomplete as a man, and out of this incompleteness, which is also that of a child or a poet, comes the art which demands unity, a continuous labor toward making sense and magic of life. The childish writer begins his career free as a cat, he believes, but in fact governed like the cat by slavery to nature; and if he survives his ignorance, he slyly accommodates to the world, like an old Jew, freed in another way by careless detachment, patient hope, and knowledge that in any case the end of his own time is soon to come. What he keeps is the element of defiance which prevents his being a wise old man like other men. Fact and ideal, history and dream, disappointment and hope, there are no ways to reconcile them but through belief and craft. Mystery overwhelms him. He believes. He does not quite believe. He labors at craft.

Golems, magic rabbis, and furious Hasidic dancing turn me into Instant Anthropologist. I am too empirically American for the mark of lamb fat on the door, although I often have highly satisfactory daymares of my enemies being visited by snail diseases and tropical plagues. "Never again!" applies to ghetto Judaism and bland Jewish Unitarianism, as well as to the fatal periodicity of pogroms. I wish the road were clear. When I was growing up, I felt nothing about the past except an uneasy abstention from history.

Now Jewish history seems fully alive once more. Jewish Unitarianism has been replaced by Jewish rebirth for many who once fled. I've gone away and returned. How to define this road except in negatives? Chicken-soup Judaism, B'nai B'rith and Israel Bond Judaism, country-club Judaism seem mere variations of an American effort to keep busy. The quick element is a responsibility to history, ancestors alive in oneself, a tribal identity with hope, joy, and suffering. That piety is surely not enough. It is only the beginning of a return, a mere recognition, but recognition of possibility is the beginning of possibility. Our isolation of soul is inhabited by a conviction that there must be some community among men with the powers of nature.

To be a Jew leads not to a final definition, but to further questions. No rest in convulsion and conversion. Much of the anxiety, outrageousness, despairing humor, careless burlesque, longing, and nostalgia of American Jewish novelists depends on the puzzle of identity and allegiance in these times. Of course, the class "American Jewish Novelists" is as loose and ambiguous a category as "Southern," "Catholic," or "Black," and the variations of talent and depth make more important classes of their own. But to the extent that we recognize an energy of origin, the class can be named as a factor in the American imagination. There is no excellent beauty which hath not some strangeness in the proportion, Francis Bacon said, and he was no Jewish writer. The persistent search for language and new proportions expresses a search for the fitting identity. *Who am I?* is a question which also asks, From what did I come? To what do I belong?

The tribal answer is only partial: to be at one with a history which continues. Despite what I was told, and especially by the Unitarian rabbi of Cleveland, Judaism is not doctrine, a credo, doing good, marrying a nice girl. It shifts with the times to mean what people make it mean. In this it is like other Eastern religions, which to the European mind are not religions at all. There is a book—but the commentaries are legion. There is only one God, but His name is mystery. Hamlet's question has a simple answer: To be *and* not to be. The peculiar Jewish inheritance, an otherworldly worldliness, offers a vision of the eternal in the here-and-now. The bewildered Mallorcan architect and bullfight judge was also trying as best he could.

"Things standing thus alone shall live behind me," but they also live ahead of me as I let the peculiar Jew within instruct the middle-aged American novelist. Why I am a Jew, why I am a writer, why I am a defrocked adolescent, why I am the father of five, why I am sometimes up and sometimes low, what it bodes to be these things, why so much fun and so much else, how can I nourish myself and the world from these questions in my history—where is the value in the astonishments of life? The puzzles and pleasures which all together make me a writer also make me a Jew. And in moments of faith that there is a possible community out there, they also give the writer moments at one with other strangers on American streets. . . .

My non-Jewish wife studied Hebrew at the Berlitz school in San Francisco after we returned from Israel. I don't speak Hebrew. I can remember certain prayers learned by rote at the Euclid Avenue Temple, but they are not the ones I need. I'll find them.

I thought to be a Jew because I was named so by others. I learned by being one that Jew is more than epithet. The content of tenuous community, risk, and history makes me feel immortal though I'm not. No matter what happens to me, I am continuous with a past which was worthy of better than me; a present when others died to be Jews; a future constructed equally of fate and intention.

On the grounds of a hospital in Biafra, after an air raid by Soviet Migs piloted by East Germans, a little crowd gathered near a rocket still smoking in the turf. The doctors were giving morphine to the hurt and dying spread out on burlap bags. An old man, pushing a bicycle, joined me. "You are from Berkeley?" he asked me.

"San Francisco."

"You think my son is safe in Berkeley? There is trouble there? Rioting?"

"Yes, but I think he's safe."

"You will take him a letter?"

"Yes."

Later, when he brought me the letter, he wanted to talk awhile. He was the sexton in the church of the Fathers of the Holy Ghost at Ihiala, an emaciated old man with a bicycle and a son getting a Ph.D. in biology at the University of California at Berkeley. "We Ibos," he said, "we are known as the Jews of Africa."

"I've heard that."

"Does that mean," he asked, "Biafra will survive?"

Being reduced, as I was, to my name alone still left me with enough. I am. I am Herbert Gold. I am the American Herbert Gold. I am the American Jew Herbert Gold, a writer. I am the Jew who is also an American who remembers he was a Jew raised among people who knew little of what a Jew is. Nor did he know anything.

And I want my children to learn what I finally learned.

As a writer and a man I have sought an impossible consolation in the words *Now I see the truth! Now I embrace it!* In this rush to resolution, the enduring griefs, my own and others, were not always real to me. When I felt sorrow, I felt it at night and waited for the good light of day to drive it off. I worked, I took pleasure, I played against others and against myself. The deepest regrets and pains refuse consolation by truth and embrace. They refuse consolation by any means at all.

I found a peculiar joy in my peculiar allegiance because I needed to join all the lost tribes. Writing and the life of a soldier, student, husband, teacher, father, restless Bohemian, clever organizer in disordered times, all these distractions were not enough. Even the lonely devotion of storytelling becomes part smuggery in isolation. The sorrow written about moves into another world from the sorrow purely suffered. *Now I see the truth!* is a boast. *Now I write the perfect story, meet the perfect girl!* is a blind.

Therefore I have been nervous, erratic, fanciful; I inherit my parents' uninhibited employment of the blundering English language as a tool, a practical device to be explored in mistakes, in the use. Every writer remembers lonely day-dreaming from his childhood, and thinks himself shy and withdrawn, both self-created and victimized by family, no matter how public and insistent he becomes in this time of aggressive celebrity. Awareness of Difference and puzzle-ment about what differences mean compelled my explora-tion of fantasy, melodrama, play, and manners. Fairly waste-ful at times. Detached by fate, I sought to join every flow of feeling with ideas. Not so detached as self-pity might have it, I found myself bound to both Cleveland and Jerusalem, the American idea and the history of Israel, each of them seeking through intention and divine favor a salvation on earth, right now; not in heaven, but today. Or at least tomorrow. Or, please God, next year in Lakewood, Ohio.

The disappointments of history govern a Jewish reluctance to rest in solutions. Neither a responsible style or a conve-nient success gives any promise of grasping the meaning of life which writers seek outside of institutional sanction. To be an American writer provides an ambiguous set of pleasures and chagrins. The decisions about life which I have come to might also come to another American writer. But being a Jew gives both ambiguity and secure reference to a passion to put words in order and in disorder, to make clear and unclear, real and magical, practical and pious, in ways not yet known. To clarify the incomprehensible is the deep dream of the novelist. Horror and possibility make him suffer and invigorate him. He reconciles briefly with the unforgivable, and then fills once more with rage and desire. And to the very end of his life, the novelist or the Jew must also leave the mystery intact.

Anxiety and hope are close cousins, related through their common expectation that the future exists. There is no resignation in Judaism. Heaven above is the roof of the house; plenty going on here below, past and future; to keep the mysteries local and at home. That makes it our own business, not God's. No wonder Jews are so nosy and persistent, since there is no pantheon of saints and angels, no tender, ascending Savior. Resignation gets a Jewish fellow noplace. The only truly resigned Jews have been those in such despair that they could only wish for death. That's not resignation. The stony wait for oblivion has no quality of grateful piety in it. But Jews have often found themselves waiting.

And so the survivors are often anxious and hopeful, optimistic and disabused. Clever as Jews are thought to be, they have never succeeded in outsmarting time and place, history and event, the cares of daily life; and in fact, they haven't wanted to. They have suffered without the promise of sweet heaven. They have clung to the notion that human life itself is the great good, provided it can be made better. They are perpetually fretting and trying to show the way. Pious Christians believe that death comes just before dawn, and then they go to heaven. Jews know that death comes at any hour, and then they go noplace. So better do your business today, make plans for tomorrow today, and when tomorrow comes, *if* tomorrow comes, thank God and see if there is still another day likely to follow.

To add to the burden of this total, irreducible value of the individual human life, property is under no circumstance an equivalent to spirit. Historically, what the talion principle meant, eye for eye and tooth for tooth, was that a transgressor could not compensate his victims' heirs by sheep or land, honey or grain. A man's life could not be redeemed by purchase. There is no buying of forgiveness. One thing only was equivalent in value to a man: another man. This is the essential difference between the law of Moses and the code of Hammurabi. It's very severe, too severe for the modern nostalgia for sweet forgiveness, and it, too, cannot face the essential fact of loss: *Nothing* is the equivalent of a man; no grief redeems another grief. But at least it avoids easy redemption. It comes as close as possible to what matters, and it makes that modern nostalgia for sweetness most touching in its effort to find divine mercy. And, too, it helps to explain the ironic Jewish interest in wealth and power for what they are: games, a way of passing the time, a fleeting pleasure, sometimes useful, maybe useful, useful *in case,* second-best and ancillary to a manly life on earth.

When a boy in Lakewood, I turned from the allegiances of unreal history toward a fantastic community in the life of art. When I discovered what that community really was, a community of Manhattan, of property and power, and how it narrows souls, I was blessed to remember that I could still discover the community given me by birthright, a connection someplace. All of us preserve alternatives, no matter how many turnings our roads take. In the light of what the world is, the life of art narrowed toward triviality, while a life joined with the history of my tribe came to parallel my own strivings to write. Much is already printed on the body before we understand anything about ourselves. I must tell what I know and what I don't know, and come to learn more than I have thus far told. And so, partway by this atavism of the Word, I discovered a new way back to the community of writers.

Within my tribal allegiance, the magic and strangeness of its history embracing me, I peer out with longing and wonder at the strangeness and diversity of other stories. Like Jonah speaking from the whale, I speak out of a belly and expect an echo of results. I'm not sure finally if the whale out of which I speak is a Jewish fish or a writer fish; it's both, of course; and the ocean in which it swims includes everyone else, plus everyone's whales.

Being a Jew in the twentieth century is a rigorous infliction and reward. I didn't realize it was also a course of training. History doesn't plan such matters, nor is history to be praised for letting it happen, but gradually a man finds how he has come to be what he is. I set out in middle age with

bonds I have discovered, not chosen. My line to the past and
future is opened in a way I suspected only lately. There are
prayers still to be written for the traditional ceremonies of
mourning and celebration. Still Alive—the repeated notation,
day after day, in Tolstoy's last journal—is one of the most
astonishing claims a man can make. Clear and defiant it is,
an essential truth seen to be merely temporary, and heedless, fearful, and accepting, all at once—a complex negotia-
tion with the unnamed Judge.

How fine it would be to write my life as if blind and dying, yet in full possession of my soul, in very simple sentences, with no possibility of revisiting the text; to be truth-
ful, and to make the first account of each event sum up the
meaning of it, no elaboration necessary, no drama required.
Then there would be a pure line leading only to the truth.

Impossible. I can't do that.

And so, to find my truth, what part of it I have been
given to find, I have had to think again and elaborate.

And yet it is not very complicated. I now have five children. I was distressed, not knowing why, by being born a
Jew. My life has been fortunate. All it takes to die is to be
alive, and all it takes not to die is to remember to live. The
first is a permanent truth and the second a temporary one.
Absurdity and laughter have protected me from clinging to
chagrins which were merely mine. Good luck and health
have been unmerited gifts from the God in whom I do not
believe but who remains a puzzle to me.

My second wife, in whom I believe, is very dear to me.
Writing is my other bride. In middle life I have become what
I was born, a Jew, and hope my new children, the grandchildren of English and Scottish soldiers and merchants,
Russian-Jewish merchants and soldiers, Americans, will understand how this came to be, since it is also a part of how
they came to be, in their turn living and then dying.

If the Jews are the chosen of God to bring the truth of
His word onto earth, then how can I be a Jew? I am willing

to let God dictate to me, but He does not speak. Perhaps I am deaf. He is silent.

But if the Jews are a people with continuous pride in their continuous history, then of course I am a Jew. My life has been lived as a function of the holiness of words I cannot pronounce, of wisdom I do not understand, and of the stern morality of a law which I have not followed.

So my being and becoming a Jew are both paradoxes. And yet paradoxes more precious to me than any good and useful idea. Even if we and the world suffer the fate of Biafra, there has been a community in history and some mark of it in seamless time.

I was present at the last birth. My wife and I had done the natural childbirth exercises. We were ready. The doctor was kind and easy.

The child was born, my fourth child, a boy. After three girls, Ann, Judy, and Nina, a boy. We would name him Ari, a Hebrew name meaning the Holy Lion.

"Okay, one more push, Mrs. Gold, Melissa, and it'll be all over. Now push."

She did what she was told. We knew the routine. It was planned and prepared and we understood everything. She pushed and it was not all over.

The doctor's face turned gray.

A baby slipped out into his hands, a tiny, perfectly healthy little boy who had been crouching unnoticed behind his brother Ari all this time, unsuspected by anyone. His cries were piping and powerful. I was crashing about the room, laughing; and also trying to console my wife for this surprise. The doctor was explaining how it could happen, it was logical, it was a surprise, it could easily happen, it happened all the time, this was the first time in all his experience; and I in my sterile white gown was consoling him, too, telling him we didn't mind at all; and my wife and I were consoling the nurses and doctors, telling them not to be upset, they didn't have to predict everything, no one needed to predict and control everything, we were surprised but pleased.

We named him Ethan, because it is an old American name and my wife is descended from Ethan Allen, leader of the Green Mountain boys, and that way we could have one Jewish and one New England Protestant twin. But it turns out that Ethan is also an ancient Hebrew name, spelled Aleph Yod Tav Nun and meaning Firmness, Perpetuity, and Strength.

Having a child, now that I have had five, does not seem to be a creative act. It's an act in which I assist nature to be creative. I enjoy a power which is not mine but in which I share.

Being a Jew has come to seem like having a child: I have given birth to the Jewishness within myself. I did not choose it; it has been given me; but I share in the power and pain which it has offered. I am a part of history, not merely a kid on a street corner or a man making out okay. The suffering of others is mine, too.

During much of my earlier smiling life, I thought I might go smiling out of my mind, and despite the modern fad for madness, it did not delight me. I covered my fears with smiles. I smiled to tell the world how sweet I would be. I made jokes to tell the world I was agreeable about things; it could trust me; I didn't care; I might be rash, but no trouble at all, sir.

Later in life, most men learn to limit their desires and dreads, and this we take for wisdom. What begins as wisdom ends, I see from other aging men, in melancholia and worse. But I am not sorry to lose the fear of madness, and as I connect myself with the history of my tribe, I know that I cannot merely die; I belong with my father, with the man with acromegaly, with Schneider and Tal, and perhaps if I'm lucky, also with the gypsies. Just as I'm not entirely sure of what it means to be a father, except that it means some joys and some responsibilities, some risks, terrors, and exaltations, so I'm not sure what my destiny as a Jew means—or what the destiny of the Jews means—except that it is a unique fate, a peculiar devotion to world and spirit wrapped together.

And that I have at last become what I was when my Old Country father and mother in Cleveland submitted to nature and conceived me.

DAVID EVANIER (b. 1940), born in Manhattan, is a former assistant editor of *The New Leader,* and has twice been awarded residence fellowships at the MacDowell Colony. His work has appeared in *Transatlantic Review, Midstream, Tamarack Review, Dissent, December,* and other magazines. Author of *The Swinging Headhunter,* he is currently at work on a second novel.

The Jewish Buddha

My psychiatrist is crazy. I sit silently, nodding my head, while Wechsler talks about my teaching "The American Jewish Novel." I could start, he suggests, with synagogues— why not call my local Rabbi? I say mildly it would be difficult—the "Jewish" part of the novel is mainly references to food and neighborhoods. He nods, smiling, goes on—*he* knows what he is talking about. He is a handsome man—a large, curly-haired ingratiating face dark and perspiring—a square, broad body—and he is a *kind* man. For I am sitting in his office for a private consultation at no fee. Outside, nervously planted on the couch, is my father. We are guests of the Wechslers for Passover. Passover! Soon we will go to services at Harvard. Surely this is a joke, a private whim; or is Wechsler cracking up? I have dreams of him announcing one day that he is giving up psychiatry, that he is becoming a Rabbi and emigrating to Israel. Goodbye and good luck. But are these delusions? He has been to Israel two years ago, last year, he's going again this year. He is there more than he is here in Boston. My thoughts are interrupted—I hear Wechsler speaking. "And then we were planning to move to Israel permanently, but there are doubts, the hardships . . ." This is no dream. My eyes roam around the room: Judaica everywhere. When you're crazy, the whole world is Jewish. Then I listen again to what he is saying: ". . . when you wrote me that you were at the writer's colony, of course I was delighted and wanted to see you before you returned to Vancouver. So you're going back to the frontier—" Oh my God, now he's unwinding a map of Vancouver, his curious eyes scanning beautiful British Columbia. What is he so happy about? The frontier—it's a city of rain and gray, you could go crazy there—put away that map, you optimistic . . . his lips are moving: "You're not happy there?"

"No. The rain doesn't end. Ever. And I have no money. I stand in the rain waiting for buses that creep up to the university—" I go on.

He nods. He understands, but keeps peeking at the map. What can you do with this man?

"Now that you are no longer in therapy with me, Bruce, of course I was hoping that our friendship could continue —" I listen closely, nodding at every word. It is what I have been waiting to hear for so long. For the silences between us while in therapy could have meant anything—but long before now he had stopped charging me—and when I called him after moving away from Boston, he was always there, ready to see me . . .

Although I am cracking and crumbling from loneliness and despair, I am listening now to every word. At the colony, I wrote well—crumbling, I wrote well about crumbling people.

He stands up, his huge frame as always curiously graceful, smiles, shakes hands: friends. Friendship in the twentieth century. And waves me into the living room.

In the living room teacups, honey cake, the Talmud, my father on the edge of his seat, Wechsler's wife . . . and now entering the room, his daughter. "I have heard so much about you!" she says. "You know," he says to her, "of Bruce's writing fellowship—"

"Have a lot of rain here, Doctor?" my father says, smiling, cupping his ear and nodding in response to the answer that will come from Wechsler. But Wechsler doesn't reply, goes on with the conversation with me and the daughter.

We plan to meet that evening for dinner and Passover services . . .

Back at the motel (across the street from Wechsler's beautiful home) my father: "He didn't even speak to me! Not once!"

"It isn't true," I say.

"All he did was talk to you. His wife was nice—she at least talked to me—but would he even answer my questions? That isn't nice."

I take two libriums secretly in the bathroom. "Shut up!" I scream. "Can't you see I'm cracking?" Without thinking, I bang my open hand against the wall.

My father quiets down and looks at me. "You go tonight. He doesn't want me—"

I pull myself together, for with my father there is little choice.

"He does—" I comfort him.

"No—no—don't mind me." My father looks ahead, crimson. "Anyway, I hate services. Ever since my father made me sit through them when I was a boy. You go, Bruce. And calm down, kid." He pats me on the shoulder. "Please."

At Wechsler's house, we prepare to leave for the ceremony at Harvard Hillel. Oh my God—Wechsler is fiddling with his prayer shawls. Trying to drape them neatly around his shoulders, getting them mixed up. I can't believe it's happening—I look away—I look back, he's still fiddling.

His daughter doesn't want to go. Neither does the Israeli friend who has dropped by: "I'm a hedonist," says the friend.

"No more than I am," Wechsler replies, laughing. I perk

up my ears. I have never heard him speak in this way. What does he mean he's a hedonist—he eats a lot of plums?

But then we are in the car: Wechsler, his wife, and me. In the synagogue, he still fiddles with the shawls. The services are good—simple, and sincere. I tell him on the way out they are the best I have ever been to.

"Yes. I've stopped going to the regular synagogues because they're so mechanical," he says in the car as we drive through Cambridge.

I am silent as we drive back home. We arrange to meet again the next day. After honey cake and tea, I say goodnight and walk across the street to the motel.

The summer has not just been the artist's colony . . . graduate school in Vancouver ended for the season in May. May, June, and July in Manhattan. August and September, the colony. Sleeping on my father's sofa in the heat. Trudging Manhattan in my one gray woolen suit, sweat pouring down my face, looking for work. I am thirty years old. My father keeps handing me nickels, quarters, when we meet at the Automat at six o'clock for dinner. First a job at the NAACP as a typist: hiding when a writer I know comes into the office. For we have published in the same places. If he were working for the NAACP, he would know (I think) it was temporary. But when I work for the NAACP as a typist, I AM a typist. My father introduces me to his friends as the typist, although, he says, I will soon be going to writers' "camp."

I rise higher in June: assistant box office cashier at a theater. The full time cashier, Bill Bird, is a homosexual in his fifties who keeps combing his hair in the reflection in the box office window. He keeps talking about his "stepson." He is not kidding; he has adopted a juicy adolescent. He is a former director whose theater has burned down. "I don't have the certainty of judgment I used to have," he tells me. He shows me scripts he likes. He is right; he has no judgment at all. I tell him my opinion; he never forgives me. He is, as people go, malevolent.

The high point of his summer comes when a famous aging playwright takes an ad in the *Times* to complain about the critics' reception of a play he keeps rewriting; he sounds suicidal in the ad. Bill Bird takes a pencil and paper, sits down in a corner, and carefully composes a letter to the playwright. The critics are nuts, he says; the play is beautiful; he, as a director, should know, and then comes to the point: he is at the playwright's disposal for directing his plays. He shows me the letter: it is obvious and hungry, but I don't say so. I hate him for writing it, for adopting the boy he keeps calling over the phone and who, he eagerly announces to everyone, is cracking up.

Suddenly there is a crisis: a phone call. "Well, that's just too bad. I've had her in my house and she has peed all over the tiles." When he hangs up, he tells me that his mother is in a nursing home and the social worker wants him to take her back to his apartment. "The woman is helpless; I will not wash up her mess."

The stepson runs away from his apartment; the mother, somehow, has been moved in. He is combing his hair furiously. The city is hot; I am cracking; he is cracking; the playwright, in his air-conditioned suite, composes suicidal notes and pays to have them published in the *Times* where, curiously, they are not really noticed.

One day, when someone inquires who I am, he says of me, "He is nothing."

If I do not keep the job, I will have to accept my father's quarters.

I am, as always, seeing a psychiatrist, at fifty dollars a week, paid for by my father. He is one of a line I have seen since leaving Boston and Wechsler six years before. In writing about him now, I cannot recall his name, although I can remember the names of janitors, teachers, and Rabbis who have crossed my path twenty years ago. I recall his grimace.

Every day my father calls me at the theater.

I visit him in his office. He is part of what is called "the bullpen," those insurance salesmen who do not produce enough business and do not have private offices. These men have known each other for twenty years. When one of them goes on a plane trip, the others hand him quarters and ask him to take out insurance policies on the flight. They handle each others' suits in appraisal. When I come into the bullpen, they look me over. I know they have been informed of the psychiatrist, and nothing else. My father likes to give the impression that he is carrying a heavy load.

I published a poem about my father in a well-known left wing magazine six years ago. It was perfect for that magazine: ideological invective. It began: "My father sells insurance for death to people who have never lived . . ." and so forth. My father carries that poem around in his wallet, and whips it out to show to everyone he meets.

The men in the bullpen gather around me, their eyes sharp. Those in their eighties are the cadaverous ones; they don't have long to go, and they long for slices of flesh. One of them addresses me, but not by name. "How old are you by now, anyway?"

"Thirty."

"That's a nice suit you got on—summery."

I feel the sweat pouring down me. His eyes are triumphant.

"You look good," he continues. "Where you living—the *Village?*"

My father sweeps over and says, "Don't be nasty, Nat."

"Me nasty?"

They stand around me, waiting to take turns. My father leads me out.

When I leave him, I go to the library. On the subway, a man leans closer and closer to me, and coughs in my face. "What are all those books for?" he says. "Who are you? You're not gonna tell me you really read those books? WHO ARE YOU?"

"Beat it, Pop," I say carefully.

"Pop? POP? I'm a lawyer of the city of New York, and you call me Pop? Who are you anyway? You show-off."

The trains comes to my stop, and I hurry off.

"Pop? POP? Give me your name, you phony. You nobody. With a pile of books you'll never read. Who do you think you are?" He shouts at me jabbing at my shoulder as we walk along the subway path beside the tracks. I stop. Another train is coming, and I want to push him off into the tracks. I start to run. "You better run. You better run. Ha ha! That's right, RUN, RUN."

I tumble up the steps into the heat of Cooper Square.

I have moved into a sublet apartment on St. Marks Place. The stout old Russian woman next door smiles at me and locks her husband out. I hear his cries at all hours. I walk up and down St. Marks among the freaks and heads, and I panic in the crowds and the heat.

A few blocks away is the girl, and the apartment we lived in together for five years. Six flights up, the two rooms, the barred windows. It was a beginning. Thinking about it on St. Marks Place, I weep, and write about the girl. I sit in the charcoaled, broiling park, where there is no refuge from the sun, and try to get with the relaxed freaks around me—no use, I am too old, or too shy, or too critical, and my scrutinizing eye makes them angry. The rock band blasts away—people are swaying in the heat. I find the music uninteresting and too loud.

I go back to the St. Marks apartment, furious and lonely, and write more about the girl.

An old girl friend discovers me. She is married to a skinny Latin businessman, and lives on Park Avenue with their baby. She finds me at the theater, and is amazed at my situation. "You're still in SCHOOL?" she says. "In VANCOUVER?" She goes on like that, and I know better, but I agree to see them because they are the first people to have invited me.

The Latin mixes cocktails for us on their breezy balcony. She says, "So you're going to CAMP in August?"

I bristle. "Writers' colony."

"Writers' camp?"

When we're alone, she says, "It must take a lot of courage to do what you are doing."

When I am alone with her husband, he says, "At thirty, some of us take a nine to five job. Others are artists, and take a chance."

On the balcony, we discuss Fellini, et al. She whispers that her husband plans on more babies, but that this one is the last.

She has a brilliant idea. She is bored. Why not have a party of all MY friends at THEIR country house? She would so like to meet interesting, creative people.

Near the end of the month, we set the date. I round up a few friends, or near friends. It doesn't mean much to me, but as the day gets nearer, it means more.

The morning of the day comes, and no message from them. I call, and there is no answer. I reach them at five. They have forgotten.

I inform my friends.

She calls me the next day. Her husband, she says, is furious at her. It is she who was supposed to remember. She begs me to come out for the weekend.

I hang up, and July ends.

The next evening at Wechsler's, he has another notion. His daughter Tammy (how can a growing girl live up to a sweet name like that—Tammy Hitler, paging Tammy Hitler) has written a piece of creative writing about Israel. Impressionistic, sort of. Wechsler calls Tammy: go get your creative writing, Tammy. She brings back fifty-two pages. I know what it will be like: oranges grow and flowers bloom in the once barren desert. Wechsler looks at his only daughter lovingly. Her favorite novel, he says, is Howard Fast's *My Glorious Brothers*. Tammy sits down beside me. She is ten years younger than I am, very sweet, and fresh. Wechsler never takes his eyes off her. Wechsler stands up, crosses the room, and joins us on the couch.

"Will you take Tammy's manuscript with you to Vancouver and let her know what you think of it?" he says.

I think of Vancouver, and all I can remember is rain, and my one-room apartment with a bridge table, one chair whose wooden legs keep falling off and I keep screwing back, a lamp, a television set, a bookcase, a bed, and dust. Yes, I say, I will take his daughter's manuscript back with me. Wechsler leaves us.

I am talking with Tammy, but hear rumbling noises and look up.

"We were in Seattle in *June,* 1965," his wife is saying.

"July," says Wechsler.

"June. I remember distinctly."

"Well, we can verify it with my correspondence—"

"June. June."

"Oh, mommy and daddy are getting into one of these again," Tammy says to me.

I look up, fascinated. Wechsler seems unperturbed. "The Jewish Buddha," a patient in Group had once called him. Wechsler had smiled.

I suddenly think that I have never discussed sex with Wechsler. There are certain subjects you can not bring up with certain kinds of people, even if they are psychiatrists. Oh, I mentioned it to him on occasion, but the atmosphere became charged, or so I thought. But then, why did he never bring up the subject himself? I remember standing in the bookstall at Harvard Square, looking at a copy of *High Heels* magazine. There was a story, "Lucky Merv," about Mervin Spott, whose dream wife kept in her closet high heels that were all the colors of the rainbow. How ridiculous, I thought, but why was my pulse pounding? I never told Wechsler.

The rest of the evening is spent on Jewish subjects; arguments about the Torah, Philip Roth as a Jewish anti-semite.

Wechsler has another suggestion for me: that I teach the Jewish Novel in Israel. He gives me a pencil and paper; I am writing down names and addresses of professors in Israel, and stacking pages of notes on top of Tammy's creative writing. I scribble industriously, look serious, and sip Manischewitz wine which makes me high with the librium I had taken before coming.

I ask about members of the Group I was in six years before. I hear my voice uneven with feeling, and I am surprised. I look at Wechsler, and I see that he is not. There is the same gentle smile that a long time ago I thought was mocking me.

The Group had lasted only six months for me, as Wechsler was going to Israel for a year. The patients were in a panic; some were booking flights to be near him. I had only been seeing him for a year, and I could not understand why they were so upset.

An old woman in the Group had stood up and said, *"Fear! Fear!* When I think back now, I know that my entire life was motivated by fear. Why? Why? Why?" Tears rolled down her cheeks. "And I am *not* free of it to this day! Not to this very day!" Her arms moved up and down fiercely.

I had listened to her words, and thought it could have been said better.

The old woman had not gone to Israel, but several members of the Group did.

Within two months, I had arrived in the airport in Jerusalem.

At the kibbutz where I worked, Wechsler had come to see me with his wife and a tubby, younger Tammy. "You came a long way to see me, Bruce," he had said.

From the time of the decision to go to Israel, on the flight, in the months before that day, I had never thought of that.

In the living room, Wechsler is saying goodnight to me and inviting me to a private session the following morning. I say goodbye to his wife, and to Tammy. I gather up Tammy's opus and the useless pages of notes about teaching in Israel. Wechsler closes the massive door behind me.

My father is waiting up for me at the motel. He is lying on his back on the bed, watching television. He tells me to shut it off.

"I saw Henry Gold tonight, Bruce. What a character. When we were kids, I was so poor I didn't even have marbles. Henry did. I would go over to his house and we would play marbles. But before he would let me leave, he would count the marbles."

A few months ago, my father mailed me a baby picture of myself, bundled up in a carriage on an apartment roof-top. "I have cherished this for twenty-nine years," he wrote me.

Now my father is talking of dying, of his will, the vault, where he wants to be buried. Then he comes, as always, to his central thesis. "I'm so lucky, Bruce. You think I'm miserable. But I'm not. You are. I have my apartment. In the afternoon I go to the stock broker's. In the evening I eat at the Automat. What more can I ask? I have good, loyal friends. You don't have any friends, do you?"

"God damn it," I shout at him. "I don't want to hear this shit. Do you know I could recite word for word what you're going to say, I've heard it so many times? Don't keep telling me about how your lonely miserable life is so great. It makes me so sad I want to cry."

My father is straining forward in the bed, his eyes bulging.

"How can you say that to your own father? *You're* the miserable one—"

"No! No!" I pound the wall with my fist. "Don't give me that. I won't have it, no more, you bastard—you're the most frightened man I've ever known, and you're my own father."

When I stop, I look over and see that my father is weeping.

"You cruel thing—"

He turns over on his side. He is wearing only his underwear. I walk over and touch his arm. He flinches, and moves away. He is red in the face.

"Dad," I say softly, "can't you see that I am drowning?"

For the first time, I really tell him about the girl.

I read him a story I wrote about him as a young man courting my mother, marrying her, and about my boyhood. In the story, I imagine my grandfather, a man who wanted to be in vaudeville, ingratiating himself with my father by dancing on a table top.

My father listens to the story, and says, "I was never as shy as you're making me out to be."

Then I read him the part about when he would sing me his favorite songs: "Let a Smile Be Your Umbrella," "Smile, Darn Ya Smile," and the song he once sang to my mother on a rare happy Sunday morning when the three of us were laughing in bed together: "The Best Things in Life Are Free."

My father does not sing this night.

But we are friends again.

He jumps up in bed. "Bruce, remember Ben Alexander? I told him I was seeing you and he gave me a message for you. He said he doesn't do it no more!"

"He said that? Again?" My father and I kicked our legs.

Ben Alexander, a fellow agent, was a man with a moustache, a dirty white shirt and tie. When I was seven or eight, we ran into him. He was stuffing an insurance circular in a baby carriage.

"Oh my God!" my father had said that day. "Do you see what he's doing, Bruce?"

I absorbed my father's attitude, and I barely spoke to Alexander. He never forgot it. For years after, he ashamedly gave my father a message for me: "PLEASE TELL BRUCE I DON'T DO IT NO MORE! NO MORE!"

My father always relayed the message to me.

Every time we ran into Ben Alexander on the street, he approached my father, shirt sticking out of his pants, and backed away when he saw me. Moving backwards, he said to my father in front of me: "Tell him I don't do it no more!" Not looking at me, he turned and hurried away.

Then my father tells me about the agent who slept on the floor in the office and bought a piano for his alcoholic girl friend who beat him.

And about Melvin. "Bruce, tell me what you think about this. I went up to Grossinger's and I was dating this lovely girl. I never liked her very much. Sheila. She had a trick knee. Then I saw on the dance floor Melvin, who I hadn't seen in five years. His wife just had her left breast removed. Frankly I never much liked Melvin, Bruce. But I felt sorry for him. 'Sheila,' I said, 'do me a favor. Dance with Melvin. His wife just had her left breast removed.' So Sheila danced with him. Suddenly I look up and they're dancing very close, and Melvin is kissing Sheila's fingers. And she's letting him! I couldn't believe it. This goes on for half an hour. Then she has the nerve to come back to my table. I refused to talk with her. 'What's the matter?' she says. 'I felt sorry for Melvin,' I said, 'because his wife had her left breast removed. But I didn't expect you to let him kiss your fingers like that.'

"So I never went out with her again. Can you imagine such a thing?"

I ask my father, "But how did you know that Melvin's wife had her left breast removed?"

"THAT'S NOT THE POINT!" my father bristles.

Before we go to bed at 3 a.m., my father tells me never to hate. "I don't hate anybody," he says, "not even Melvin," and turns over.

A few minutes later, he says, "Wechsler is a nice man, isn't he, Bruce? Do you remember when his father died, and we read in the paper that he had been an insurance salesman?"

"I remember," I say, and I suddenly do.

In the morning my father presses two expensive ties on me to give to Wechsler as a gift. I refuse. My father is furious. I leave him at the motel to visit Wechsler for the last time. I am deliberately early, and approach his house by a wide radius, circling around it. I pass through the spacious tree-lined streets, and walk down to the park where children play. Wechsler's strength is so great that it extends to the streets around him: they have a serenity for me that I can never find in my own life. The houses are not the brown-stones of the Boston I love; they are the solid, well-fed edifices of Brookline. Yet I feel that if Wechsler lives here, it must be all right.

And I keep trying to remember that I am here this morning not as a patient, but as a friend. I approach the house, and take a side glance at the screen door near the garage: the patients' entrance, and stride up to the wide wooden door in front.

He waves me in, and we go into his office. He leans back in the swivel chair, looks at me, and smiles. He starts in on Israel, and I want to scream. He is asking me a question: would I like to listen to a news broadcast from Israel on the short wave radio? He checks the time on his watch and says it is six p.m. in Israel.

We listen together to fifteen minutes of news. Produce prices in Haifa are holding steady. He nods, satisfied. I too nod.

He flicks off the radio. He watches me. All the time I have known him I have kept some secrets from him so as not to disappoint him. And yet I know that he has caught them all. I sift through all the subjects I want to pour out to him, eliminating the things I feel will trouble him. "Thomas Mann—" I begin. His eyes light up. What I forget is that this is a subject that makes me happy as well. And that he knows this.

I cannot hold back any longer. "Do you remember Sarah?" I ask him.

"Who?"

"Sarah. In Group. I can't forget the words she said to us one day. She said: *'Fear! Fear!* When I think back now, I know that my entire life was motivated by fear. Why? Why? Why?' " I clench my fists as I speak.

"Yes, I remember. It must have had a strong impact on you."

"Not at the time. At least I didn't think so. I didn't understand it then, but now I know what it means. *When do we get rid of it?*"

He was silent for several moments, looking at me.

"Well, it varies. In your case, it has been receding for some time."

"You think this is a temporary setback because of the girl?"

"Yes I do," he says.

"So do I." I take a deep breath.

I pause. There is one expression of thanks I can give him that I know will mean something, and I can give it: "You know, going to Israel changed my life. As I have become more of a writer, it has become interwoven with being more of a Jew. And I do not understand why."

I say it passionately: yet it is so much what he wants to hear that I will never know if it is the truth or not.

He rises and we walk to the door. We shake hands.

"Visit us whenever you come back," he says. "Next time why not stay here?"

I grin, and using a Jewish inflection I have always been too embarrassed to use reply: "Why not?"

At the airport, my father is as taut and strong as a pretzel. He jolts back and forth with my bags, not letting me lift them because he is afraid I will get a hernia.

"Caroline——" he begins. My girl's name has been enough to break me down all summer.

I say to him: "I saw Caroline in Tompkins Square Park in July. She was doing what she wanted: smoking pot, and cuddling a queer. She suddenly saw me and said, 'You can't change a girl by pouring a glass of water over her head.' "

I embrace my father, and stop to wave at the exit door to Vancouver.